Supernumerary Intelligence

A New Approach to Analytics for Management

2015

Supernumerary Intelligence

A New Approach to Analytics for Management

John W. Dickey
Virginia Tech

Ian A. Birdsall
LMI Government Consulting
Walden University

2015

G. Richard Larkin
Walden University

Kwang Sik Kim
Sungkyunkwan University
Universiti Teknologi Malaysia

INFORMATION AGE PUBLISHING, INC.
Charlotte, NC • www.infoagepub.com

Library of Congress Cataloging-in-Publication Data

A CIP record for this book is available from the Library of Congress
http://www.loc.gov

ISBN: 978-1-62396-829-8 (Paperback)
          978-1-62396-830-4 (Hardcover)
          978-1-62396-831-1 (ebook)

Printed in the United States of America

To the great and very patient ladies in our lives:
Joyce, Dixie, Martha, and Jung Sik Hwang

"We are living in a—

Radius of Empathy:

A Radical and Radiant Relationship

With the Unknown"

Hakuin Rose
April 29, 2013

Contents

Preface xv

1   **Introduction** 1
    1.1   Supernumerary Intelligence (SI) 2
        1.1.1   Art and Science of SI 3
        1.1.2   Categories of Knowledge... 4
    1.2   Quantitative Cyberquest (QCQ) 5
    1.3   The Public Administration Genome Project (PAGP) 6
    1.4   A Model of a Model (Meta-Model) 6
    1.5   A Simple Example.. 8
    1.6   What to Do? What to Do?.. 10
    1.7   Traditional Approaches.. 13
        1.7.1   Regression 14
        1.7.2   Systems Analysis and Dynamics 15
        1.7.3   Research Methodology.. 16
        1.7.4   Qualitative Research.. 17
        1.7.5   Artificial Intelligence (AI) 18
    1.8   Crosscutting Concepts... 18
        1.8.1   Big/Wide Data 19
        1.8.2   Analytics 19
    1.9   The Making of Supernumerary Intelligence, Part I.............. 20

2   **A Different Approach** 23
    2.1   A Model of a Model (Meta-Model) 24
    2.2   Quantitative CyberQuest (QCQ) 24
    2.3   The Public Administration Genome Project (PAGP) 26

2.4 A Semi-Real Exercise 28

    2.4.1 QCQ Step 1: Situation Description 28

    2.4.2 QCQ Step 2: Theory Search.................................... 29

    2.4.3 QCQ Step 3: Theory (Local) Development............ 29

    2.4.4 PAGP (Temporary Interruption to Use the PAGP) ...30

    2.4.5 QCQ Step 4: Data Specification and Collection 33

    2.4.6 QCQ Step 5: Individual Relationship Development... 34

    2.4.7 QCQ Step 6: Relationship Evaluation Development... 38

    2.4.8 QCQ Step 7: Forecasting....................................... 39

2.5 The Making Of Supernumerary Intelligence, Part II 40

3 Case Study: Shopping Center Parking Lot Accumulation 43

3.1 Step 1: Situation Description 44

3.2 Step 2: Theory Search 44

3.3 Step 3: Theory Development... 45

3.4 Step 4: Data Specification and Collection 46

3.5 Step 5: Individual Relationship Development 47

3.6 Step 6: Relationship Evaluation 48

3.7 Step 7: Forecasting 50

3.8 Recapitulation: A Higher Quality, Higher Quantity,
    Higher SI Situation 51

4 Step 1. Situation Description 53

4.1 Identify Basic Case Information 54

4.2 Identify Goal Variables with Checklist 56

4.3 Search Literature and Discuss with Experts—Conduct
    Content Analysis... 56

4.4 Collect and Organize Descriptive Material 58

4.5 Cull Goal List 60

4.6 Recapitulation 61

4.7 An Expanded Learning Case: Accident Insurance Claims ... 62

5 Step 2. Theory Search...67

5.1 The Theory Search Process.. 67

5.2 Identify Causal Variables from Dimensions Checklist 71

5.3 Conduct Content Analysis of Literature and Expert
    Discussions... 73

5.4 Identify Invariates from Invariates Checklist........................ 73

	5.5	Find New Variables and Theories via Information Technologies	73
	5.6	Undertake Crowdsourcing	75
	5.7	Recapitulation	77
	5.8	An Expanded Learning Case: The Medicaid Data Disruption	77
6	**Step 2. Theory Search (Continued)**		**81**
	6.1	Identify New Variables and Theories with CyberQuest	81
	6.2	Search "Previous Theories" Database	83
	6.3	Use the Public Administration Genome Project (PAGP)	85
	6.4	Use Supposedly Dated Material	86
	6.5	Undertake Situation Structuring	87
	6.6	Cull the List of Variables and Theories	93
	6.7	Recapitulation	93
	6.8	An Expanded Learning Case: The New Minivan	94
7	**Step 3. Theory Development**		**95**
	7.1	The Theory Development Process	95
	7.2	Identify Specific Variables	97
	7.3	Identify Possible Links	100
	7.4	Identify Variable Roles	102
	7.5	Determine the Type of Mathematical Structure	103
	7.6	Undertake Cause/Effect Analysis	104
	7.7	Recapitulation	108
	7.8	An Expanded Learning Case: Boyle's Law	108
8	**Step 3. Theory Development (Continued)**		**109**
	8.1	Specify Time Affinities	109
	8.2	Identify Exact Theories, Assumptions, Etc.	113
	8.3	Recognize Situational Constraints	115
	8.4	Detail Related Experience and Confidence	115
	8.5	Avoid Errors	116
	8.6	Recapitulation	116
	8.7	An Expanded Learning Case: The Agricultural Plots Experiment Case	117
9	**Step 3. Theory Development (Continued Again)**		**119**
	9.1	Review the Main Model	119
	9.2	Categorize Variables	122

9.3	Explore Connections	126
9.4	Determine Minimum Time (Variables) Paths	126
9.5	Check on Meeting Goals	127
9.6	Develop Graphics	129
9.7	Recapitulation	129
9.8	An Expanded Learning Case: Travel Time among Three Points (Two Link)	132

10 Step 4. Data Specification and Collection **139**

10.1	Specify Definitions and Other Information on Variables	140
10.2	Identify "Accounting" and "Outside" Equations	144
10.3	Enter/Edit Data in a Database Management System	145
10.4	Establish Operational Range for Each Variable	145
10.5	Recapitulation	146
10.6	An Expanded Learning Case: The Gasoline Tax Model	146

11 Step 5. Individual Relationship Development **151**

11.1	Some Drawbacks to Regression	154
	11.1.1 Negative Forecasts	154
	11.1.2 Symmetric and "No Cause" Correlation	154
	11.1.3 Lack of Policy/Decision Variables	155
	11.1.4 Incorrect Signs	156
	11.1.5 Direct and Indirect Influences	157
	11.1.6 Domains and Goals	158
	11.1.7 "Accounting" and Deduced Relationships	160
	11.1.8 Sign Switching and Coefficient Magnitudes	160
	11.1.9 Controlling	161
	11.1.10 Necessary and Sufficient Conditions	162
	11.1.11 Value of Different Equations for Extrapolation	162
	11.1.12 Extrapolating Percentages	163
	11.1.13 Data Requirements in Time Series	163
11.2	Recapitulation	164

12 Step 5. Individual Relationship Development (Continued) **165**

12.1	The "Pre-Equalization" Process	166
12.2	Example 1: An External Variable (Function of Time)	166
12.3	Example 2: A Simple One But in More Detail	168
12.4	Warrants	172
12.5	Intercept Types	173

12.6 Determine if "Reachability" is Desired and Possible.............176

12.7 Specify the Goodness of Fit (GoF) Criterion 178

12.8 Example 3: COC vs. VMT and PE 179

12.9 Curve Fitting with S-Shaped Structures............................... 183

12.10 Handling "Outside" Equations 184

12.11 Example 4: Grade Point Average 184

12.12 Incorrect Signs (Again) 189

    12.12.1 Example: COC vs. VMT... 189

    12.12.2 Example: VMT vs. POP and GDPPC 191

    12.12.3 Automatic Checking 192

12.13 Simultaneity.. 192

12.14 Delays, Anticipations, Catalysts, and Pre/Reaction Times..... 192

12.15 Recapitulation 193

12.16 An Expanded Learning Case: Newton's Gravity Model....... 194

13 Step 6. Relationship Evaluation...201

13.1 The Set of Equations... 201

13.2 Undertake Quantitative Evaluation...................................... 206

13.3 Undertake Qualitative Evaluation 208

13.4 Another Type of Model... 211

13.5 Recapitulation 214

13.6 An Expanded Learning Case: The Olympic Gymnastics
Performance Model 214

14 Step 7. Forecasting...221

14.1 Develop Scenarios... 221

14.2 Make Forecasts 223

14.3 Use Qualitative Models... 224

14.4 Recapitulation 224

14.5 An Expanded Learning Case: The Hamurabi Game 225

15 The Public Administration Genome Project (PAGP) 229

15.1 Introduction 229

    15.1.1 What Exactly Is the PAGP? 230

    15.1.2 Where Did the Name Come From? 230

    15.1.3 Why Do It? 230

    15.1.4 How Does It Work?... 231

    15.1.5 Where Do Things Stand Now?................................... 231

   15.1.6 How Is It Being Used Now? 232

   15.1.7 Who Would Be Interested? 232

   15.1.8 More Information? 232

  15.2 Building and Contributing to a Case 232

  15.3 Views of a Case 234

  15.4 Using the PAGP 237

  15.5 Recapitulation 239

16 Major Case: Preparing Tomorrow's Teachers for Technology 243

  16.1 U.S. Department of Education: Preparing Tomorrow's
Teachers for Technology (PT3) Program 243

  16.2 Project InSight 244

  16.3 Barriers to Infusion 245

  16.4 Learning 248

  16.5 Lessons Learned 249

   16.5.1 Lesson 1: Breadth over Depth 249

   16.5.2 Lesson 2: Variables 249

   16.5.3 Lesson 3: Sparcity 249

   16.5.4 Lesson 4: Extracting 250

   16.5.5 Lesson 5: Accumulation and Forgetting 250

   16.5.6 Lesson 6: Generality 250

   16.5.7 Lesson 7: Paths 250

   16.5.8 Lesson 8: Strength 251

   16.5.9 Lesson 9: Verification 251

   16.5.10 Lesson 10: Mind Models 251

   16.5.11 Lesson 11: Connecting Chunks 251

   16.5.12 How? 252

  16.6 Evaluation with Quantitative Cyberquest 253

  16.7 Recapitulation 253

17 Major Case: Reorganization of the Seoul Bus System 255

  17.1 Background 255

  17.2 Introduction 256

  17.3 A Case Description 257

  17.4 A Simpler Example 259

  17.5 Categories and Ontologies 260

   17.5.1 The PAGP Ontology 260

   17.5.2 Use of the Ontology: Case Example 263

17.6	Connections	265
17.7	Description of a Variable	267
17.8	Recapitulation	267

**18 Major Case: U.S. Department of Defense: Joint Total Asset
Visibility (JTAV) Project** **269**

18.1	Introduction to the JTAV Case	269
18.2	Concept of Forces	270
18.3	Procedure	272
	18.3.1 Methodology	272
	18.3.2 Developing Initial Data Codes	272
	18.3.3 Data Analysis	272
	18.3.4 Data Synthesis	273
	18.3.5 Likert Scale Rating of Driving Forces	274
	18.3.6 Likert Scale Rating of Restraining Forces	275
	18.3.7 Determination of Higher Order Forces	275
18.4	Determining Level 1 Forces	275
18.5	Relationships	278
18.6	The Framework	279
18.7	Recapitulation	280
18.8	Behind the Scenes	281
	18.8.1 How the Government Saves Money	281
	18.8.2 How the Government Accounts for Money	281
	18.8.3 Priorities	281
	18.8.4 Discipline inside the Beltway	282
	18.8.5 The Color of Money	282
	18.8.6 Can I Get a Little Help?	282
	18.8.7 The "Real" Work	283
	18.8.8 The "B" Team	283

19 Supernumerary Intelligence in Perspective **285**

19.1	Putting It All Together	286
19.2	The Public Administration Genome Project (PAGP)	286
19.3	Quantitative CyberQuest (QCQ)	286
19.4	Contribution to Analytics	288
19.5	Contribution to Management	289
19.6	Contribution to Education	289
19.7	Development of Visualization	290
19.8	Recapitulation—In Search of Supernumerary Intelligence	290

A **Some Basic Statistics and Mathematics** **293**

    A.1   A Brief History of Regression 293

    A.2   A Statistical Slide Show 294

    A.3   Variations from the Average (Mean) 294

    A.4   Goodness of Fit Measures 298

    A.5   The Mathematics of Minimization of the MAE and MAPE ... 303

B **Some Additional Case Studies** **307**

    B.1   The Rainfall Model Case 307

    B.2   The Auto Scrappage Case 309

    B.3   The Stock Market Case 310

    B.4   The San Francisco BART Case 311

    B.5   The Trip Generation Case 315

C **Characteristics of Supernumerary Intelligence (by Step in QCQ Process)** **317**

D **Checklist for Cause and Effect Considerations** **329**

E **Necessary and Sufficient Conditions** **347**

F **Data** **357**

G **Warrant-Based Equation Development** **361**

References **367**

About the Authors **373**

Index **377**

Preface

Life presents us with various types of challenges. Some of the solutions to those challenges are easy, while others are beyond our capabilities to achieve. Some challenges can be tackled by individuals, while others require group efforts. Some challenges involve competition, politics, or technology, while others may be void of all these elements.

This book attempts to make some sense of the world by looking at how people can and do approach various problems and opportunities, especially those from the field of public policy. The book represents over 150 combined years of experience thinking about and developing approaches to diverse, multifaceted problems and opportunities. We place special, but not sole, emphasis on the analytic dimensions of problem solving. Our goal is to:

> Create and apply tools within a problem-solving process (called "QCQ") to achieve "supernumerary intelligence"—knowledge, capabilities, and answers beyond the usual numerics and logic.

In those cases when we seem to be achieving our goal, the requisite efforts seem to noticeably contribute to individual as well as organizational analytic capabilities and, more importantly, to greater understanding of certain problem areas in our world.

Like most goals, ours is destined to remain elusive; however, as is often the case, striving for such an ambitious outcome leads to substantive

Supernumerary Intelligence, pages xv–xix
Copyright © 2015 by Information Age Publishing

progress. For example, we have been able to identify and briefly illustrate over 125 characteristics of "supernumerary intelligence."

In Chapter 1 we build on the substantial success of some fairly generic analytic approaches such as qualitative analysis, regression analysis, systems analysis and dynamics, research methodology (social science), and artificial intelligence ("scientific discovery"). We then illustrate some of the limitations of those approaches in Chapter 2 and provide examples of how they might be improved in Chapter 3. Particular attention is given to traditional regression analysis. Although regression analysis provides an easy and well-known target for us, we also recognize its numerous successes over hundreds of years.

The first three chapters serve as a prelude to Chapters 4 through 19 that describe and illustrate the seven-step "problem solving" process of Quantitative CyberQuest (QCQ). We use QCQ to bring together the 125 aforementioned characteristics of "supernumerary intelligence" under one umbrella or technique. To serve as an illustrative example, we use an air pollution case (the AIRPOL case), which involves an investigation of carbon monoxide concentrations in the most polluted U.S. cities. Data for the case are from 1975 through 2010, supplemented with forecasts to the year 2020.

The final chapter gauges our progress in achieving supernumerary intelligence in comparison to the basic approaches noted in the first three chapters.

Three points should be made about QCQ and the example case. First, despite its name, we consider QCQ to be an analytic rather than a quantitative discovery tool. The naming convention may seem strange given the title of this book; however, in our investigations and musings we have found that much of the development of good quantitative models starts way back in the nebulous mist of the qualitative. Somehow the vague, intuitive, and unsubstantiated impressions about a situation under investigation are transformed into much clearer, well-integrated, and "hard" models that can be used for forecasting purposes. One of QCQ's goals is to capture that transition process and thereby actually have a considerable number of "qualitative" elements in it.

Second, what is presented in the book about QCQ is a combination of what already existed in the associated computer program and what might be reasonably obtainable in the near future. For the purposes of this book, we are focusing on the philosophy and mechanics of the process and not particularly on the computer program. QCQ, like the search for supernumerary intelligence, is a never-ending project.

Third, the example of the AIRPOL case is limited. We never were clever enough to find a way to include all of the 125 identified characteristics of supernumerary intelligence in one illustration. We had to place that task in the "too hard to do" stack in the near term. As a result, we resorted to using many small examples, billed as "expanded learning cases" and placed them individually at the end of the most relevant chapter or made them part of a large appendix (Appendix B) to help demonstrate our points. We apologize for the gear switching that takes place.

To assist the reader in developing a better understanding of the origins and nature of the concepts and examples in this book, we thought it would be helpful to burden you with some knowledge about our very diverse backgrounds. See About the Authors at the end of this book.

Because of our diverse backgrounds and experience, we have learned many valuable lessons. We also have obtained a much broader understanding of the nature of "knowledge" from our colleagues and students, particularly in public administration and policy. These lessons are especially pertinent as we all try to comprehend and make some useful decisions about some of the "messes" that are placed at government's door. Particularly intriguing are those situations where some of the evidence is being hidden or, worse yet, is fraudulent.

Some of our time in the last 15 years has been spent investigating the aspects of artificial intelligence that might be used in analytic endeavors. This search led us to develop one of the first personal computer versions of an expert system "shell." More importantly, we started to look into the creative or discovery process. This resulted in an interactive, multimedia "problem solving and innovation support system" called CyberQuest (CQ). CQ, as the forerunner of QCQ, has been employed in over 600 cases, mostly "real world." The range of the cases has been far beyond anything we ever could have imagined and included such diverse endeavors as reducing delay and congestion in state courts, developing better coordination in the design of the surface combatant ship of the 21st century, marketing cemeteries, testing very large scale integration (VLSI) chips economically for computers going to the moon; designing a state scenic highways program, and yes, even improving communications between perfect God and imperfect man. The outputs for the CQ cases were lists of ideas, usually rated for importance and combined into implementation packages. There was very little quantification.

Until we stumbled into the opportunity to work on all these kinds of cases, we had no inkling of the vast diversity of problems and problem solving processes "out there" in the world. We have attempted to capture the major elements of these in QCQ and subsequently in this book, but we still have to continue to work hard to build up the highest possible level singular process within QCQ.

The case experiences with QCQ are diverse but somewhat limited when compared with CQ. They include assessing the future of next generation manufacturing systems (NGMS), forecasting the number of people in the U.S. without health insurance, estimating the success of group sessions with CQ, and understanding the factors and relationships in decisions to make a person a "ward of the state."

Even with the mathematical/statistical capability of QCQ, most of the cases involve no numbers. The largest case, for example, with 2000 "variables" and 4000 "relationships," was defined mostly in the heads of the users. The nature of the case outputs offers support to our earlier contention that "Analytic CyberQuest" (ACQ) may be more appropriate than QCQ.

The universe of tools and techniques gets even larger with the introduction of the Public Administration Genome Project (PAGP). The PAGP is fashioned after the Human Genome Project as a searchable data base of about 80 case studies, put together mainly with QCQ applications. The emphasis is on identifying useful strategies ("genes") for an issue a public administrator may face and tracing logical paths from these strategies to their impacts.

Despite wide exposure through CQ, QCQ, and the PAGP, we think that our knowledge is extremely limited. A field like artificial intelligence (AI), for example, is changing so rapidly that it is virtually impossible to keep up with it. Therefore, the implications here are twofold:

1. While the baseline approaches we have employed (e.g., Langley, Simon, Bradshaw, & Zytkow's 1987 *Scientific Discovery* in the case of AI) may be superseded in one arena they still may be useful, through analogy, in others.
2. Some of what has been written will be obvious and repetitive for some groups (e.g., "domains" for systems analysts; "recursion" for AI people) but brand new to others.

Regardless of its shortcomings, the book should be informative and useful for those willing to cross over and learn from other disciplines/arenas. The value of the book comes from the way various approaches are synthesized. We have learned that most innovations usually are new combinations of old things.

Who are the intended readers and users of the book? Our target audience includes basically, anybody who has an interest in either quantitative or qualitative analytics. We hope that our work will aid problem solvers/consultants, students, managers, educators, policy analysts, "expanders" (e.g., AI researchers, mathematicians, management scientists, statisticians, research methodologists, systems analysts, financial analysts), and the like.

Finally, there is a need to understand some basic statistics, mainly regression. Appendix A describes most of the statistical concepts/techniques used in this book.

It should be noted that over the past 25 years or so, several versions of the QCQ software have been developed. None of these quite made it to the point where they could be made available to the general public. Most of the subroutines can be found, however, in the marketplace, albeit with some additional searching.

One more note: We did not like the way references for Internet items had to be displayed *in full* in both the text and reference section. So, we are trying out a different approach. Each web reference is presented in full at the end of the book in a separate Internet reference section. You will notice there that each website is preceded by a code—starting with "[INT-##" and followed by a short, descriptive text. An example found in text would be something like [INT-23 Calibration Errors]. The reference section would have a more descriptive text, as well as publication dates, full URL, date accessed, etc.

We hope this will make the reading a little smoother.

1

Introduction

Much of our life is consumed looking for quantitative relationships. At the personal level are questions such as: How much more sleep do I need at night to make me feel better? How many calories do I need to eliminate to lose weight? How many times do I need to pass by that special someone before he or she will be more likely to notice me?

On the job are questions like: How much larger does my budget need to be for me to be more effective? How much will my profits be reduced if the government enforces a new regulation? How much can import quotas be increased in some countries before they begin reducing international competitiveness?

All these quantitative questions actually are preceded by another, more qualitative set: What factors affect your "feeling good" and in what manner? For example, before I decide how much extra sleep I need at night, I need to determine if extra sleep will actually make me feel better. In another example, I need to determine if a larger budget will make me more effective on the job before I think about how much more money I will need. Sleep, weight loss, and romance may only be three of the determinants, and perhaps not

Supernumerary Intelligence, pages 1–21

the most important. What elements influence job performance, and how do they interact? Budgets, regulations, and competitors may play significant and interconnected roles, but other variables also may be equally significant.

We spend much of our life trying to find answers to such quantitative questions—as well as the qualitative issues that surround, precede, and accompany them. We are, then, in search of a kind of intelligence that includes but also is above and beyond numbers. We call it "supernumerary" intelligence (SI).

1.1 Supernumerary Intelligence (SI)

As is the case with numerous other topics (strategy comes quickly to mind), SI can be divided into content characteristics and process characteristics. Content consists of the essential quality of a thing. If you were able to bore deep into a thing, the content would be what it consists of. So, what does SI consist of? What is SI's essential quality? Data. SI is data, information, knowledge, and, yes, intelligence. We have already alluded to the fact that SI consists of quantifiable data as well as data "above and beyond" the quantifiable. Data that are not quantitative must be qualitative. Quantitative data have (usually) been observed and collected empirically and can be manipulated using a mathematical process.

Qualitative data is that which cannot be quantified within a certain degree of validity and reliability. Qualitative characteristics deal with subjective qualities such as aesthetics and functionality. The repository for much of the SI data that we have developed can be found in the Public Administration Genome Project (see Section 1.2). The contents of SI are characterized in Figure 1.1.

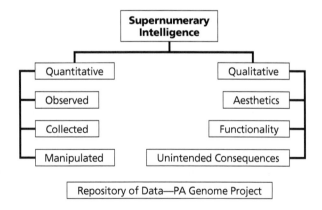

Figure 1.1   Content of supernumerary intelligence.

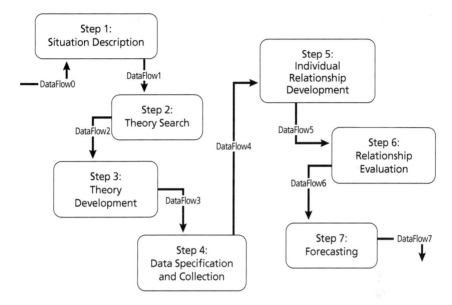

Figure 1.2   Using QCQ to develop and analyze SI.

"Process" consists of how a thing works. In order to determine how SI works, we need an analytic process. The one we will use is Quantitative CyberQuests (QCQ), perhaps to be better thought of as Analytic CQ (or ACQ). QCQ's process will not only provide us with a metamodel of SI but will also allow us to evaluate and forecast using a portion of the SI data. The QCQ process as applied to SI is displayed in Figure 1.2.

1.1.1   Art and Science of SI

Is SI an art or a science? It is neither fully an art nor is it fully a science—but in its totality is both. SI, in its most basic form, consists of two elements—quantitative and qualitative data. Quantitative data requires a process to logically break the environment into its component parts and to find relationships between those parts. This process is best conducted using a structured, analytic approach. Thus it is a scientific, linear, logical process.

Qualitative data comes from a process of creative thought that synthesizes those parts into observable and inferred patterns and trends. These two processes—analysis and synthesis—require different types of thinking, using different sides of the brain and based on different outlooks and perspectives. Analysis of quantitative data requires a scientific, rational, pragmatic cause and effect approach. In addition, it needs a systematic and rational method to analyze the strategic environment in a fact-based manner. Synthesis of qualitative data, on the other hand, requires the art of discerning trends and patterns.

1.1.2 Categories of Knowledge

To carry SI further, it includes the same surprises and unknowns that we planned for (the things that we know we do not know) but also includes the chaos and disorder that we do not yet understand (the things we do not know that we do not know). This concept is often credited to former U.S. Secretary of Defense Donald Rumsfeld and gives rise to four categories of knowledge:

- Information that you know you know—you know the question and the answer;
- Information that you know you do not know—you know the question but not the answer;
- Information that you do not know that you know—you do not know the question but know the answer;
- Information that you do not know that you do not know—you do not know the question or the answer.

These four categories of knowledge create the 2×2 matrix in Figure 1.3.

		Question	
		Know	Not Know
Answer	Know	Things that you know that you know (You know the question and the answer)	Things that you do not know that you know (You do not know the question but know the answer— Tacit Knowledge
	Not Know	Things that you know that you do not know (You know the question but not the answer)	Things that you do not know that you do not know (You do not know the question or the answer— Unintended Consequences)

Figure 1.3 Categories of knowledge.

What is striking about Figure 1.3 is the differences in the right and left sides of the matrix. On the left side of the matrix we have "things that we know we know" and "things that we know we do not know." Thus we know something about everything in those two quadrants in the first instance— we know the question, and we can place them in the appropriate quadrant.

On the other hand, on the right side of the matrix we have "things we do not know that we know" and "things we do not know that we do not know." Thus as we do not know those things in the first instance—we do not know the question and we cannot place them in the quadrants on the right, because we do not know them. If we knew the questions they must go in the quadrants on the left. Thus, the types of things that would theoretically be placed in the right quadrants would be tacit knowledge and unintended consequences, respectively.

Ironically, as soon as we realize that we have the tacit knowledge (i.e., we know the question) it moves to the left quadrants, and immediately as we notice the unintended consequence it also moves to one of the left quadrants. The lesson here is clear. Our goal should be to identify, as quickly as possible, those items that are hidden from us in the right quadrants and move them into the left quadrants so we can deal with them. QCQ is particularly well-suited to help us in that task.

1.2 Quantitative CyberQuest (QCQ)

Quantitative CyberQuest (QCQ) is a philosophy as well as an analytic tool that we will use to help in exploring the supernumerary. QCQ is particularly well-suited for sorting out the kinds of variables suggested previously as well as their interrelations. It involves a combination of statistics, systems analysis, research methodology, qualitative research, and artificial intelligence. QCQ provides a relatively easy-to-understand but still powerful set of tools and guidance mechanisms to pilot (the "Cyber" part) users in their "Quest" for supernumerary relationships.

A major premise in this piloted quest is that people often are not aware of the wide range of factors that may come into play in many situations they encounter. Some apparent boundaries and constraints are simply that— "apparent," not real. This premise comes from the extensive experience with QCQ's parent CyberQuest (CQ; Dickey, 1995a).

CQ is a qualitative tool and process used to help people generate ideas *and* ways to implement them. Over 600 cases with QCQ's parent system have shown that different ways of looking at a problem situation can lead to a variety of different approaches to solutions that enhance the benefits and reduce the costs associated with that situation.

Similarly, QCQ attempts to get users to look at quantitative relationships in a different way so that new perspectives and understandings can be gained and, as a result, new ways can be found to help improve decision making. One of the primary advantages of using QCQ is its ability to help identify the items on the right side of the knowledge matrix and move them to the left side so they can be dealt with.

As stated earlier, you can see that QCQ is more than quantitative; it also has a large qualitative component. This combination makes ACQ a more appropriate, but not possible now, handle.

1.3   The Public Administration Genome Project (PAGP)

Associated with QCQ is another system known as the PAGP. By way of background, according to the most recent census there are about 89,000 "governmental units" in the U.S. Obviously, there can be many problems associated with that large a number of public organizations acting at the same time. These problems include duplicative effort, conflicting purposes and goals, gaps in oversight of procedures and funds expenditure, confused mission values, and so on. Some new approaches to these and other issues appear to be needed.

To help respond to these needs, we have exerted a great amount of preliminary thought and action on an innovative, long term endeavor known as the Public Administration Genome Project (PAGP). The basic aim is to improve administrative theory, strategizing, decision-making behavior, and the general effectiveness of public managers.

The PAGP is composed of numerous unique one-word topics (the "genes"), variables containing combinations of these topics, and relationships between the variables. All of these are captured from source cases and stored in an information and guidance system (the COMprehensive Public Administrative Support System, or "ComPASS") to help use this knowledge in every day strategy development.

1.4   A Model of a Model (Meta-Model)

As might be anticipated, we refer to the factors, components, and the like associated with a given situation as "variables." In identifying such variables and their relationships in that situation, we are basically developing a "model," or analytic resemblance of reality, that can be employed to "explain" that situation. Under favorable circumstances, that model also can be used to make forecasts with respect to various decision possibilities (strategies, policies, programs, treatments, etc.). A model of such a model is presented in Figure 1.4.

There basically are six major types of variables (or conditions, factors, elements, etc.) that enter into a QCQ model—strategy, external, intermediate, time clock, reaction time, and goal. These are shown in Figure 1.4 along with many of the alternate names that crop up in the literature and in discussions in different fields of study.

Strategy variables are those presumed under the control of the client for whom the study is being made. In other words, it is assumed that the client is free to select any level of the strategy variable. Strategy variables are not affected by any other variables (no incoming arrows). External

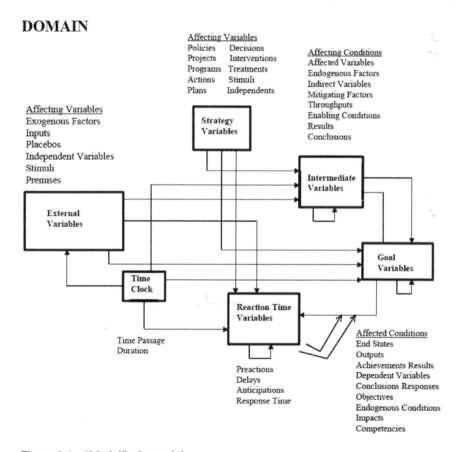

Figure 1.4 "Model" of a model.

variables, by contrast, are completely beyond the client's control. It is assumed, moreover, that nothing else affects them (except, perhaps, the passage of time). This assumption is made because there is a law of diminishing returns in regards to the number of variables that can be analyzed. We simply cannot study everything. We thus have drawn those limits because the benefits from studying those third and fourth echelon variables usually do not warrant the resources expended.

Goal variables are those that the client is explicitly trying to maximize or minimize. These may be factors like profits or costs or program benefits (for government projects). These variables are generally affected by other variables and occasionally also affect other variables.

In the middle of the show come the intermediate variables because they can affect or be affected by other variables. Intermediates are included to give a complete picture of the major interconnections in the system under study. They are influenced by strategy, external, and other intermediate variables. They also can influence themselves and, more importantly, the goal variables.

"Time" is another type of variable. It can be reflected in two ways—as points on a clock and as a reaction period. The former marches on constantly without ceasing—it is the ultimate invariate (with apologies to Einstein). The latter modulates in amount, depending on how it is influenced by different catalysts—other types of variables that affect the length of delay between cause and its associated effect. In other words, a reaction time is part of the relationship between a pair of variables (symbolized in Figure 1.4 by the crooked arrows that generally point to the connecting lines).

None of these relationships result in immediate impacts, however. All take a period of time to occur. Thus the "time clock"—documenting the passage of time—is an important causal factor in most situations. Moreover, this duration may not be constant but might depend on other variables (which may be thought of as catalysts, as in chemical reactions). The model resulting from all these considerations subsequently may turn out to be a rather complicated set of temporally-varied relationships.

1.5   A Simple Example

As an illustration of the meta-model in Figure 1.4, consider attempts by government to reduce traffic accidents and fatalities. These can be considered to be two goal variables. Possible strategy variables are speed limits and police enforcement levels. In the 1970s, for instance, the speed limit on Interstate highways in the U.S. was reduced to 55 miles per hour. This change was made primarily to save fuel (another goal variable) but also for safety purposes.

A primary external condition at that time was an increase in fuel prices brought about by the OPEC (Organization of Petroleum Exporting Countries) cartel. These increases affected the amount of driving that people did (an intermediate variable), as, according to basic economic theory, the quantity of a good or service consumed will decrease as the unit price of it increases. Less travel then meant fewer occasions for accidents (again, a goal variable). The speed limit reduction also contributed, in combination, to safety since it lead to slower travel (an intermediate condition) and thus to fewer and less severe accidents (e.g., an injury instead of a fatality).

If the units of the time clock were considered to be "years," then the reaction time ranged from –1 to 3 years since different states took different amounts of time to reset their speed limits (the minus sign indicates that some states did it in advance of the federal requirements—a "pre-action" time). The reaction time generally was influenced by the fuel price. As prices went up, the delay was less. This progression thus affected the length of time for the strategy to take effect.

A schematic of the connections among the selected strategy variables can be seen in Figure 1.5. This follows the framework of the meta-model in Figure 1.4 and provides a basis for further, more detailed exploration

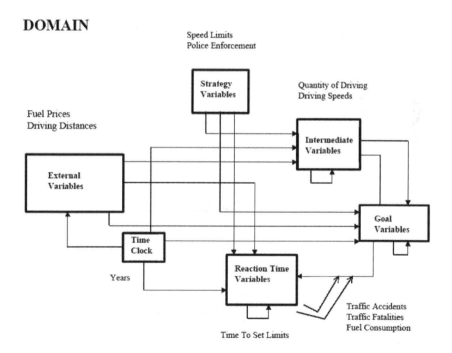

Figure 1.5   Model of traffic accidents and fatalities.

of the variables and their interrelationships. Such research can lead down some unusual "roads," so to speak. As one instance, an accident involved the turnover of a truck carrying a load of 11 million bees (this really happened), which opened their way for a major escape. Needless to say, the highway was closed for a period of time while a capable removal expert was found, hired, and cleared the area. In general, there could be hundreds of unique stories like this (another one was about a 60 foot bridge in Scotland being "stolen"), so the dimensions of a chart like that in Figure 1.5 could turn out to be immense.

1.6 What to Do? What to Do?

The possible combinations of elements in a case seem overwhelming. This is illustrated in the "causal diagram" in Figure 1.6. This was created in the "CAVE" at Virginia Tech (a virtual 3-D immersible environment) and contains almost 2,000 variables and over 1,300 relationships, most of which have been identified by Peter Hall and Ulrich Pfeiffer (2000) in their book on

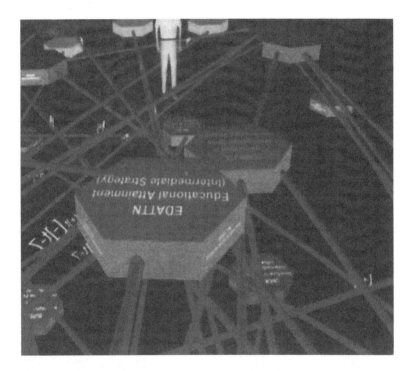

Figure 1.6 Looking at educational attainment in the CAVE. (Photo: Virginia Tech/ Rick Griffiths)

Figure 1.7 Another view of factors and relations affecting educational attainment. (Photo: Virginia Tech/Rick Griffiths)

the future of cities. The fun part of being in the CAVE is that you can "walk through" the "diagram/image" (actually, most of the time the person wielding the controller directs the diagram/image to move past him/herself). Regardless, the symbolism here is enticing—the entrance of the human controller (see Figure 1.7) allows for a much wider picture to be experienced.

Perhaps the main (and most general) symbolism here is that those tools and techniques that allow users to widen their experiences and sample cases more than likely will prompt these same users to make more informed designs, plans, policies, works of art, and the like. In sum, we assume that these tools will increase the users' SI, where some of the insights will be beyond what numbers alone can provide, particularly where numbers already play a leading role. We are not necessarily picking on numbers. In fact, a great example of what we are aiming for can be found in Brasilia (the new town capital of Brazil). In the 1960s, when many of the new structures were designed and built, the architect Niemeyer devised bridges, cathedrals, and other structures that theretofore would have been very difficult to analyze mathematically for safety and stability purposes (see Figure 1.8 and Figure 1.9). But they stood fast, and the computational approaches as well as aesthetics were copied over many years thereafter. So Niemeyer added a great sum to the SI in that arena.

The preceding division of SI into quantity and quality views certainly has its advocates and advantages, but there certainly are people on the other polarity. To make matters worse, there seems to be a strong division between "qualitative" and "quantitative" dimensions, with people in the latter category sometimes called "quants" or "quant-heads." It must be remembered on both sides, however, that the identification of any variable starts

Figure 1.8 A unique bridge design in Brasilia . (Photo Courtesy: Glaucia Maia)

Figure 1.9 The cathedral in Brasilia. (Photo Courtesy: Glaucia Maia)

with a fuzzy notion and works its way up to a clear statement. For example: What is our country's population? Does it include citizens working out of the country? Children of visiting workers? Those who do not have a birth certificate? Dual citizens? After we get these issues settled, we may then possibly get into some serious quantitative analysis.

In any case, we have identified five general approaches to quantitative-qualitative analysis and synthesis that have helped guide our thinking in developing QCQ and the PAGP together as a form of supernumerary intelligence. These approaches are:

- statistics (primarily regression),
- systems analysis and dynamics,
- research methodology,
- qualitative research, and
- artificial intelligence.

All of these have some very powerful features that have been used widely and with some success in the past. They also have some drawbacks—mainly, although far from totally, is their lack of coverage of the features of the other four approaches.

Since the QCQ/PAGP represents an attempt to meld these five into one (while also incorporating some additional unique features), it is worthwhile to review the five to point to their general strengths and weaknesses. This will help considerably in developing a "wish list" of characteristics for a supernumerary intelligence. In each area we have selected one book that we feel best represents that area and used it as a takeoff point for discussion.

──

Important Note
A fairly exhaustive set of characteristics for a "wish list" for SI is presented in Appendix C.

1.7 Traditional Approaches

The conceptual diagram in Figure 1.4 gives a vision of the nature of the desired end product—a set of quantitative and qualitative variables and relationships (a model) that enables us both to explain and to forecast the impact of selected strategies on goal variables of importance. In this section we review our traditional approaches with a view as to how they help us and how they might fall short.

1.7.1 Regression

Regression as a technique for curve fitting goes back to the mid-1800s [INT-17 Regression], although there is evidence that Gauss [INT-6 Gauss] and D'Alembert employed a similar technique for analyzing the motions of rigid bodies in the late 1700s [INT-5 d'Alembert]. It was around that time that the notion of the squared deviation arrived. This gave birth to the process of minimizing the sum of the squared deviations, followed by the now well-known goodness of fit (GoF) (e.g., the correlation coefficient).

Pedhazur (1982) has summarized nicely and completely many of the techniques and philosophies that have grown from these starting points. His discussion includes linear bivariate and multiple regression, "controlling," covariance analysis, some nonlinear regression, time series, and then development of systems of linear relationships via path analysis and LISREL. Techniques dealing with a mixture of ratio-scaled and nominal-scaled variables also are addressed. As with most statistics texts, Pedhazur's book deals extensively with experimental designs as well as sampling and hypothesis testing.

The overwhelming advantage of regression is that it enables us to replace what may be a large amount of data with one equation (or a small set). Prediction therefore is made much more systematic, generalizable, and faster. Moreover, literally hundreds of variables can be taken into account at one time, a feat that basically is impossible for the human mind left to its own devices. Add to these the capabilities to:

1. determine the goodness of fit of the relationship (with the correlation coefficient),
2. assess the contributions of individual variables through partial correlation and "controlling,"
3. derive conclusions based on samples of data,

and the power of regression is seen as very convincing.

The overwhelming disadvantage of regression is, strangely, its ease of use. Readily available software packages make it extremely easy simply to "drop" data into the program. This can be done without giving much thought to the:

1. nature and appropriateness of the definitions, measures, validities, precisions (and so on) of the variables;
2. limits on variable range, which might make all-too-common linearization improper; and

3. adoption of the squared error—which may give undesired emphasis to outliers—as the sole measure of goodness of fit.

Moreover, as in most statistical procedures, the focus is on a relatively shallow understanding of a large number of cases as opposed to an in-depth comprehension of a few (as in case studies).

1.7.2 *Systems Analysis and Dynamics*

Systems analysis is best known for its use in the military and for its great success in the space program. It is doubtful that the U.S. would have been able to land a person on the moon without it. Systems dynamics is one kind of systems analysis developed primarily by Forrester (1968). It is the study of how systems change. It has been used extensively for dissecting—and making long term forecasts for—social, economic, and environmental systems in the famous "Limits to Growth" studies. (Meadows, Meadows, Randers, & Behrens, 1972; Meadows, Randers, & Meadows, 2004) [INT-19 Smithsonian magazine].

Forrester has laid out the principles of systems in his book of the same title (1968). The basic theory is that systems change as the variables within that system change. The current level of a variable in a system is determined by: (1) the level of other variables in that system in the preceding period of time; (2) the rate of change of selected variables; and (3) the length of the period of time under consideration. The rates of change, meanwhile, are determined by levels and differences in levels.

The strengths of systems analysis and dynamics are many. For example, very large systems, with 1,000s of variables, can be addressed. These systems are clearly seen as dynamic—that is, changing over time. Indeed, it is difficult to conceive of any system not being so. Second, nonlinear relationships are the rule rather than the exception. Third, data for checking can be brought in at any point or combination of points in the process—or not at all. The latter allows well-developed theories to be incorporated without need for data to calibrate them again.

Systems dynamics models tend to replicate real world processes and incorporate strategy/policy variables. Because variable ranges can be established and maintained, systems dynamics models can be used to set up different scenarios and extrapolate future impacts. In so doing, various temporary and permanent "shocks" and smaller random deviations can be applied to the system.

Since systems dynamics models are very explicit and rely on specified orders of calculations, they rate very highly on logical consistency, conceivable refutation by skeptics, and changing of thought about the scientific and policy-making world.

Perhaps the greatest drawback to system dynamics is that it offers no explicit way to calibrate and/or validate the equations vis-à-vis data. Hence there is little to insure that the proper variables are being used, that they are defined in meaningful ways, and that estimated and/or forecasted values are close to "real" ones. In sum, a systems dynamics model cannot be tested without some further enhancement of the technique.

1.7.3   Research Methodology

Education in almost every scientific discipline requires a course in research methodology. This focuses on the basics of the scientific process that has brought so much understanding and worthwhile progress to the world.

Babbie's (1998) book on social science research methodology is a continually updated classic text in the field. Although it does deal briefly with analytic techniques, its main emphasis is on the nature, collection, and interpretation of data and information. This emphasis places the focus on such issues as the:

- character and structure of inquiry;
- nature of theory;
- notion of causation;
- definition and measurement of variables as well as identification of scales, indices, validity and accuracy;
- unobtrusive and obtrusive surveys, case studies;
- specification of reliability, representativeness, measurement error, and the handling of missing values.

The main advantage of research methodological thinking is that it forces users to be very careful and systematic in their approach to studying a topic; otherwise, it is difficult to draw any logical conclusions. Words and mathematical symbols quickly lose their meanings and the world becomes a jumble of unsubstantiated and often erroneous claims.

On the negative side, research methodological thinking generally does not go far enough to enable estimation and forecasting. The basic understanding it provides is fine, but that understanding has to be turned into worthwhile forecasts that will help us live the rest of our lives in order to be truly beneficial.

1.7.4 Qualitative Research

As might be imagined, this topic has some close alliances with research methodology. Although it has a heavy concern for the way in which data are specified, collected, and interpreted, its main concern is in the breadth of factors that are identified and their agreed-upon meaning.

Lincoln and Guba (1985) as well as Spradley (1979) are perhaps the best known authors in this field. A combination of their methods employed by Roe and Dickey (1992) involved:

- Data collection in the natural setting in which activities were occurring, so that the varieties of realities can be seen;
- Use of a human "instrument" for the fullest interpretation of the nature and extent of the activities;
- A focus on tacit knowledge—that which people cannot talk about or express in direct ways—as well as stated knowledge;
- Purposeful sampling—that in which the goal is to expand the variety of information received so that the next interview (observation) is based on the results of theories of information relevant to the concepts being investigated—also, analysis of the semantic relationships, including cause-effect, rationale, sequence, location, and so on;
- Taxonomic analysis—putting things in categories—and comparing to previous results;
- Domain analysis—to find relationships and areas of similarities and differences;
- Grounded theory—identification of recurrent themes—and general assertions that can be applied to other situations.

The strengths of qualitative research are manifold. A wide variety of important factors and relationships can be identified and viewed from a variety of perspectives so that little of significance is missed. Purposeful sampling provides a direction and an economy in data collection, and semantic analysis helps break down wording into relevant scientific categories (e.g., cause–effect). Finally, a set of theories is derived, grounded in all the data collected and the analysis previously undertaken.

The weakness of qualitative research is that, like general research methodology, it does not go far enough. While an in-depth understanding of an existing situation obviously is helpful to have, it may not be directly convertible into beneficial future actions. Changes in client strategies and external forces may lead in directions and amounts somewhat different from the past. Thus, some type of quantitative forecasting mechanism is needed to supplement the in-depth analysis.

1.7.5 Artificial Intelligence (AI)

In its beginning AI research specifically avoided any focus on the quantitative. More recently, there have been many efforts to fill in this missing gap. The book *Scientific Discovery* by Langley, Simon, Bradshaw, and Zytkow (1987) perhaps has been the prominent forerunner in this effort.

These authors looked at the history of a set of scientific discoveries and tried to develop a set of techniques that would replicate the process used to create the associated mathematical relationships (e.g., for Boyle's Law, connecting the pressure, temperature, and volume of a gas).The process involved combining variables and raising them to powers depending on the nature of the current discrepancies with the data. This recursive procedure was continued until the fit of the resultant mathematical relationship was judged to be "close enough."

The main advantage of the Langley et al. (1987) approach is that it gets away from the traditional linear relationship. There is also some evidence that scientists actually may have thought in the way simulated by the process. This kind of "scientific expert system," in typical AI fashion, would open the door for others (and/or computers) to use the same approach without having to be on the same intellectual or resource level as scientists.

Two major and immediate drawbacks to the Langley et al. (1987) approach are that it cannot handle very many variables nor can it deal with simultaneity. A much broader disadvantage, however, is the underlying assumption that "scientific discovery" essentially is curve fitting. In actuality, much important scientific work is manifested in finding the important variables and concepts; defining and measuring them correctly; carrying out novel, well-conceived experiments; and interpreting the results in a fashion that leads to further discoveries. Basically, the Langley et al. approach lacks the "front end" that, for example, research methodological thinking provides.

1.8 Crosscutting Concepts

Now built in to many government and private business projects are expanded efforts to collect more and more information and to improve analysis methods. These two tasks generally crisscross the five approaches described above and have been referred to lately as "big data" and "analytics," respectively.

1.8.1 Big/Wide Data

As alluded to above, lurking behind the five approaches in many instances is the need for, and provision of, "big data" as well as the hardware and software to gather and analyze it. According to Wikipedia [INT-7 Big Data]

> In information technology, "big data" is a collection of data sets so large and complex that it becomes difficult to process using on-hand database management tools or traditional data processing applications. The challenges include capture, curation, storage, search, sharing, analysis, and visualization.

Further along in that article:

> the trend to larger data sets is due to the additional information derivable from analysis of a single large set of related data ... allowing correlations to be located in a variety of arenas: business opportunities, relevant research, criminal activities, expressway traffic and associated weather conditions.

There is some question about where "big data" starts and where "smaller, wider data" drops off (if, in fact, it does so). We are more familiar with having a large number of databases of a smaller size. For instance, Birdsall (2004) was overseer of a Department of Defense project to meld over 700 logistics information systems into one central capability (see Chapter 18). Kim was heavily involved in the substantial transformation of the Seoul (Korea) bus system, including databases (no small task given a city the size of New York; see Chapter 17). And Larkin is the director of what is thought to be the largest PhD program in public administration in the world (Chapter 16). No lack of data there.

The point is that no matter whether it is bigger or wider data sets, there is a great potential to sift out some very interesting relationships that may lead to significant gains in SI.

1.8.2 Analytics

"Analytics" is the discovery and communication of meaningful patterns in data. Especially valuable in areas rich with recorded information, analytics relies on the simultaneous application of statistics, computer programming, and operations research to quantify performance. Analytics often favors data visualization to communicate insight [INT-3 Analytics].

Analytics has two sides to it. One side involves descriptive and predictive models to gain useful knowledge from data—that side is "data analysis." On the other, analytics uses insights so derived to suggest or to guide decision making.

Analytics therefore is not so much concerned with individual analyses or analysis steps, but with the entire *methodology*. There is a pronounced tendency to use the term analytics in business settings—for example, *text analytics* versus the more generic *text mining* to emphasize this broader perspective [INT-3 Analytics].

From these descriptions of analytics and comparisons to QCQ and the PAGP it is easy to see some of the many ways in which they are complementary to each other.

1.9   The Making of Supernumerary Intelligence, Part I

SI is more than merely bringing the quantitative and the qualitative together. If that's all we were trying to do, it would be little more than a mixed methods approach to research. Our goal is to develop a cohesive philosophy and strategy that actually melds the two methods into one. The purpose of QCQ, as noted earlier, is to serve as an analytic tool to help users develop meaningful models within the framework of the meta-model in Figure 1.4. The PAGP serves as a main data repository for the effort. Once developed to their fullest, such models can help people forecast the future (since, as it is said, that is where we will be spending the rest of our lives). These forecasts can be made for different "what if" strategy conditions and various anticipated external condition levels. Such analyses hopefully will lead to more beneficial decisions, plans, projects, policies... (let us just leave it as very generic "plans").

As the subtitle of this book suggests, it is focused primarily on considerably improving the analytics aspect of the resulting plan or process. While this may be enough, there also is a substantial interest in developing and/or revising the whole process, involving as it does all the components of SI.

The scorecard for all our efforts thus will be measured in terms of how well we improve the:

- outputs of QCQ and the PAGP, both qualitative and quantitative;
- inputs from the five traditional (and other?) fields;
- usefulness of big/wide data sets;
- nature, "awareness," and applicability of analytic tools.

An example along these lines that always appealed to us is Yuzo Yasuda's (1991) *40 Years, 20 Million Ideas: The Toyota Suggestion System* (Japan Management Association).

The rest of the book focuses on the details and applications of the QCQ seven step process for exploring, developing, and using variables and relationships to help address problems and/or achieve identified goals. Then, periodically, the PAGP is called upon to demonstrate its role in helping to develop ideas to overcome the aforementioned problems. Each of the seven steps in QCQ subsequently is elaborated in one or more succeeding chapters thereafter. By the end, the reader should have a good grasp of the fundamentals and the way in which QCQ and the PAGP have been and can be utilized to help develop and apply analytical models that assist in bringing the user to a greater "know what we know" state.

Three expanded examples of this process are provided. The first, in the next chapter, deals with some of the managerial aspects for a school district that bought tablet computers for all its teachers and staff. The second application is focused on the provision of adequate parking spaces in planned shopping centers. The last application, seen across the succeeding chapters, uses U.S. urban carbon monoxide concentrations as the main variable of concern. This is seen as depending on such factors as GDP per person, CO emission rates, federal air pollution control expenditures, and a catalyst affecting abatement program development times.

2

A Different Approach

Now that a broad overview has been presented, we will be able to illustrate, in this and the next chapter, the development and use of QCQ and the PAGP on two different problems (or, seen another way—two different "opportunities"). These will be followed by an extended example that covers most of the remaining chapters.

To start on the first case: suppose an elementary school teacher along with all her colleagues recently was given a popular tablet computer by her school district to use in her teaching activities. This led us to think about what we would do under similar circumstances, including scenarios that involved tablets in a variety of educational management situations, and also, of course, involved the use of QCQ and the PAGP. We felt that this would make a more concrete (make that "silicon") way to illustrate the process and the outcomes.

Suppose you were appointed the manager of this tablet program for a medium-sized school district. A rash of announcements about similar programs elsewhere lately had convinced the local school board that they wanted to investigate the possibility here. You suggested, wisely, that the project start small so as not to cost the Board a lot in early misapplications.

Supernumerary Intelligence, pages 23–41
Copyright © 2015 by Information Age Publishing

From many years of experience and education you knew that you and those working with you on this project would have to develop a "model" (which sounded rather sophisticated, but really was what was fairly basic) that would be a guide for the group in finding the best (forecasted) approach to the opportunity at hand.

2.1 A Model of a Model (Meta-Model)

"When we are trying to discover and utilize variables and relationships in a situation," you said to your newly appointed team, "we basically are trying to develop a 'model,' or analytic resemblance of reality, that can be employed to 'explain' that situation." That model then can be utilized to make forecasts with respect to various decision possibilities (strategies, policies, programs, treatments, etc.). A model of such a model, you pointed out, was presented in Figure 1.4.

You continued talking with the team about the six major types of variables (or conditions, factors, elements, etc.) that enter into a model—strategy, external, intermediate, time clock, reaction time, and goal. You also showed them the exhibit in Figure 1.4, along with many of the alternate names that can crop up in discussions with people from different social, academic, and professional backgrounds.

You subsequently walked the team through the "rules" about the nature of each of the variable types (see Section 1.4). A schematic of the connections among the selected strategy variables can be seen in Figure 1.5. "This follows the framework of the meta-model in Figure 1.4 and provides a basis for more detailed exploration of the variables and their interrelationships," you said in closing the team's first meeting.

2.2 Quantitative CyberQuest (QCQ)

In a succeeding set of small training sessions, you had to become a quick learning manager, reiterating that Quantitative CyberQuest (QCQ) was intended to expand your effort into greater analytic (qualitative as well as quantitative) discovery arenas. QCQ basically is a combination of the qual and quant, the five traditional approaches, and the two cross-cutting concepts (analytics and big/wide data) described in Chapter 1.

QCQ guides the user through what eventually should become a familiar seven step process that is presented graphically in Figure 2.1.

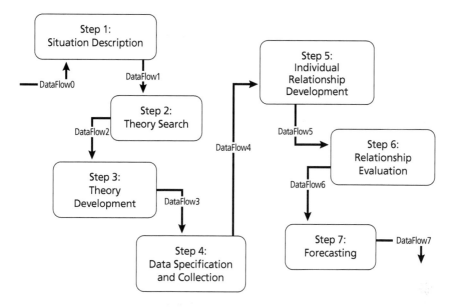

Figure 2.1   Steps in the QCQ process.

In the first step the background of the situation under study is documented, focusing on such items as the aim, client, user, horizon, developer, and date. Various goals for the project also are elicited.

The next step (Step 2) involves "theory search." This is a somewhat academic way of saying that if no useful explanation ("theory" or model) is immediately available to show the client how to reach an acceptable level of the prescribed goals, then an exploration is made to locate the best available causal variables and relationships.

In Step 3, "theory development," the findings from the preceding steps are utilized to produce a "possible links" diagram (i.e., an outline of a new theory/model). The included variables then are classified into goals, intermediates, externals, strategies, time clock, and reaction times. See Figures 1.4 and 1.5.

QCQ Step 4 focuses on the specification and collection of data relevant to the model. For each potential variable, questions are asked about such items as measurement, validity, reliability, and sample size as well as completeness and coverage of extremes. If some of the variables are quantified, then operational ranges can be established for them.

In the fifth step individual relationships are developed. The user is questioned about the likely structure of the relationship for each dependent (goal, intermediate, and possibly reaction time) variable. The eligible combinations of mathematical forms to represent these structures, while keeping within the operational ranges of the associated variables, then are identified. Time affinities (delays or anticipations) are specified, as well as catalysts that may influence these. Regression-like fits subsequently are made to the available quantity data to help come up with sets of what are referred to here as "pre-equalities" (potential equality relationships from which a final one will be selected) for each dependent (goal, intermediate, reaction time, and catalyst) variable.

In Step 6 the set of relationships (pre-equalities) thus developed is evaluated and a choice is made of the best representative for the respective dependent variable. This assessment and decision is based not only on goodness of fit but also on such qualitative factors as logical consistency, confirmability, novelty, resolution of paradoxes, and even beauty and harmony.

In the last step the model is employed to make forecasts. These can made under various "what if" scenarios where the values of the external and other variables can be changed. Perhaps more importantly, different settings for each strategy (or policy or decision) variable can be assumed and the impacts of these on the goal variables predicted.

These kinds of outputs then will allow the team to move from a relatively unknown state to a relatively known state (Figure 1.3) in their understanding of the situation. That gain in intelligence creates one of the most solid approaches for the eventual successful design and implementation of a plan.

2.3   The Public Administration Genome Project (PAGP)

The PAGP presents an almost wholly different but integratable aspect and methodology from QCQ. Although different, the PAGP can be an influence upon every step in the QCQ process (see Figure 2.2). As imagined so far, the PAGP has many analogies to the genes in the human body. The latter has a set of about 35,000 genes replicated in each of the body's trillions of cells. Similarly, we estimate that there may be approximately 35,000 mainly single word "topics" that guide public administrative behavior and thus can be found in complicated situations in numerous public organizations.

Similar to the Human Genome Project (HGP), one of the long term goals for the PAGP is to "map" these PA "genes" (that is, "topics," formally called "cistrons"). The developers also want to map clusters thereof (call them variables or "operons") and their relationships ("kineses"). The hoped for outcome should be improved PA theory and a better understanding of administrative actors and their actions. Perhaps equally important is

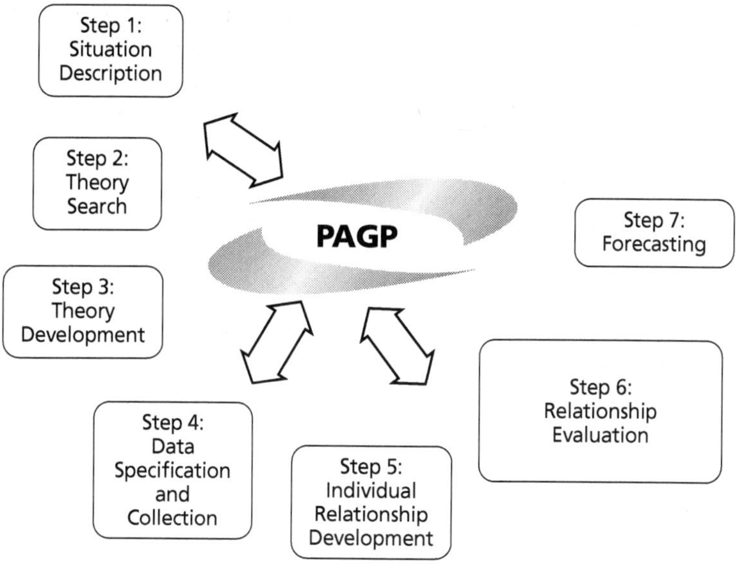

Figure 2.2 The PAGP can be employed in any step in the QCQ process.

the continued formalization and "filling" of an information and guidance system (called "ComPASS") to help use this knowledge, both in every day and in unusual strategy development situations—all to enhance general PA decision making.

As mentioned above, a "topic" usually has been taken as being a single word (noting that, for many people, a "topic" is thought of as a much broader concept). Meanwhile, a "variable," as defined above, is a combination of one or more topics, assumed to be preceded by a phrase like "The amount of…" or "The level of…" or equivalent. To illustrate, in one example case there is a variable called PRIVVIO, which is ("the amount of") privacy violations. This variable thus contains the two topics—"privacy" and "violation."

As a further elaboration, the developers of the PAGP have analyzed one version of Nobel Laureate Elinor Ostrom's (1999) institutional analysis and development (IAD) theory (Dickey, 2009) and found 272 variables and 254 relations. From the former were derived 426 unique topics (which was a surprisingly large number, indicating the complexity of some theories).

The PAGP currently is estimated to contain over 5,000 topics, more than 14,000 variables (vars), and about 1,500 bivariate relationships (rels). All of these come from over 75 "source cases," about 70 of which are on the web.

"These source cases now can be searched," you as tablet manager said to the team, "as part of any step in QCQ for similar situations (whole cases, 'chunks' thereof, or individual variables, and/or relations), all to see what can be learned and applied successfully."

2.4   A Semi-Real Exercise

With the preceding background and a little extra research, the team was ready to try a "real" (but scaled down) exercise. Their immediate question was "How can we keep up with the number of purchases and repairs of hundreds of the tablets throughout the school district, especially if we do not know how many tablets we have and how many more we need?" These questions led to the initiation of QCQ (the reader can follow the steps in Section 2.2 and below). With each step we will show some sample qualitative illustrations.

2.4.1   QCQ Step 1: Situation Description

The first task (step) involved identification of the client, central aim (goal), and other background information as well as all the other main goals to be addressed.

- ▪ main aim (goal): good estimate of computer tablets purchased
- ▪ client: school district maintenance and operation team (DMOT)
- ▪ person developing model: team leader (TL)

Another goal then came in sight as part of an initial informal team get-together:

- ▪ get quicker learning of the machines

This turned out to be nothing brand new, but it did not surface (go from "Things that you did not know that you knew" to those you knew) until a perusal of a "dimensions" checklist in QCQ (see Chapter 4) under a topic on that list of "general economic climate."

At this point (we pretend) the team had run out of new goals to be made part of the study. They then went on to Step 2.

Sample Qualitative Items:
The aim itself and all the preliminary descriptions of variables.

2.4.2   *QCQ Step 2: Theory Search*

Having identified the main goals to be achieved, the DMOT's exercise in this step involved the search for well-known, general theories and also not-so-well-known, localized theories (e.g., the boss's concept) that may help in understanding the situation—and, as a result, the variables and relationships that could affect the current set of goals and any already connected variables.

The first source to be tackled was a "search of informational networks." So, naturally, the team went to the Internet. One member happened upon The Weather Channel and came up with the rather important idea (variable):

Get tablets that are least affected by the sun's glare.

This produced a strange reaction. "Yes," the team guessed, "you would be likely to get more and better usage in a low glare environment, but the cost may be much higher." Nonetheless, the DMOT was not hesitant to keep this seemingly high-cost idea alive (and part of the "possible links" model they were building). They could always eliminate it later. Meanwhile, many other ideas for variables affecting the goals were being generated (but, to keep this example simple, let us assume they were ignored).

After a rest, the team members still wanted to keep going, so they went on to the next QCQ step.

Sample Qualitative Items:
All the descriptions, definitions, and measures of the variables.

2.4.3   *QCQ Step 3: Theory (Local) Development*

Now that some of the main goals and the variables that affect and are affected by them have been envisioned, the objective in Step 3 became to start putting together a rough "parts and relations" for the tablet group.

The team scoured the literature and interviewed experienced people nearby. No clearly superior model (theory) was found. But they did find a need for a very basic model that captures one type of the connection between the number of students, teachers, staff, and tablet computers in possession of the teachers and staff.

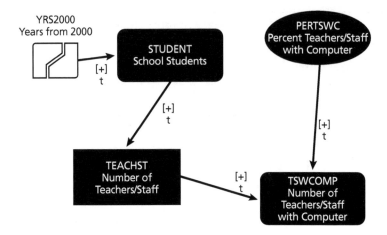

Figure 2.3 The basic model.

The team subsequently identified five basic variables and potential linkages for the new model. They then put them in a QCQ-style diagram (see Figure 2.3), followed by a tabular presentation (see Table 2.1) showing the variables and their influences placed appropriately under QCQ's role headings.

The fundamental notion is that the number of tablet computers purchased and distributed essentially is student-size driven (an external force of about 1,000 that is anticipated to grow approximately 3% per year). The number of faculty/staff hired (intermediate variable) is roughly 10% of that level. The quantity of tablets purchased to date is a strategic variable that, for budget purposes, has been set up by the school district as an increasing percentage over the years of the number of faculty/staff on board. The percentages are roughly in a normal distribution. One-hundred percent is reached in 2018.

Sample Qualitative Items:
Descriptions of variables and their relations in the basic model.
Assumptions.

2.4.4 PAGP (Temporary Interruption to Use the PAGP)

Just to demonstrate that it can be useful to stop temporarily at certain points in QCQ, the DMOT started a separate interaction with the Public Administration Genome Project (PAGP, see Chapter 15). The sequence of events in this endeavor was as follows:

TABLE 2.1   Variables Along with Influences in Basic Model

CASE: School Computers
DATE: 08-28-2013 TIME: 14:09:22
===
ID CODE and DESCRIPTION (Subject and Action/Status)
===
      UNSPECIFIED VARIABLES
―――
,,
      CLIENT STRATEGY VARIABLES
―――
* 1* PERTSWC Percent Teachers/Staff with Computer
,,
      TIME CLOCK VARIABLE
―――
* 1* YRS2000 Years from 2000
,,
      INTERMEDIATE VARIABLES
―――
* 1* TEACHST Number of Teachers/Staff
    {+}[t](0) STUDENT School Students
,,
      GOAL VARIABLES
―――
* 0* TSWCOMP Number of Teachers/Staff with Computer
    {+}[t](0) PERTSWC Percent Teachers/Staff with Computer
    {+}[t](0) TEACHST Number of Teachers/Staff
,,
      RE/PRE ACTION TIME VARIABLES
―――
,,
      EXTERNAL [f(Time)] VARIABLES
―――
* 1* STUDENT School Students
    {+}[t](0) YRS2000 Years from 2000
,,
      EXTERNAL [Data] VARIABLES
―――

Note: Legend
  xx Number of Other Variables Directly Influenced by that Variable
  {xx} Type of Relationship (e.g., {+ } is Monotonically Increasing)
  [xx] Time Relationship (e.g., [t-2] is a Delay of 2 Time Periods)
  (xx) Number of Cause-Effect Questions Answered Positively (Out of 6)
  <C> Catalyst Affects the Reaction Time of the Relationship)

1. The team picked a word that best summarized the aim of the whole exercise. After some debate, they agreed that, being that they were at the beginning of their efforts, the most important word probably was "mission."
2. They then went to the home page of the PAGP, which was pagenome-compass.pbworks.com. Even though they were new-comers to the PAGP and therefore should have studied it more

thoroughly beforehand, like everyone else in the world, they were pressed for time. So they took a quick look at the list of cases, saw some titles that appeared promising, and returned to the PAGP front (home) page.

3. They had heard that there were three different databases (views) of the cases, so they clicked on the one that they felt looked most promising—"Variables in Relationships." This got them to the front page of that database.

4. They subsequently entered the "mission" word in the search box in the upper right corner and pushed "enter." The result was a listing of the (many) cases in which the word "mission" appears.

5. They browsed through that list of matching cases and decided that the one dealing with "Food Program Management" could have the most similarity to theirs. They then pressed the "Ctrl-f" keys together, causing another search box to enfold. They again entered the word "mission" and pressed "enter." The matching variables *inside* the case then were made known.

6. The team subsequently picked out the variables:
   - AWARD Recognition/Awards Given Achievers
   - EMPOWER Empowerment of Front-Line Staff
   - ERROR Food Stamp Benefits Accuracy Percentage
   - MANAGE Managers are Good at Management
   - MEDIA Unfavorable Media Exposure
   - UPWARD Upward Mobility of Career Path

   Also, another matching variable (ACCOMP) affects three other variables (thus the *3* in front of it), and these three also can be considered as influencing variables.

7. In the informal brain-storming session that followed, the team was particularly taken by the "UPWARD" variable. This made them realize, first, that the mission should reflect the rule that there always has to be a path to reach at least one goal from any place in the network, and, second, that each goal has to have at least one path to get to it. They subsequently wanted to add two temporary variables (called "OUTWARD" and "INWARD") to reflect these concerns. The DMOT decided, however, to postpone these until the next version.

Later discussions led to the conclusion that the PAGP trial results and process gained much appeal with the DMOT.

Sample Qualitative Items:
PA Cases in the PAGP. Matching words in the search progress.

2.4.5 QCQ Step 4: Data Specification and Collection

Having now identified most if not all of the desirable variables and relationships needed for the model in this case, it now was time for the DMOT to get as much "hard" data as possible to help bolster their case for the kind of organization and operations to which they seemed to be heading. They certainly faced no dearth of data, since it seemed to be almost as much as in those organizations who worked with so-called "big data."

The team started to focus on the sources, nature, quantity, and quality of what was available. In fact, the manufacturer of the tablet had a definite Japanese total quality management (TQM) style (Deming, 1986)), which produced lots of data, and the school district superintendent also had worked hard at collecting performance data from its operating arms. As a result, the team created a second team to start immediately on collecting data in a format that reflected the nature of the five "variables" already "in play" (see Table 2.2). For example, the STUDENT variable's data reflected those people in attendance (not formally on health leave) in at least two courses for at least 80% of each course's class time.

Figure 2.4 shows a chart of one set of data. As can be seen, it is rather smooth in its acceleration. If it were chaotic, this naturally would be difficult to use productively.

The manufacturer was to undertake a nationwide sample survey of possible education buyers in a relatively common "research methods" endeavor. The hypothesis to be addressed was that those education buyers who had worked at a full-time job before—ranging from auto mechanics to computer hacks—were more likely to enroll.

TABLE 2.2 Full Set of Historic Data

YEAR	PERTSWC	STUDENT	TEACHST	TSWCOMP	YRS2000
2003	0	1000	100	0	3
2004	4	1031	104	4	4
2005	6	1070	109	7	5
2006	15	1110	114	17	6
2007	24	1115	117	28	7
2008	39	1140	123	60	8
2009	46	1150	123	69	9
2010	55	1190	124	86	10
2011	66	1234	131	102	11
2012	76	1289	133	113	12
2013	83	1330	135	121	13

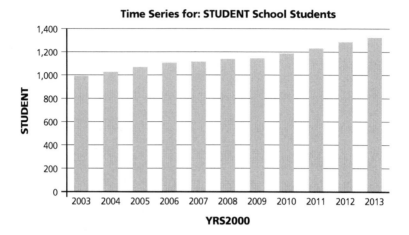

Figure 2.4 Example student data vs. time.

Meanwhile, the DMOT and their leader (you) were working face-to-face with individuals in smaller, local groups but on the same topic. The researchers were using predominately qualitative research methods, getting close to a small number of families, watching each decision on education very carefully, and recording those that seemed to result in an enrollment (or a loss). From these they hoped to create a manual of sorts to aid future work in predicting enrollments.

One immediate difficulty was that the team needed a mathematical model to make the calculation procedure quicker and less questionable than that supported just by individual human "biases." In preparation for such a model, QCQ first asks if there is an upper and lower limit on any of the variables. For instance, the strategy variable (PERTSWC—%Teachers/Staff with a Computer) has a lower limit of 0 and (assumedly) has an upper limit of 100 (%) . Meanwhile, YRS2000 marches on from 0 (year 2000), conceivably to be a large number (taken as + infinity).

2.4.6   *QCQ Step 5: Individual Relationship Development*

Continuing from the previous step, the DMOT now turned to creation of each individual relationship. First it asked about the expected or desired sign (+ or –) of the relationship. It then presented the user with some choices—called "warrants"—for a two dimensional association of one of the applicable mathematical (regression) options. The 2-D displays are available for calibrating part of an equation to represent the situation at hand. One of those options (generally as a fallback) is a linear regression.

A sample of some of the "art work" shown to users when they are in the process of establishing a warrant can be seen in Figures 2.5a and 2.5b. The users then have to make a choice, while they wait for the computer to establish and/or straighten out the data and some of the corresponding qualitative materials. In this situation it is an exponential (Warrant 22) that looks best statistically. (See Appendix G for table of warrants.)

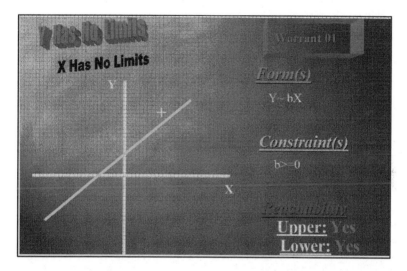

Figure 2.5a Warrant 01: Linear.

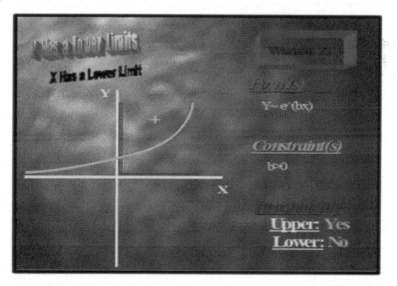

Figure 2.5b Warrant 22: Exponential.

TABLE 2.3   Calibration Report: STUDENT vs. YRS2000

EQUATION(S) FOR: STUDENT School Students

   With 11 Eligible Observations

Where the Objective is to:

Maximize the Coefficient of Determination (R2)

BASE STATISTICS ###### for STUDENT<t>

Upper Limit = 1E+38 Lower Limit = 0 Mean = 1150.727

Standard Deviation = 103.2454

Maximum Absolute Deviation (MAXAD) = 179.2727

Maximum Absolute % Deviation (MAXPD) = 15.57908

Mean Absolute Deviation (MAD) = 80.01653

Mean Absolute % Deviation (MAPD) = 6.953562

Maximum Value = 1330 Minimum Value = 1000

EXISTING EQUATION

   (None Currently)

UNCONSTRAINED LEAST SQUARES LINEAR REGRESSION

     STUDENT<t> = c1+c2*{YRS2000<t>}

     Where: c1 = 905.41 c2 = 30.66

|||||| Descriptions ||||||

STUDENT = School Students YRS2000 = Years from 2000

||||||||||||||||||||||||||

*** Associated Goodness-Of-Fit (GOF) Statistics ***

Standard Error = 18.76089

Maximum Absolute Error (MINIMAX) = 31.39099

Maximum Absolute % Error (MINIMAX%) = 2.729651

Mean Absolute Error (MAE) = 14.17346

Mean Absolute % Error (MAPE) = 1.200213

Coefficient of Determination (R2) = 0.9702828

Correlation Coefficient (R) = 0.9850293

++++ Advantages ++++

  Usually Best Goodness-of Fit-Value

  Linear Usually Best for Forecasting

    (If No Other Problems Exist)

  Linear Equation Usually Easiest to Understand

  Parsimonious (Uses Just 2 Parameters)

  All Observed Values of STUDENT<t> are Reproducible by the Equation

---- Disadvantages ----

  Potentially Illogical Situation: This Equation Will Give a Value for

  STUDENT<t> of 905.4 when All the Independent Variables

    Are 0 (or at Their Corresponding [Usually Lower] Limits).

  This Equation Will Give a Value of No Less than 905.419

  for STUDENT<t>. This is Higher than its Lower Limit of 0.

(continued)

TABLE 2.3   Calibration Report: STUDENT vs. YRS2000 (continued)

LEAST SQUARES LN LINEAR REGRESSION

STUDENT<t> = 1000*{c1*Exp(c2*{YRS2000<t>})}

Where: c1 = 0.9271246   c2 = 0.0265548

|||||| Descriptions ||||||

STUDENT = School Students YRS2000 = Years from 2000

*** Associated Goodness-Of-Fit (GOF) Statistics ***

Standard Error = 16.67031

Maximum Absolute Error (MINIMAX) = 27.42029

Maximum Absolute % Error (MINIMAX%) = 2.384373

Mean Absolute Error (MAE) = 12.34795

Mean Absolute % Error (MAPE) = 1.050226

Coefficient of Determination (R2) = 0.9765368

Correlation Coefficient (R) = 0.9881988

++++ Advantages ++++

   Usually Best Goodness-of-Fit Value

   Fairly Good for Forecasting (If No Other Problems Exist)

   Parsimonious (Uses Just 2 Parameters) No Violation of Limits

---- Disadvantages ----

   Less Easy to Understand Than Linear

   This Equation Will Give a Value of No Less Than 2527.232

      for STUDENT<t>. This is Higher Than its Lower Limit of 0

   There is (are) 11 Observed Value(s) of STUDENT<t>

      Too Low to be Reproducible by This Equation

The output of this exercise is a calibration report like that in Table 2.3. This not only presents the alternate equations but all the relevant statistics and several notes on the advantages and disadvantages of the equation under some situations.

The preceding process definitely needs an illustration, which the DMOT got at a special training section. Suppose, for instance, they were trying to develop an equation to best fit the data for STUDENT (Y) vs. YRS2000 (X). The historical (by year since 2000) data are:

Y	1000	1030	1061	1093	1126	1159	1194	1230	1267	1305	1344
X	3	4	5	6	7	8	9	10	11	12	13

There are at least two kinds of equations warranted for this situation:

Warrant 22 Exponential: $Y = 927.1*e^{\wedge}(0.02655*X)$ $R^2 = 0.976$ (2.1)

Warrant 01 Linear: $Y = 30.63*X + 905.8$ $R^2 = 0.970$ (2.2)

These are referred to (temporarily) as "pre-equalities," until the final choice is made between them. The first is nonlinear (exponential) and actually has a slightly higher R2. The second is the traditional linear regression version. The first is more difficult to discuss. While not true in this case, the linear can go negative within the X range, which makes it a little unreliable. Still, the DMOT call in this situation, as mentioned earlier, was for the linear, apparently because it was easier to understand.

Two other equations were required for this case. The first was for teacher/staff (TEACHST) vs. STUDENT. Again a linear version was chosen:

$$\text{TEACHST} = -24.75 + 0.1250*\text{STUDENT} \quad \text{with } R^2 = 0.923 \quad (2.3)$$

The remaining equation does not require regression:

$$\text{TSWCOMP} = (\text{PERTSWC}/100)*\text{TEACHST} \quad (2.4)$$

since it is just a proportion.

Sample Qualitative Items:
Statistical measures (definitions of cause, effect, truth, precision, accuracy).

2.4.7 QCQ Step 6: Relationship Evaluation Development

The next step in the QCQ process is to assess the relationships, both graphically and mathematically/statistically, that have emanated from the preceding efforts. This assessment also is likely to be both quantitative and qualitative. Much of the needed information can be obtained from the calibration reports. As an example, the coefficient of determination (R^2 or R2) for the (non-linear) exponential equation is almost perfect (0.976), as is that for the linear version (0.970). This also means that, looking ahead, the forecasts for, say, 2020 (YRS2000 = 20) will tend to be close and agreeable.

In QCQ the qualitative side of the evaluation, among other factors, lies on the response to five criteria:

■ logical,
■ empirical,
■ sociological,
■ historical, and
■ aesthetic.

For example, the first category concerns logical (Root-Bernstein, 1989):

- offers unifying idea that postulates nothing unnecessary,
- is logically consistent internally,
- is conceivably refutable,
- is explicitly bounded in application, and
- is consistent with previously established laws and theories.

A consistent response to the fourth point, to illustrate, would be difficult for almost any analyst to produce. There are so many different reasons why, for instance, a high school graduate might go one place for college or another. One can easily generate a list of 20 variations—boyfriend, sickness at home, insufficient income, too far away, and so on. Hence it is extremely difficult to declare that our equation absolutely separates those who would be going to our institution under study from those who would not.

Sample Qualitative Items:
Choice of statistical measures.

2.4.8   QCQ Step 7: Forecasting

The job of the team and other managers in this step is to develop various appropriate scenarios for the future of the endeavor, assess the results in terms of gains and losses, and, under many circumstances, start the QCQ + PAGP process all over again.

The "no change" (NC or "null") scenario quantities are shown in Table 2.4. To arrive at this, it is proposed that by 2018 and thereafter every teacher/staff person will have been given a tablet. That amounts to 159 by 2020.

TABLE 2.4   Calculations for "No Change" Scenarios

YEAR	PERTSWC	STUDENT	TEACHST	TSWCOMP	YRS2000
2014	88	1334	139	122	14
2015	93	1365	142	132	15
2016	97	1395	146	141	16
2017	99	1426	149	147	17
2018	100	1457	153	153	18
2019	100	1487	156	156	19
2020	100	1518	159	159	20

An alternate scenario would be that the number purchased would be, say, 80% of the number of teachers/staff, assuming that 20% would already have bought a tablet on their own. That 80% would amount to only 0.8*159 = 127 machines to be bought by 2020.

The simple model is taken as a good start on accomplishing the aim (QCQ Step 1) of making a good estimate of computer tablets purchased. Assuming a good response to the model, it then may be possible to respond to other goals (like the "quicker learning" one generated in Step 1), to other features (like the "reduced glare" one in Step 2), and to the set of mission-affecting variables generated with the aid of the PAGP. Although desirable, it may not be possible to quantify some of these additions, but that does not mean they should not be included.

Then too, a lot of strange and unexpected things can happen in the future. Just for instance:

- The head person has a heart attack and is out six months (hence many decisions are kept up in the air).
- The student body becomes overwhelmingly Hispanic (hence a request that more "apps" on the machines be in both Spanish and English).
- But also a large coalition is formed that advocates for the technologies for which the DMOT is in charge.

───

Sample Qualitative Items:
The descriptions of alternate scenarios and previously unanticipated futures.

2.5   The Making Of Supernumerary Intelligence, Part II

The main purpose of QCQ, as noted earlier, is to help users develop meaningful models within the framework of the meta-model in Figure 1.3. Once developed to their fullest, such models can help people make forecasts of the future (since, as it is said, that is where we will be spending the rest of our lives). These forecasts can be made for different "what if" strategy conditions and various anticipated external condition levels. These analyses hopefully will lead to more beneficial decisions.

The QCQ + PAGP combination has a unique mixture of analytics and ideation, qualitative and quantitative entities, big and wide data, and the five traditional fields (regression, systems dynamics, research methods, qualitative research, and artificial intelligence). All these, used in proper concert, subsequently come to add form to the body and mind of Supernumerary Intelligence (SI).

The rest of this book focuses on the seven step process in concert with the PAGP for exploring, developing, and using qualitative as well as quantitative relationships. In the succeeding chapters a series of case studies are employed to bring out a large number of problems with current approaches. These same examples are reexamined to show many of the improved approaches taken in QCQ plus the PAGP to overcome the aforementioned problems. Each of the seven steps in the QCQ process subsequently is elaborated in a succeeding chapter. By the end, the reader should have a good grasp of the fundamentals and the way in which QCQ and the PAGP can be and are utilized to help develop a useful model, whether it be explicit or carried in his/her head.

A relatively simple example of this process, dealing with the adequacy of parking spaces at planned shopping centers, is provided in the next chapter. Then, using U.S. urban carbon monoxide concentrations as the main problem of concern, we take a more detailed chapter-per-step look at each part of the process. Thus, to give a quick glance ahead, CO concentration levels (COC) will be seen as depending on such factors as gross domestic product per capita (GDPPC), CO emission rates, federal air pollution control expenditures, and catalysts affecting abatement program development times.

3

Case Study

Shopping Center Parking Lot Accumulation

The previous two chapters have supplied the basic background for, and description of, the nature and basic operation of QCQ and the PAGP. In this chapter we bring out a relatively simple (as if any are) case study to give a quick example of the inner operating mechanics of the two interconnected methodologies. The succeeding chapters then highlight many of the qualities and quantities that make themselves apparent as analysis and synthesis proceed as part of the seven step QCQ process and interaction with the PAGP.

Here is the hypothetical issue to be addressed: a problem (if it may called such) that arises periodically in various localities has to do with the impacts of a new planned shopping center on traffic flow and parking. This case is addressed to the latter, with the focus on the maximum number of parking spaces needed for shoppers, office workers, center employees, and the like, assumedly when the center is completely developed and fully employed.

The local government agency responsible for arriving at this maximum number is the planning department. This case has to do with determining the maximum number of vehicles that would accumulate in the parking lot

Supernumerary Intelligence, pages 43–51

TABLE 3.1 Daily Traffic Generation and Max Accumulation at Seven Planned Shopping Centers

Center	Type	Goods	Area (acres)	Per Day	Stalls	Accum
Bay Fair	R	S&C	50.0	10,000	3,000	1,800
Stonestown	R	C&S	42.0	19,167	3,500	3,100
Stanford	R	S&C	44.0	11,554	4,200	3,200
Capwells	R	S&C	30.6	8,990	2,486	2,350
Broadway	R	C&S	37.5	18,017	2,823	2,500
Bon Air	C	C	4.7	2,360	328	150
Safeways	N	C	2.6	2,088	217	200

Note: Center Types: R = Regional; C = Community; N = Neighborhood Good; S = Shopping;
     C = Convenience (put in order of ranking)
Source: Harding (1960), except for last column, which is notional.

of a planned shopping center. This was seen as depending on the daily traffic coming into the center. Much of the introductory data can be found in Tables 3.1 to 3.3. The case now will be addressed using the QCQ seven step process and employing the PAGP in selected spots in that process.

3.1 Step 1: Situation Description

The first step in the process was to identify the aim for the study as well as other pertinent background information. The results of this effort are shown in Table 3.2. The aim, as noted above, was to be able to estimate maximum parking lot sizes. This translated easily into the single goal variable of "estimating the maximum accumulation."

3.2 Step 2: Theory Search

Next on the agenda was a search for a relevant theory. A review of the literature and conversations with knowledgeable people produced nothing of

TABLE 3.2 Situation Background Information

Aim: Determine future shopping center parking lot capacity needs
Client: Traffic engineers, commercial center developers, local city officials
User: J. W. Dickey
Horizon: 10 years.
Budget: small
Time available: 6 months
Goal Variable: Maximum vehicle accumulation (MAXACUM)

substance (assumed here for illustrative purposes). Only one influencing variable—incoming traffic—was identified as being relevant. This external variable certainly met the test of being a "cause" since it was obvious that if traffic were prevented from entering, none would accumulate.

The analysis then went on to look at constraints. The first limitation, on lot capacity, would seem to be most pressing, so the dependent variable might be stated as the "maximum accumulation versus the lot capacity."

The eventual aim, however, is to determine the desired capacity, so we do not want to constrain the variable at this point. We do know, too, that accumulation cannot exceed the incoming volume, but we will *assume that the lot capacity would have been reached first anyway.*

3.3   Step 3: Theory Development

A simple "possible links" diagram is shown in the middle of Table 3.3. TRS/DAY is taken as an invariate since it will be supplied by another agency.

TABLE 3.3   Theory (Variable & Relationship) Information

Goal (Y) Variable: MAXACUM

Definition—Maximum accumulation of parked vehicles in a lot of a planned shopping center. The unit of analysis is for a single day, which may be at a different time of the year for each center. The maximum accumulation is *for that day only (not for the year as a whole).*

Measure—Count of vehicles in the parking lot at the point in time when the count is a maximum during the day (taken as the maximum difference between the cumulative in and out traffic volumes, which is totaled every 15 minutes).

External (from data) (X) Variable: TRS/DAY

Definition—All licensed vehicles entering the center by all entrances, regardless of purpose (e.g., delivery, employment, bus drop-off, etc.) in the selected day (only 8 am to 6:30 pm at Capwells Shopping Center). (CONFID)

Measure—Counts at every entrance summed for every 15 minute period.

Cause/Effect: X meets all tests of being a cause of Y (see Appendix D).

X by itself probably is not sufficient, however (see Appendix E). More variables are needed, but will not be used in this example.

Possible Links Diagram: TRS/DAY ----------> MAXACUM

Anomalies/Paradoxes:

Vehicles may enter but not park (drive around and exit).

Some entering vehicles may be for delivery, not customers or employees.

Employees may be required to park off site during busy times.

3.4   Step 4: Data Specification and Collection

The next step in the process is to become familiar with the data in detail so that we are intimate with its limitations. A set of pertinent information for each variable is presented in Tables 3.4 and 3.5, respectively.

TABLE 3.4   Variable (MAXACUM) Specification Information

Variable: MAXACUM

Agreement on Definition: yes

Validity: standard definition by professional organization.

Measurement scale: ratio

Integer/continuous: integer, but is large so can be treated as continuous.

Ranges: *Calibration data:* 150 to 3200
Conceivable: parking lot capacity, incoming traffic (which may be limited in turn by entrance capacities)
Operational: use 0 to +∞ since want to know needed capacity.
Data values are not influenced by constraints.

Statistical Element: shopping center

Universe: all planned shopping centers in the U.S.

Statistical Population: not specified exactly, but possibly all planned shopping centers in San Francisco area.

Statistical Sample: no systematic sampling scheme specified; 7 centers taken in the years 1957–1959.

Unit of analysis: a particular shopping center on a particular day.

Measurement error: not specified. Guess of about +/– 3%. Likely to be evenly distributed.

Precision: exact to one vehicle.

Reliability: would get the same results again, although might get some differences in inclusion of motorcycles, buses that take more than one parking space, etc.

Predictive volatility: low. Some weather, behavioral variations.

Sequential order: yes, but not that relevant here.

Note: See Chapter 7 for definitions of terms.

TABLE 3.5   Variable (TRS/DAY) Specification

Variable: TRS/DAY

Agreement on Definition: yes

Validity: yes, standard traffic engineering definition.

Measurement error: not specified, but probably low: say 2%. Likely to be undercounted.

Forecast error: +/– 20%

Precision: to 1 vehicle.

Ranges: *Calibration data:* 2088 to 19,167
Conceivable: 0 to sum of entrance capacities
Operational: Use 0 to +∞ since conceivable>>data

3.5   Step 5: Individual Relationship Development

We now are left with two variables. While they both would have limits (e.g., MAXACUM would be limited by the capacity of the incoming entrances), these boundaries are far in excess of both the range of the collected data and those likely to occur in reality (called "conceivable limits" in QCQ). Hence the operational ranges of the variables are taken to be from 0 to infinity (see Tables 3.4 and 3.5).

Taken together, these ranges imply that the resultant relationship must be contained in the upper right hand quadrant (called a "union" in QCQ) of the X:Y graph. We now search for a structure with equation forms that increase monotonically in that area. Furthermore, these forms must go through (0,0) since, logically, there cannot be any accumulation of vehicles in a lot if none enter the premise.

There are two eligible "pre-equality" possibilities (denoted by the "<=>" symbol) that meet the preceding selection criteria. Results of calibration on these can be found in the middle of Table 3.6.

TABLE 3.6   Relationship Calibration Information

Variable Operational Ranges: see Tables 3.4 and 3.5.

Select MAPE as the Goodness-of-Fit criterion since there is a particular concern that small centers are built with no more parking spaces than they need.

RELATIONSHIP:
Combination of variable ranges (union) is upper left hand quadrant.
MAXACUM (Y) is increasing monotonically with TRS/DAY (X).
Equation has to go through 0,0 since if there were no incoming traffic, there would be no accumulation in the parking lot.
No limit on Y as X increases.
No time delays to consider.
Graph of relationship (Figure 3.1) shows some varied scatter, so *no* form will fit perfectly.
Eligible pre-equality forms:
1. Linear: Y <=> 0 + bX   2. Power: Y <=> 0 + b(X^c)
Results: Mean = 1900; MAD = 1014; MAPD = 53.4%

Form	GOF*	b	c	MAE	MAPE	R^2
Linear	MAE	.162		456	37.4	.70
Linear	MAPD	.180		485	34.8	.73
Linear	R^2	.178		481	35.0	.73
Power	MAE	.0044	1.39	639	34.3	.53
Power	MAPE	.0044	1.403	697	29.1	.36
Power	R^2	.0044	1.39	639	34.3	.53

Conclusion: Take Power Curve (optimum MAPE); Degrees of Freedom = 7 – 2 = 5 (OK).

Note: The current version of QCQ optimizes only on R^2. This optimization here was done using the "Solver" routine with the GRG non-linear solving method in Microsoft® Excel.

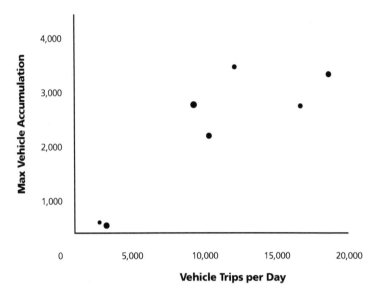

Figure 3.1 Maximum parking accumulation vs. vehicle trips to center per day.

While the decision has been made to focus on minimizing the MAPE (so that small centers will not greatly overbuild lots), the regressions for the two other criteria also are displayed. Note that the amount of scatter in Figure 3.1 shows, though, that no form should be expected to fit exactly.

The power curve:

$$\text{MAXACUM} = 0.0044*(\text{TRS}/\text{DAY} \wedge 1.403) \tag{3.1}$$

has the lowest MAPE at 29.1% and thus has been selected as the "official" equation.

3.6 Step 6: Relationship Evaluation

The resulting equation now is reviewed from the standpoint of other statistical and non-statistical perspectives. It is interesting, for example, that the R2 of Equation 3.1 is relatively low (0.36 compared to the best of 0.73) and the MAE is relatively high (697 compared to the best of 456).

Do we have the right variables? The maximum accumulations shown in Table 3.1 actually are not necessarily the maximums over all time, just recorded values on particular days (to find the yearly maximums would require data collection throughout the year). It therefore is important to record this fact in the definition (Table 3.3).

There are many other candidates for the independent variable(s). Perhaps the floor area of convenience stores as a percentage of total floor area, the spread of store hours (e.g., 9 AM to 10 PM = 13 hours); and many more. We will, however, stick with the incoming traffic volume since this is an output of most metropolitan transportation studies and thus is a readily available, predicted external factor.

What about a limit on parking lot accumulation? The first limitation, on lot capacity, would seem to be most pressing, so the dependent variable perhaps might be better stated as the maximum accumulation divided by the lot capacity. Much like before, our eventual objective, however, is to determine the desired capacity, so we do not want to constrain the variable at this point. We do know, too, that accumulation cannot exceed the incoming volume, but we will assume that the lot capacity would have been reached first anyway.

The current version of QCQ optimizes only on R^2. This optimization here was done using the "Solver" routine with the GRG non-linear solving method in Microsoft® Excel.

In terms of the other criteria mentioned in Table 3.3, the equation is:

- Logical—consistent and explicitly bounded;
- Empirical—based on data, but not on a good sample;
- Sociological—helpful in resolving a problem but also poses new ones (e.g., lack of good statistical data);
- Historical—surpasses predecessors (there presumably are none); and
- Aesthetic—has simplicity, but still requires interpretation.

The next and last step is to make a forecast. The process for this is detailed in Table 3.7 and diagrammed in Figures 3.1 and 3.2. We assume that the potential owners of a new center, which is anticipated to draw 5,000 incoming vehicles a day on the peak day, also want to be extra careful that sufficient parking space is available for all customers.

TABLE 3.7 Forecasting Information

Forecast: (see Figure 3.2) (highly conservative)

    Presented forecast = 5000 vehicles/day

    + Measurement Error of 2% = 100; total = 5100

    + Forecast Error of 20% = 1020; total =6120

    Y forecast of $.0044*(6120^{1.403}) = 904$

    + Forecast Error of 29.1% 263; total =1167

    + Measurement Error of 3% = 35; total = 1202. (vs 681 without errors)

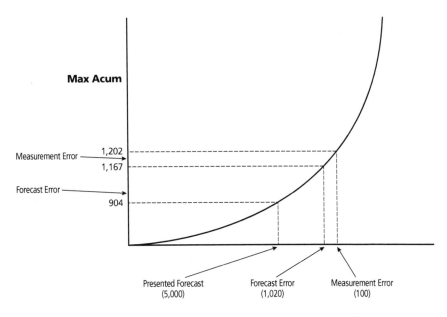

Figure 3.2 Impact of possible errors on estimated accumulation of parking.

3.7 Step 7: Forecasting

We first note that there could have been a measurement error of about 2% in counting the incoming traffic in developing the charts in Figures 3.1 and 3.2. We therefore add 2% of the 5,000 (= 100 vehicles) to the chart in Figure 3.2. Next we take into account the possible forecast error in the incoming traffic of about 20% (= 1,020 vehicles) and add that to the total. At this point we use the power curve in Equation 3.1 to estimate the maximum forecasted accumulation, which turns out to be 904.

Remember, though, that the MAPE (or average absolute error) for this equation is 29.1%. So to be entirely safe, we add this amount (29.1% of 904 = 263) to the predicted maximum accumulation. Last, we take into account the likely error (about 3%) in measuring the dependent variable and add that (35 vehicles) to the total. The final number is a forecasted maximum accumulation of 1,202 vehicles.

The resultant forecast can be compared to the value of 681 if none of the errors were considered. The 1,202 forecast obviously is fairly conservative, especially since the two types of errors have been added (they may actually help cancel each other out). On the other hand, we have employed only the *average* (mean) error in the calculations, and some will be much greater than the average.

3.8 Recapitulation: A Higher Quality, Higher Quantity, Higher SI Situation

Our hope is that, as we went through each of the seven QCQ steps, it became apparent that there was a lot of detail that entered the picture. Most of it was quantitative, as for instance in the creation of a regression equation focused on minimization of the mean absolute percentage error (MAPE) rather than the usual coefficient of determination ($R2$). But there also was an increased amount of qualitative information, as exemplified by the possible assessment of the equation for MAXACUM in terms of the "aesthetic"—having simplicity, but still requiring interpretation. It is these kinds of additions to the analysis that increase its "supernumerary intelligence" and, we feel, make for an improved product.

The chapters to follow now go through each of the QCQ seven steps and the use of the PAGP in more detail.

4

Step 1. Situation Description

This chapter serves as an elaboration of the AIRPOL case mentioned briefly in the previous chapters. The hypothetical story deals with the relationship between air pollutant concentrations (specifically carbon monoxide—CO) from mobile sources and federal expenditures aimed at reducing such. The focus is on urban areas across the United States. It is assumed in the example that the Environmental Protection Agency (EPA) has hired a consulting firm (Data Cruncher Consulting Services—DCCS) to develop a model (to be called "AIRPOL") to show how increased federal expenditures might influence CO concentration levels in the cities.

Let us imagine that DCCS now is in the first stage of the Quantitative CyberQuest (QCQ) process. The purpose of that stage is to describe the situation under study. This may seem a fairly straightforward task but can (and usually does) require an expansion of current thinking to get the greatest possible perspective. In our experience this is crucial. Far too often analysts simply "rely on the numbers," never bothering to talk to the people involved or even going to investigate the situation first hand. Much can be missed in this way. QCQ therefore guides the user through a series of steps that help draw out the significant aspects of the situation (see Table 4.1).

Supernumerary Intelligence, pages 53–66
Copyright © 2015 by Information Age Publishing

TABLE 4.1   QCQ Step 1: Situation Description

1. Identify the aim, client, user, horizon time, study resources (budget), and developer.
2. Identify relevant goal variables with dimensions checklist.
3. Search literature and have discussions with experts (content analysis).
4. Collect and organize descriptive materials.
5. Cull variable list to get most important goals.

In the first step an identification is made of the aim to be achieved, the nature of the client for whom the model is being developed, the horizon time (period in which goals are to be achieved), and several other pieces of basic case information. A search then can be made of the literature and discussions held with experts to identify the most important goal variables.

Content analysis is helpful in this regard. Reference also can be made to various kinds of checklists to help identify additional goals. Frequently it helps to compile and organize all past information (including reports, pictures, videos, and databases) about a case to highlight and give further insights into the context of the goals being sought. At the end the list of resulting goal variables, which can be quite extensive, needs to be culled.

4.1   Identify Basic Case Information

What is the most basic information needed about any case? QCQ requests six items (Table 4.2) about the situation being analyzed.

The first item is specified by completing, as simply as possible, the sentence:

> The aim is to develop a new (or new way to) _____

For the AIRPOL case, the blank might be filled with:

> ...reduce carbon monoxide pollution concentration.

TABLE 4.2   Basic Case Information

Aim: Main objective (goal variable) for the study.
Client: Person or organization most directly impacted by the study results.
User: Person or organization supporting the analysis and most likely to use the resulting model.
Horizon: Furthest point in time for which forecasts are to be made.
Budget: Amount of money, person-months of effort, and/or time allotted to do this project.
Developer: Name of person or organization responsible for actually doing the analysis.

The client in this case would be citizens in the CO polluted areas, with the user (and more direct client) being the Environmental Protection Agency. Assume that "now" is the end of 2015. Since any actions by this agency will require time for their impacts to be felt—from 5 to 10 years—the horizon point thus has been taken as the year 2020. As a result, forecasts will be made out to that time.

Relatively little funding (only enough for 10 person-weeks of time) has been made available for the study, so the model cannot be elaborate. Moreover, it has to be produced in a very short period of time (6 weeks). While the need for the first piece of information is fairly obvious, some may question the rest. Why, for example, identify the client or the amount of resources employed in the study? The answers actually may be critical to understanding why certain goals and affecting factors have been selected. See Table 4.3.

As an illustration, the AIRPOL case centers right from the start on variables of direct interest to the client (namely, CO concentration and federal expenditures to reduce it). Presumably the EPA is concerned about getting a quick resumption of spending in the process. This situation may be contrasted with one in which we imagine a single, lonely scientist studying CO concentrations in one location over a period of many years. He or she may be focusing specifically on these concentrations as a function of, say, wind patterns and speeds, precipitation, and traffic mix (proportion of cars and trucks). The "client" in this second case may be simply the self-interest of the scientist. In either case, the aim is roughly the same, yet the underlying purposes—as characterized by the nature of the "client," the quantity of resources, and the manner in which they are spent—are quite different. The person trying to understand and/or assess these cases thus should be aware of these differences.

TABLE 4.3   Summary Background Information for the AIRPOL Case

Aim: Reduce carbon monoxide (COC) air pollutant concentrations.

Client: Citizens living in highly COC polluted areas.

User: The Environmental Protection Agency (EPA).

Horizon: 6 years from the current time (2020).

Budget/Time Available: 10 person-weeks over 6 weeks.

Developer: Data Cruncher Consulting Services (DCCS)

Report Due Date: April 15, 2014.

4.2   Identify Goal Variables with Checklist

A primary task in the situation description step is to identify the variables that represent the various goals that the client thinks are important ends to be achieved. The aim, of course, is of central concern and usually would be translated into the first goal variable in QCQ. The aim to:

> reduce carbon monoxide air pollutant concentrations

thus becomes the goal variable:

> carbon monoxide concentrations.

Other goal variables are relatively easy to identify, but it also is relatively easy to overlook some that may be of merit. Just as we hope that even the best trained and most highly experienced airline pilots are thorough in reviewing their checklist before takeoff, so too do we want even experienced developers of models to be thorough in their review for possible goal variables. This process is aided in QCQ with a generic "dimensions checklist." This list is displayed in Table 4.4. It gets the user to think about goals in a broad variety of areas, as illustrated by the following specific goal possibilities for the AIRPOL case in Table 4.5.

4.3   Search Literature and Discuss with Experts— Conduct Content Analysis

While checklists certainly can be helpful, they still may be limited. Any worthwhile academic paper, as an example, involves a literature survey, and any worthwhile policy study involves discussion with as many relevant stakeholders and experienced professionals as possible

There are many techniques and tools to help in both these arenas. Face-to-face meetings can be held, telephone conversations can be initiated, library searches can be undertaken, and so on. The role of the Internet at this point is obvious (see Section 6.2). To help in some of these endeavors, QCQ has built into it a "content analysis" procedure. This can be applied to any ASCII (American Standard Code for Information Interchange) file, whether from the literature or from notes or transcriptions of conversations with experts. A "content analysis," at least for this version of QCQ, is simply a process to create an alphabetical listing of all of the "nontrivial" words (no a's, an's, the's, etc.), along with their frequencies of occurrence, in a text file. The assumption is that the more often certain words are mentioned, the more central they are to the situation at hand.

TABLE 4.4   Dimensions Checklist

1. Technological

Competing technologies	Stage of development	Level of understanding of theory
Complementary technology	Availability of trained people	Supporting technology

2. Economic

General market conditions	Financing	Cost of land, labor, capital
General economic climate		

3. Managerial

Number of managers	Experience	Training
Organizational arrangement Techniques	Procedures	

4. Political

Power	Beneficiaries	Losers
Rights, Duties, Privileges	Tradeoffs for other things	"Looking good"
Electability		

5. Social

Population	Geographic distribution	Church, family, work
Gender, race, age	Institutional groups	

6. Cultural

Values	Practices	Prohibitions
Gusto	Exhortations	Attitudes

7. Intellectual

Prestigious Organizations	Decision makers	Opinion leaders
Academics		

8. Religious/Ethical

Doctrines	Teachings	Standards
Institutions	Answers to man's ultimate destiny	Hierarchy
Control		

9. Ecological

Flora, Fauna	Control	Pollution (air, water, heat)
Balance		

10. Health

Physical	Psychological	Sight
Care	Institutions	Regulation

11. Sensual

Taste	Feel	Hearing
Vibration	Smell	

12. Legal

Laws	Regulations	Contracts
Policies	Intellectual Property	Courts

TABLE 4.5   Some Statements of Possible Goal Interests

Technological: Maximize use of "clean burning" fuel.

Economic: Develop as many new pollution control industries as possible.

Managerial: Train as many governmental managers as possible about air pollution laws.

Political: Show every Congressperson the benefits for his/her state.

Social: Optimize appeal to new, young drivers.

Cultural: Restrict as many automobile ads as possible.

Intellectual: Provide technical training in all high schools.

Religious/Ethical: Increase the number of religious organizations sanctioning air pollution reduction.

Ecological: Reduce CO pollution concentrations.

Health: Minimize morbidity and mortality from CO exposure.

Sensual: Better understand human limits to CO exposure.

Legal: Maximize public adherence to air pollution laws and regulations.

The process can be illustrated with text on "Environmental Pollution," based somewhat on that found in *The Electronic Encyclopedia*™ (CD-ROM), Grolier, Inc., 1990. A first paragraph is shown in Figure 4.1.

A sample from the resulting printout can be found in Figure 4.2. The word "area," for instance, appears six times in the text, which might imply that the goal variable should be specified by geographic area (the CO concentration data are for the nation as a whole, but the monitoring stations are mostly in selected high pollutant urban areas).

4.4   Collect and Organize Descriptive Material

Rarely is a study done that has no precedents. There always are previous exercises, accompanied perhaps by reports or articles and possibly even databases, drawings, quantitative analyses (e.g., on spreadsheets), pictures, and videos. All these obviously are helpful in understanding what has taken place to date and in exposing developers and users to a virtual experience with the situation being investigated.

Environmental pollution is any release of substance or energy into water, land, or air that causes or may cause short-term (acute) or long-term (chronic) detriment to the Earth's ecological balance or that lowers the quality of life. Pollutants may cause primary damage, first with an identifiable impact on the environment, or second, with damage in the form of minor changes in the delicate balance of the biological food web that are detectable only over longer time periods ranging from months to decades.

Figure 4.1   Adapted first paragraph of definition of "Environmental Pollution."

> 1 abate 1 abated 3 abatement 3 ability 1 able 1 about 1 above 1 absorb
> 1 accelerate 1 accelerates 1 acceleration 2 acid 1 acres 1 action 1 active
> 1 activities 1 activity 5 acute 2 addition 1 additional 1 additionally 1 adequate
> 1 advent 1 aesthetic 1 aesthetically 2 affect 1 after 1 agencies 1 aging
> 5 agricultural 2 air 1 airborne 1 algae 1 algal 3 all 1 alleviated 1 almost 5 also
> 2 alternatives 3 although 1 aluminum 1 ambient 3 amount 1 angeles 2 animals
> 1 another 2 any 1 appliances 1 application 1 applied 1 approximately 1 apr
> 4 aquatic 3 area 3 areas 1 arsenic 4 associated 1 atmosphere 1 attention
> 1 attitude 1 auto 1 automobiles 1 available 1 average 1 awareness 2 body
> 1 both 1 break 1 breakdown 1 brighter 1 building 1 burning...

Figure 4.2   Sample list of word frequencies in "Environmental Pollution" article.

QCQ helps in collecting and organizing digital material by incorporating a program originally called "CRISTAL" but now available as an application on Android devices and known as the "Quantum Matrix" (or "QM"). This essentially is a spreadsheet (or, more specifically, a set of spreadsheets) where a cell can be almost anything (any computer object, that is). It can be

- Text
- A picture
- A CAD (computer-aided design) drawing
- An executable file
- A macro
- A number
- A word processor
- Sound
- A button
- A database
- An equation
- A video
- A graph
- A list box

A spreadsheet cell can even be another spreadsheet!

An illustration can be found in Figure 4.3. Information can be stored directly, as is the case for the numbers on the middle right section and the "slide" immediately above. Or it can be stored by file (path) reference, as is the case for the four items on the top right. A double click on the file name brings forth the file, which was what was done to raise the picture on the middle right.

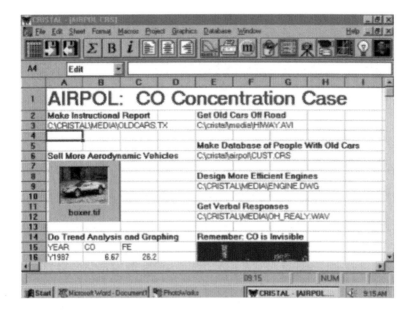

Figure 4.3 Illustrative "QM"™ spreadsheet. (Courtesy: Dennis Jones)

The QM also can be employed to make more elaborate visual representations through "image maps" like that in Figure 4.3. This has on it two pictures, a CAD drawing (middle right), a spreadsheet, a text editor and text file (bottom right), and an Audio Video Interleave (AVI) file, the first frame of which is shown in the top right corner). All are fully operational.

The point to be reinforced here is that understanding of the situation being investigated can be enhanced considerably with the aid of pictures, graphs, spreadsheets, text, and other objects. The bus and truck shown in the middle left picture in Figure 4.4, for instance, highlight the fact that the composition of traffic has been changing over time—with greater proportions of trucks (U.S. Bureau of the Census, Statistical Abstract, 2012)—and that such a trend perhaps might be reflected as a goal variable.

4.5   Cull Goal List

Most studies start by expanding the list of factors to be considered so that as few relevant ones as possible are overlooked. By the same token, there often are too many such factors and some tough decisions have to be made as to which to ignore.

To illustrate the kind of thinking that goes into the latter decisions, consider the "health" goal elicited in Section 4.2 to "minimize morbidity

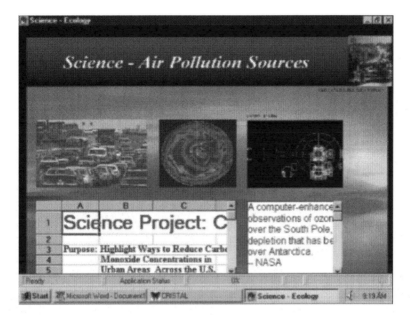

Figure 4.4 Example "image map" for air pollution project. (Courtesy: Dennis Jones)

and mortality from CO exposure." That goal most likely would be of more direct interest to the Department of Health and Human Services, so we might imagine EPA opting to stay with the single goal: the aim of reducing CO concentrations.

QCQ has no specific tools to help in the task of culling goal variables, but it does require that the user select and enter the most important ones. To keep the AIRPOL case simple for illustration, we have chosen to stick with the single goal variable, derived from the aim, of "reducing carbon monoxide concentrations." In a more realistic case, there obviously could be many more.

Naturally, good data are indispensible to be able to produce a graph like that in Figure 4.5, a very desirable end point for this step in QCQ. Although only 114 of the total of 332 measurement sites had sufficient history to be included, they gave good evidence to show that there has been a very rapid decrease in CO concentrations and that the major battle was one that was well on the way to being "won." (See also [INT-1 Air Trends].)

4.6   Recapitulation

The techniques presented in this chapter have allowed a vague, fuzzy situation to be clarified to the point where a small number of relevant goals could be identified. In the beginning the only known factor was the aim of

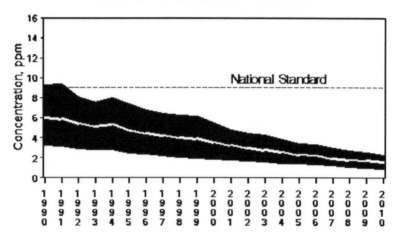

Figure 4.5 CO air quality (Courtesy EPA).

reducing carbon monoxide concentrations. The variety of potential goals to be considered then was expanded, via content analysis and review of QCQ's dimensions checklist. Greater depth of understanding subsequently was achieved through collection, organization, and display of relevant reports, pictures, videos, and other objects. The list of goal variables then had to be condensed for purposes of simplicity.

Important Note:
In this chapter and most of the ones to come we have attached a short "Expanded Learning Case." This usually (but not always) contains a short elaboration and further development of one of the concepts in that chapter.

4.7 An Expanded Learning Case: Accident Insurance Claims

Ann Landers was a very famous advice columnist (in "Dear Ann"). She took over this column in 1955 and ran it until she passed away 56 years later. Her column continues under the heading of "Annie's Mailbox." One older column just seemed to appear out of nowhere and grab our attention. It was published in our local newspaper, *The Roanoke Times and World News,* on October 24, 1994, and it had to do with Auto Accident Insurance Claims. Apparently some anonymous person with access to such records at an insurance company found and sent in some humorous excerpts of the reasons drivers gave for being involved:

"It happened this way:"

"The other car collided with mine without giving warning of intention."

"I thought my window was down but found it was up when I put my hand through it."

Our interest in these, besides the humor, is that they are structured representations of one approach to formalizing cause and effect. They bring out some interesting aspects not addressed in various other kinds of analyses. The first statement, for instance, shows that a variable with a value of "0" ("no warning given") still can be a cause.

The second statement ("put hand through window") highlights the fact that several variables may need to be active in *combination* before an effect takes place. "Thinking that the window is down" by itself is not going to cause many (if any) accidents. Yet it might lead to a great number more if combined with "the window actually was up" and "put hand through window" (and, presumably, "lost control of car"). Hence, if any one of these variables were "0," the accident probably would not have happened. There thus is a need in, say, regression analysis (Appendix A) to identify a set of both necessary and sufficient conditions.

This statement also shows that a *sequence* of causes and effects might be operative. "Putting hand through window" precedes and causes "lost control of car," which in turn precedes and causes "car accident." *Two* equations therefore would be needed to express these relationships.

A follow-along comparison of these two statements with each other and with a third:

"I pulled away from the side of the road, glanced at my mother-in-law, and headed over the embankment."

presents a further dilemma. There are totally different sets of (necessary and sufficient) conditions that lead to the *same effect* (an accident). "Putting hand through window" presumably did not occur (although it could) while "glancing at mother-in-law" did. Theoretically, then, there could be hundreds of different sets of equations all leading to the same result.

Another issue that the "glancing at mother-in-law" variable presents is whether this is a "symptom" rather than a "cause." The former can be defined as "a variable that accompanies another and is an indicator of its occurrence." It is not a cause in itself.

To illustrate, suppose the "glancing at mother-in-law" statement really was just an indicator of overall lack of attention to driving given by the driver. If the mother-in-law had not been there, the driver still would have been distracted by something else (a flashing light, a nearby pedestrian, etc.) The "glancing at mother-in-law" thus was not the "real" cause, but just an indicator. A regression (see Appendix A), say, that used this symptomatic variable thus would be questionable.

The letter to Ann Landers brought out some interesting aspects of cause and effect that are not frequently addressed in, say, regression analyses. The first statement, as mentioned in the beginning, shows that a variable with a value of "0" ("no warning given") still can be a cause.

This situation can be handled in a regression by insuring that there is a nonzero intercept when X is 0. Possible forms are a linear equation:

$$Y = a + b*X \qquad (4.1)$$

or an exponential:

$$Y = a*e^{\wedge}(b*X) \qquad (4.2)$$

or some other, more complicated entities. In the case where Y has to be ≥ 0 (as normally assumed in QCQ), Equation 4.1 would not be viable if b were negative (since Y eventually would become negative).

The second statement ("put hand through window") highlights the fact that several variables (say X_1 and X_2) may need to be active in *combination* before an effect takes place. Note that if Y has to be ≥ 0 (again, as assumed in QCQ), this implies that Y must *increase* as X_1 and X_2 increase. This condition can be replicated in regression via an equation like:

$$Y = a* (X_1{}^{\wedge}b_1)*(X_2{}^{\wedge}b_2) \qquad (4.3)$$

where b_1 and b_2 are positive. Y will be 0 if either or both X1 and X2 are 0.

This second statement also shows that a *sequence* of causes and effects might be operative. "Putting hand through window" (X_1) precedes and causes "lost control of car" (X_2), which in turn precedes and causes "car accident" (Y). Two equations therefore would be needed to express these relationships:

$$X_2 = f(X_1) \qquad\qquad (4.4)$$

and:

$$Y = f(X_2) \qquad\qquad (4.5)$$

The next issue surfaced by the accident claims letter is that there may be different sets of (necessary and sufficient) conditions that lead to the *same effect* (an accident). There are at least three ways to approach this situation:

1. Ignore it by focusing on only one set of circumstances (variables and relationships)—namely those of most concern to the client (this, by far, is the most common approach).
2. Develop wholly different models for different sets of circumstances (these may include some of the same variables and/or relationships, however).
3. Develop relationships that include variables from different sets of circumstances. For forecasting purposes, treat those variables that should not be considered part of a given circumstance as "not applicable."

These alternatives can best be demonstrated with another example related to auto accidents. In one circumstance accidents (Y) are caused as people try to drive in a hurricane (X_1); in another in the glare of overly bright sunshine (X_2). These obviously are completely different or mutually exclusive (sets of) circumstances since there is no or limited unblocked sunlight in a hurricane.

In the first approach we focus only on, say, the hurricane situation, developing a single relationship between Y and X_1. This obviously is only employed to forecast hurricane-related accidents. In the second approach we create an equation for Y versus X_2 also, which naturally is utilized for forecasts for sunny days. The two predictions can be added, if desired.

In the third a regression is run with *both* X variables at once. An observation might consist of the number of accidents (Y), hurricane inches of rain

TABLE 4.6 Hypothetical Accident Data

Day	1	2	3	4	5	6	7
Accidents (Y)	1	0	3	3	1	1	4
Rainfall (X_1)	2	0	0	0	0	0	3
Glare Level (X_2)	0	0	5	6	3	0	0

(X_1), and average glare level (X_2) during a given day. An illustrative set of fictional data can be found in Table 4.6. Note first that X_1 and X_2 are mutually exclusive of each other, yet they still have a correlation of 0.50. So there is not necessarily a theoretical connection between "mutual exclusiveness" and "correlation."

Continuing on, the resultant multiple linear regression is:

$$Y = 0.182 + 1.007 * X_1 + 0.478 * X_2 \qquad (4.6)$$

with an R^2 of 0.741.

If a forecast now were to be made for a circumstance where there was a hurricane with, say, 3.2 inches of rain (X_1), the glare level (X_2) would be treated as "not applicable" and given a corresponding value of 0:

$$Y = 0.182 + 1.007 * (3.2) + 0.478 * (0) = 3.4 \text{ accidents}$$

Similarly, if there were sunshine, X_1 would have to be taken as 0

In the situation where Y was *declining* as some independent variable (e.g., X_2) was increasing (and where $Y \geq 0$), the equation would be something like:

$$Y = a * (e^{\wedge}(b_1 * X_1)) * (X_2{}^{\wedge} - b_2) \qquad (4.7)$$

If X_2 were not applicable in a forecast, it should be assigned a value of 1 since an input of zero would lead incorrectly to an infinite value for Y.

5

Step 2. Theory Search

The main activity in this QCQ step is to identify variables that *directly influence the goals* (preceding chapter) as well as their general relationships. As in the recognition of goals, these associations are based first on literature reviews and on discussions with knowledgeable people. Both of these assist in bringing out theories and analogues (or, as we say, "theologues") that will help to explain and forecast the variables of concern.

5.1 The Theory Search Process

There can be numerous approaches to this stage of the QCQ process. Some of these are summarized in Table 5.1. To make matters more complicated, there is neither any requirement to use any of these techniques nor necessarily much order in the way in which they should be employed. In fact, there may be much jumping back and forth (even with other stages in QCQ). This lack of sequentiality is symptomatic, of course, of the creative nature of this (as well as the next) step in QCQ.

Supernumerary Intelligence, pages 67–80

TABLE 5.1 Possible Techniques in QCQ Step 2: Theory Search

Identify causal variables from dimensions checklist
Do content analysis of literature and expert discussion
Identify invariates from invariates list
Find new variables and theories via information systems
Try crowdsourcing

==

Identify new variables and theories with CyberQuest
Search previous theories database
Use the Public Administration Genome Project
Use supposedly dated material
Undertake situation structuring
Cull the list of variables and theories
Set up a tentative "possible links" diagram

It is important to recognize that a recursive questioning process needs to be employed in the theory search process. This starts with the identification of those variables that affect the goal variables, then those that affect the affecting ones, and so on. The end point is reached when one or more of either "invariates" or client strategy variables have been reached. The former are variables that can be safely assumed to be constant or changing at a highly predictable rate. With all these factors identified, we then can proceed to draw a "possible links" diagram showing the likely connections in each relationship.

Figure 5.1 is a demonstration of the initial result of this kind of recursive thinking for the AIRPOL model. It starts with the goal variable—COC (CO concentrations)—and imagines it as being affected by federal air pollution control expenditures (PE) and CO emissions (COE). But, since these variables *also* have to be explained and predicted, there is a need for a theologue for both of them. COE, for instance, is seen as being influenced by GDPPC and thereon to TIME. VMT (vehicle miles of travel) has still not been "hooked up" to a dependent variable.

Where does this process end? While it can retrogress forever, it can be established that both GDPPC and POP have a nice relationship with YEAR—the passage of time. This is helpful because YEAR is the ultimate invariate. Its future value is easy to forecast—the year 2000 will always be 10 years from 1990, 2005 will be 15, and so on. Meanwhile, PE also is ultimately connected back to YEAR as well as to additional federal air pollution control expenditures. (APE). The latter is a client decision variable and need not be predicted. The *assumption* (perhaps fairly heroic) is that APE is under the client's control and can be changed at the will of the client.

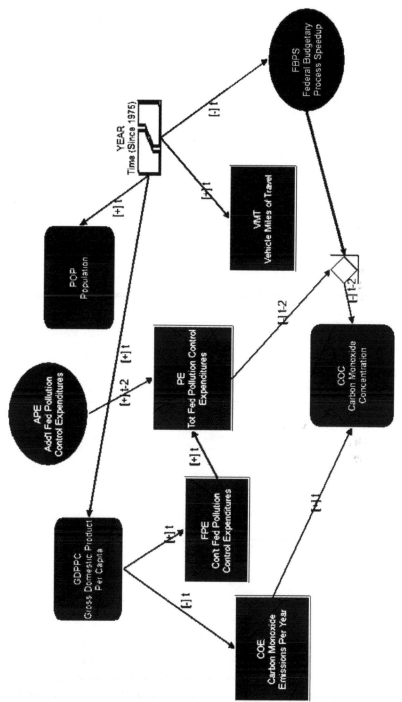

Figure 5.1 An example of an early "possible links" diagram (alpha model).

The whole set of identified variables and relationships subsequently is cut off from the rest of the world, put in a box, and called a "domain." These actions highlight the fact that, while it is *theoretically* possible to seek out and find numerous further connections (e.g., variables like unemployment and wage rates that might affect GDPPC), time and resource constraints make this neither useful nor practical for the DCCS team at the moment.

Let us now leave the AIRPOL story and return to Table 5.1. If the process in that table were sequential, it would flow somewhat as follows for each dependent variable, beginning with the goal(s): The first step would be to identify affecting or influencing variables. An approach uncluttered with substantial biases would start with some kind of broad, generic list of factors. QCQ supplies this in the form of a "dimensions checklist."

The next step is to read as much of the relevant literature and talk to as many relevant experts as possible. A "content analysis" then can be undertaken to extract the most significant variables and potential relationships. QCQ aids this process with a procedure that does counts of words in articles and/or notes (i.e., text files).

After several recursions, interest would turn to identifying potential invariates, a process that would be aided by the "invariates checklist."

Next (in Section 6.1) is an exploration for relevant theologues. QCQ contains "previous theories" databases of potentially associated concepts. These can be examined to help identify appropriate existing theories and/or provide a basis for new ones.

Use also can be made of CyberQuest (the parent of QCQ), which is known as a "problem solving and innovation support system." It not only has more concept databases, but it takes the user through a six-step process ranging from problem identification to implementation.

Another two sources involve electronic information systems. First are CD-ROMs. Over time the consultant DCCS specifically has employed the *McGraw-Hill Concise Encyclopedia of Science and Technology* (Parker, 1982), mainly because of its obvious connection to, and summarization of, physical science and engineering. Note the age of the source. We have found it to be of no drawback (see Chapter 6).

The second source is the Internet or World Wide Web. This also has obvious benefits since the Internet was established originally to aid scientific study. QCQ provides a "hook" to the user's Web browser program.

At this point the number of possible variables may be quite large for the DCCS, and so some categorization and simplification may be in order.

The "situation structuring" technique in QCQ helps in this by grouping diverse variables into smaller sets of relatively homogeneous factors. Additional culling still may be necessary, however, and can be done simply by combining and deleting those variables of marginal value.

5.2 Identify Causal Variables from Dimensions Checklist

The first task in the theory search stage is to employ the QCQ dimensions checklist to help identify relevant variables that affect the goal(s) established in the previous chapter. The checklist can be found in Table 4.4. Its use can be illustrated by focusing on, say, the economic dimension (group 2 on the list) as a source of important variables influencing CO concentrations. There are, of course, a great many economic factors in the world, including those listed in Table 5.2.

The last entry in Table 5.2 illustrates a variable (i.e., an index) that is a *combination* of several other ones. Since many combinations of this kind are possible, the number of potentially relevant variables can be substantial.

From this list DCCS tentatively selected three economic possibilities for the AIRPOL model:

- Household income needed to buy and operate new vehicles,
- Interest rates (for loans), and
- Federal spending for pollution control.

A sample of factors other than economic that might influence CO levels is shown in Table 5.3.

TABLE 5.2 Example Economic Variables Uncovered While Pondering Dimensions Checklist

Price of baked beans in Boston
Number of bank holiday days in France
Total wealth in the world
Dollars spent at local convenience stores
Household income to buy and operate new cars and trucks
Interest rates (for loans)
Federal spending for pollution control
(Interest cost + car purchase price)/household income

TABLE 5.3 **Sample Noneconomic Factors that Might Influence CO Levels**

Legal:
  Compatible court decisions
  Enforcement of emission control regulations
  Number of localities/states having emission control laws
  Amount of local political defense of local industry
  State legislators supporting environmental laws
Managerial:
  Number of governmental personnel dealing with the problem
  Time needed to produce a required budget
Political:
  Time required to implement an environmental program
  Personnel with environmental training
Technological:
  Use of catalytic converters
  Use of lighter, more fuel efficient cars
  Use of low/no emission fuels
  Vehicle CO emissions
  Miles of expressways and arterial streets
Ecological:
  Heating degree days
  CO dissipation rates
  Number of atmospheric inversions per year
  Wind speed
  Terrain (maximum height differential)
Sensual:
  Degree of "smell" of CO
  Days big buildings can be seen from a given distance
Social:
  Geographic distribution of jobs vs. housing location
  Travel behavior (e.g., vehicle miles of travel)
  Total population
Religious:
  Degree of remorse of drivers about polluting environment
  Number of clergy preaching environmental morality
Intellectual:
  Number of studies indicating travel as a polluting factor
  Number of newspaper articles on the topic
Cultural:
  Frequency of automobile advertisements
  People seeing the auto as symbol of "individual freedom"
Health:
  Leaks in catalytic converters
  Mental health of drivers

5.3 Conduct Content Analysis of Literature and Expert Discussions

The purpose of this next task also is to get a broader understanding of the variables involved in the situation under study. This is done by accessing knowledge about the topic, available both in written form and verbally through the experience of those who have dealt with similar situations for many years. As demonstrated in the preceding chapter, QCQ has a content analysis (word frequency count) procedure that can be applied to most text files, whether from the literature or from notes of conversations with experts.

This process will not be repeated here. The reader is referred to Section 4.3 for an illustration. Let us assume, however, that the variables identified at this point in the exercise are: population, industrialization, automobile ownership, and growth in goods and services. These were suggested in many articles and conversations as influencing environmental pollution and, more specifically, the goal variable of carbon monoxide concentration.

5.4 Identify Invariates from Invariates Checklist

In the beginning of this chapter it was mentioned that building the relationships between variables is a recursive process that goes back to invariates— variables that change little, or at least in a very predictable fashion. These are necessary because, in trying to make a useful forecast, it does not help to predict one variable on the basis of another that itself is unpredictable.

Table 5.4, taken from QCQ, has a list of factors that might be considered as invariates, that is, essentially constant in many circumstances. The table has the same major headings as the dimensions checklist (see Table 4.4) and is accessed in the same way (see Section 4.2). For example, under the "Technological" heading comes the ultimate invariate—"Passage of Time"—which could play a significant role in the AIRPOL model particularly because of delays involved in implementing governmental environmental programs

5.5 Find New Variables and Theories Via Information Technologies

Another way to locate potential contributing theologues and variables in QCQ is through searches using information technologies. In the AIRPOL case the DCCS team employed the *McGraw-Hill Concise Encyclopedia of Science and Technology* (Parker, 1982) on CD-ROM, with the key words of "Carbon" AND "Monoxide" AND "Concentration." Twenty-seven matching articles

TABLE 5.4 Examples of Invariates

1. *Technological*
   Speed of light
   Hours in a day (by definition)
   Passage of time (minute, year, etc.)
2. *Economic*
   Taxation
   Import controls
   A black market
3. *Managerial*
   Span of control (# of people that can be managed at once)
   Ability to fire government workers
   Budgets (money and personnel)
4. *Political*
   Turf battles
   Power struggles
5. *Social*
   Continued worldwide population growth
   The formation of groups
   Gender
6. *Cultural*
   Prohibited behavior
   Standard practices
   Survival instinct
7. *Intellectual*
   Knowledge absorption rate
   Highest degree obtainable
8. *Religious/Ethical*
   Proscribed behavior (e.g., the Ten Commandments)
   Belief in higher being(s)
9. *Ecological*
   Each person has a mother and father
   Evolution continues
10. *Health*
    Maximum age of death
    Pain and death
11. *Sensual*
    Smells that make a person sick
    Human environmental limits (e.g., exterior temperature)
    Hearing range
12. *Legal*
    Workplace regulations
    Restriction of free speech
    Patent Laws

TABLE 5.5   Summary Air Pollution Facts from the WHO

The World Health Organization (WHO) has estimated that approximately 2.7 million deaths are attributable to air pollution each year. Among the air pollutants of greatest concern are ozone (O_3), suspended particulate matter (SPM), nitrogen dioxide (NO_2), sulfur dioxide (SO_2), carbon monoxide (CO), lead (Pb), and other toxins. Ozone is one of the most prevalent air pollutants in large cities, and suspended particulate matter has great impact worldwide. The sources and formation of these two air pollutants are described elsewhere. A review of the distribution and concentration of air pollutants worldwide is available from the WHO.

---

were found in which the three words appeared within 100 letters of each other. One, reproduced in Table 5.5, dealt with the topic of "air quality."

Three of the variables that emerged from DCCS thinking about this article were:

1. Organization of environmental activities into independent units;
2. Development of nationwide regulations, standards, and requirements; and
3. Firm institutionalization.

Note that none of these variables are new, but they may not have been remembered by the DCCS staff. They forgot that they knew but now they know that they know (see Figure 1.3). This rediscovery may be important for the end product.

5.6   Undertake Crowdsourcing

"Crowdsourcing" is the practice of soliciting solutions from a large group of people (the crowd, usually online) rather than from traditional sources. Often the people in the crowd are unknown. The crowd submits solutions to the crowdsourcer, and ownership of the solutions transfers at that time. Sometimes the solution provider is compensated, and sometimes all they get is the satisfaction of providing the solution.

The term "crowdsourcing" is a combination of "crowd" and "outsourcing." It is often assumed that crowdsourcing is a recent outgrowth of the Internet, and although it is true that the Internet has brought crowdsourcing more into the mainstream, it was used prior to the advent of modern telecommunications. For example, *The Oxford English Dictionary* is a pre-Internet example of crowdsourcing. The publisher requested that any volunteer could contribute to the dictionary by submitting an index of words and examples of their use. The "crowd" submitted more than six million items during a 70 year period [INT-11 Lanxon].

The Internet has brought crowdsourcing into more widespread use, as it is an excellent platform to interact with many people simultaneously. In addition, the Internet has several other advantages for crowdsourcing. For example, people have a tendency to be more open in Web environments, as they can be incognito and criticism is not as personal.

Some of the types of crowdsourcing are:

- *Crowdvoting*—Crowdvoting is when a website gathers the crowd's opinions on a certain topic. This can be used in politics to help predict elections, government to determine the peoples' opinion on public policy, and by business to help determine everything from product design to marketing strategies. Domino's Pizza has crowdvoted a new pizza, and Heineken crowdvoted a new bottle design [INT-12 Prive].
- *Crowdfunding*—Crowdfunding is the process of funding a project by a large number of people each contributing a small amount. This is the method touted by Barack Obama as the main strategy he used to finance his first run for president. There are questions of how the SEC is going to regulate crowdfunding in the U.S. Advocates of regulation claim that crowdfunding will open up the flood gates for fraud. The process currently allows for up to one million dollars to be raised relatively free of regulatory issues.
- *Wisdom of the crowd*—This type of crowdsourcing collects and aggregates large amounts of information to gain a complete and accurate picture of a topic. It is based on the idea that a group of people is usually more knowledgeable than one individual. The Internet is an excellent platform for this type of data collection because people from diverse backgrounds can contribute in real time within the same forum.

Crowdsourcing has generated two major categories of criticism [INT-24 Woods] [INT-18 Rosenberg]:

- The value and impact of the work received from the crowd—some people believe that "you get what you pay for," so if the crowd solutions are free, they are also not useful. There are also concerns over the knowledge base resident in the crowd as well as the motivation.
- The ethical implications of low wages paid to crowdworkers—particularly in the business world, where crowdsourcing solutions can be used to generate significant income.

5.7   Recapitulation

What DCCS is trying to do at this step in the QCQ process is to find some readily available and worthwhile concepts (that is, "theories" or "models") that will allow them to eventually make reliable forecasts of the factors (that is, "variables") that affect the goal variables, mostly identified in the preceding chapter. Several readily available tools for this purpose have been located and illustrated. Several others are documented in the next chapter.

5.8   An Expanded Learning Case: The Medicaid Data Disruption

Note:
See Appendix A for an explanation of the statistics herein.

Sooner or later we have to deal with the issues surrounding the availability and "cleanliness" of the data associated with the variables and relationships we seek. Particularly difficult are the situations where there simply is no data or something has happened to change it.

In this case a model was being developed to forecast Medicaid (medical program for the poor) expenditures for Virginia. One part of the data—for outpatient hospital service payments—had a substantial downward "jolt" in it, followed by an even more substantial upward jolt. These turned out to be temporary, not permanent (see Figure 5.2).

After some investigation it was found that the main reason for the jolt was a paper mistake. Apparently the national agency responsible for the program changed the forms employed for hospitals to claim their reimbursements. More importantly, the new forms were delayed about three months in getting out, so no one could request reimbursements. There thus was a significant drop in payments during that time period, followed by a huge increase as the backlog was cleared.

This case, like that in the preceding section, begs the question of whether to include the "errant" data in the regression analysis. It also begs the question of whether to place large, temporary shocks somewhat arbitrarily in the forecasted values. Perrow (1984) refers to these shocks as "normal accidents," emphasizing the fact that something similar can normally be expected to occur again (although we may not be able to say exactly to whom, for what, why, when, where, or how).

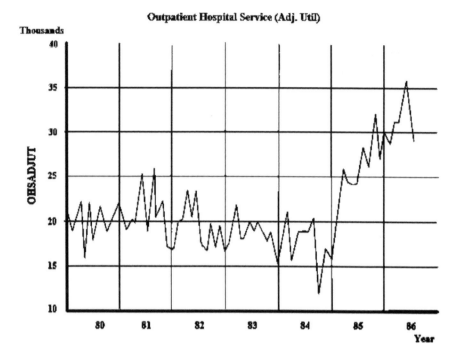

Figure 5.2   Monthly outpatient hospital recipients (OHSADJUT) at time of service.

"Normal" accidents or errors need not be restricted to large deviations. Every point in Figure 5.2 has a deviation of some amount, however small, and a "story" behind it to explain that deviation. This would imply that some degree of randomization should be built into the forecasting process.

Another aspect of the Medicaid project that was instructive was the focus on the *percentage error* as the desired goodness of fit (GoF) indicator. The highest allowable value for this was set at 4% (it turned out to be about 2%). Since Virginia was spending about $660 million a year on Medicaid at the time, an error of even the 2% size would translate to over $13 million (MAE).

The correlation coefficient (R) thus was *not* considered useful in showing how well the estimated values fit the actual data, perhaps because it is a *relative* measure. This is demonstrated in the two diagrams in Figure 5.3. In the first a regression was run on the six points. It is plain to see that each point is in error by one unit. The sum of the squared errors (ESS) thus is 6. Similarly, a regression was run on the six points in the second diagram. Four of the points are in error by one unit, and two by two units. The ESS thus can be computed as:

$$(1)^2 + (1)^2 + (2)^2 + (2)^2 + (1)^2 + (1)^2 = 12.$$

Note that the ESS of the second is twice that of the first. As an aside, this seems excessive since only two of the six points have a bigger error. But this

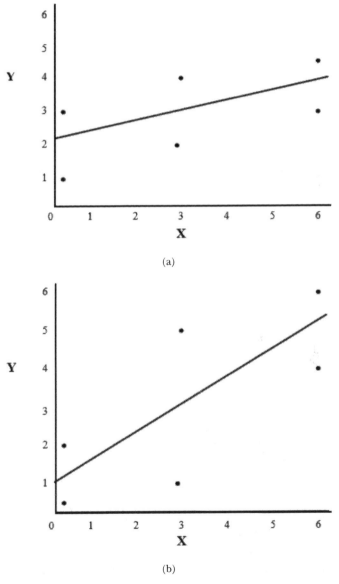

(a)

(b)

Figure 5.3 (a) Example fictional data set for regression trial; (b) Other example fictional data set for regression trial.

is a consequence of the squaring action and shows that that approach may not be in harmony with our "gut" feelings as to goodness of fit.

The main point, however, is that the correlation in the second diagram is *larger* than that in the first—0.850 versus 0.632. It thus is possible to have a higher correlation despite a greater error (in an absolute sense). This occurs because there is more initial variation in Y in the second diagram and a greater proportion of it is reduced via the regression line.

The MAPE is not without its problems either. For the equation in the first diagram it actually is slightly *higher* than the MAPD—35.5% versus 33.3%. The reason for this is, in part, the comparatively large errors on the comparatively small numbers for the two leftmost points (e.g., an error of 1 unit versus a predicted value of 2 brings the large percentage error of 50%). Big errors on small numbers thus can blow up the MAPE considerably.

The question still left to be answered is: how should a substantial but temporary "jolt" like that in Figure 5.2 be handled?

One approach would be simply to ignore those time periods during the jolt, with its substantial drop-off followed by a substantial upswing. A second approach would be to "fill in" that period with a reasonable facsimile of what might have happened had the jolt-inducing factor (a paper work screw up) not occurred.

Looking now at the forecast period, we might decide somewhat arbitrarily to place large, temporary shocks in some of the scenarios. These would represent the possibility of Perrow's (1984) "normal" accidents or errors. In other words, jolts of some magnitude are bound to happen normally in most time frames.

6

Step 2. Theory Search (Continued)

This chapter continues on the track of the previous one, which is to find old or create new theories (concepts, analogues, models, etc.) that help to explain, elaborate, and predict relevant future changes associated with a given project domain. Particular emphasis is given to those theories that relate to secondary goals in a situation (see previous chapter).

Five more techniques are presented to help in this "theory search" cause (see Table 5.1). These generally are synthesis (creative joining) techniques compared to the preceding analysis techniques.

6.1   Identify New Variables and Theories with Cyberquest

CyberQuest (CQ) is a multimedia software/hardware system intended to help in problem solving, strategic planning, and innovation support (Dickey, 1995b). It assists individuals and groups in business and government in coming up with ideas *and* ways to implement them. CQ contains databases of diverse concepts drawn from art, music, management, education, engineering, physics, sociology, science fiction, religion, and many other fields.

Supernumerary Intelligence, pages 81–94
Copyright © 2015 by Information Age Publishing
81

The six basic steps in CQ are:

1. Problem description and analysis
2. Word selection
3. Generation of ideas
4. Idea screening
5. Idea packaging and evaluation
6. Reporting

Along the way the user also has a variety of other options. These include (1) entering notes associated with any idea, (2) identifying goals that supplement the aim, (3) accessing various kinds of analytic tools (e.g., a spreadsheet), and (4) accessing a cross section of information sources. All these give the user a high degree of capability and flexibility in developing ideas and finding ways to analyze and implement them.

In the final step, reports are generated showing the ideas, sources, screening results, and final packages. Another feature of CQ is that the ideas generated can be put back into the system's databases and employed by any succeeding user facing a similar type of problem or opportunity.

Once the aim (main goal) has been identified (Step 1) and key words have been chosen (Step 2), the user employs them in Step 3 to match against concepts in various databases. These concepts come from over 20 sources and cover a variety of topical areas. They, too, have four key words describing them, again taken from CQ's list. If a match is found between the words describing the aim and those associated with a concept, the assumption is made that there is some similarity. The matching concept then is displayed on the screen and the user asked to draw an analogy to obtain an idea to help achieve the aim.

In Step 4 the ideas are screened. This involves assigning a "status" to each, depending on whether the idea has been done before or not, and its implementability. Each idea then is rated for its importance and the effort required to implement it.

Packaging and evaluation, in Step 5, require that the user look for *combinations* (i.e., "packages") of ideas that are more productive, beneficial, and/ or cost-effective than any idea individually. The resultant packages subsequently are evaluated according to selected "themes" or criteria and decisions made among them.

The last step involves the preparation and dissemination of reports.

A full example of CQ is too detailed to be illustrated here, but the idea generation Step 3 is part of the process described in the next section.

6.2 Search "Previous Theories" Database

QCQ contains several different databases of what are called "relational theories or analogues" (together called "theologues"). These simply state that a particular (Y) variable or "conclusion" is related to (or "depends on," or "is influenced by") one or more (X) variables.

These sets of theories or analogues come from many different fields—economics, negotiation, budgeting, and so on, with two having entries from miscellaneous areas. The hope is that one or more concepts may provide a good direct fit for the model to be developed for the case at hand. This idea generation process works basically by analogy, which is the way many top scientists and inventors make discoveries (Root-Bernstein, 1989). The connections may be quite startling: an art object may give an image for an engineering process, or an economic theory may lead to a new type of biological relationship.

Every theologue has four words associated with it. Two have been chosen from a list of nouns or subjects. The other two come from a list of descriptor pairs (adjectives). Both lists have been taken from CyberQuest (1995b). The associated words are intended to form a fairly exhaustive set of categories describing people, places, physical entities, and abstract concepts in the world. For instance, the subject list has the main categories of:

- group of people
- natural environment
- bodily functions
- manmade environment
- abstract concepts

where the last classification contains words like:

- art
- attitude
- behavior
- being
- borrow
- wisdom

The descriptor pairs are divided into categories following those in the old style (non-dictionary) thesaurus (Morehead, 2002). One category, for example, is "Abstract Relations," which contains the pairs:

- abstract<>nonabstract
- agreeable<>disagreeable
- defended<>defenseless
- natural<>artificial
- new<>old
- numerous<>scarce
- organized<>chaotic
- powerful<>weak
- professional<>unskilled

The search involves:

1. Selecting one subject word on the list that describes the dependent variable being considered;
2. Selecting a descriptor pair on the list that describes the dependent variable being considered;
3. Searching the chosen database for theologues that match on either one or both of the selected words.

If a match is found, the assumption is made that there is some similarity. The matching concept then is displayed on the screen and the user asked to draw an analogy to obtain an idea about relevant variables and/or theories.

In the development of the AIRPOL model, the DCCS team started the search by selecting the first so-called "miscellaneous" set of theologues. They then made the choices of "institution" and "powerful<>weak" to associate with the potential client decision variable of government spending on air pollution controls. Next, they looked at:

- law of thermo (energy conservation)
- Newton's law of gravity
- executive derailment
- force (Newton's equation)
- Bernoulli's equation

None of these seemed to have a *direct* correspondence with the "government spending" variable so, somewhat arbitrarily, the team focused on "Newton's law of gravity" as a potential source of analogy:

The *conclusion*:

Force of attraction between two bodies

is influenced by

Mass of first body

Mass of second body

Distance (squared) between the two bodies

An analogy that came to mind at the time was:

- "Force of attraction": Amount of spending attracted to a particular urban area
- "Mass of first body": Amount of money made available by the federal government
- "Mass of second body": Extent of pollution problem in a particular urban area
- "Distance between the bodies": Distance of particular urban area from Washington, DC

These new variables and new relationship then were added to the list of possibilities, to be assessed in depth later.

6.3   Use the Public Administration Genome Project (PAGP)

Deployment of the PAGP has been demonstrated in Chapter 2, so we will follow the same seven-part process but with less commentary. It also is described in detail in Chapter 15. So assume we still are looking for influencing variables related to the identified goals.

1. The DCCS picked the word "action" to best summarize the aim of the exercise at this point.
2. They then went to the home page of the PAGP, which was http://pagenome-compass.pbworks.com, took a quick look at the list of cases, saw some titles that appeared promising, and returned to the PAGP front (home) page.
3. They decided to investigate the first of the three different databases (views) of the cases—"Variables in Lists." This got them to the front page of that database.
4. They subsequently entered the "action" word in the search box in the upper right corner and pushed "Enter." The result was a listing of the (many) cases in which that word appears.
5. They browsed through that list and decided that the "Institutional Analysis and Development" case may have the most similarity to theirs.

6. They then pressed the "Ctrl-f" keys together, causing another search box to be shown. They again entered the word "action" and pressed "Enter." The matching variables inside the case then were made known.

7. The DCCS team subsequently picked out the variable: ACTAREA Action Arena, which was defined as "a conceptual unit (of analysis) containing two sets of variables: the action situation and the actor." In other words, it is "the social space where individuals interact, exchange goods and services, solve problems, dominate one another, fight, etc." (Ostrom, 1999)

The DCCS decided that most of this material certainly could be turned into relevant "variables" in this case. For instance, one could be the "number of people willing to fight for the cause." In addition, the ACTAREA concept also could be employed as a description of the background domain for the case.

6.4   Use Supposedly Dated Material

Many times we overlook relevant material because it "looks" old. While some may be outdated, there also may be a great deal of historical evidence of value, particularly in terms of the paths taken by decision makers and the resultant effects. As an example, the quote in Table 6.1 was taken from one of the earliest CD-ROMs (also in hardback).

The paragraph is instructive in that it brings out a potential new *goal* variable—long term, low level exposure. If this were considered important, it could be recorded in this stage for future evaluation.

The second information technology employed from QCQ by the DCCS team was the Internet. A search on the World Wide Web using the phrase "carbon monoxide con" turned up over 300 sites.

TABLE 6.1   Quote from McGraw-Hill *Concise Encyclopedia of Science and Technology*

The matter of low level intakes of known or suspected toxicants through a life of 65 to 75 years cannot be resolved by present toxicological and epidemiological information or methods. Decisions on . . . use . . . control . . . issues are politically . . . socially sensitive.

Source: Chanlett, 1982. (Also available on CD-ROM but may or may not work on today's equipment).

TABLE 6.2   Quote on Carbon Monoxide from a World Wide Web Page

Novelli et al (1994) attempted to estimate the possible cause of the recent decline of CO
   concentrations, but concluded that no single cause...greatest rate of...decrease began
   in late 1991, which corresponds to the eruption of Mt. Pinutabo...

Note: Taken from:
   U.S. National Report to IUGG, 1991–1994
   Rev. Geophys. Vol. 33 Suppl., (c) 1995 American Geophysical Union
   http://www.agu.org/revgeophys/penner00/node3.html (See also [INT-2])

In a different part of the report it was pointed out that CO has about a
two month lifetime in the atmosphere and is more concentrated in places
that are:

1. near large biomass burning facilities,
2. near the ocean, or
3. in the northernmost latitudes.

CO also was higher during the winter months.

A side note to be made here is that the URL given for this Internet page
was not operational when an attempt was made to access it. This usually is not
a happy occasion, especially if, say, the DCCS wanted some exact information.
On the other hand, if they only wanted to get some basic ideas, like in identifying conceptual goals (see, for example, Table 4.5), they could visit other
Web Pages and perhaps find something transferable there.

6.5   Undertake Situation Structuring

The next task in this step of QCQ is "situation structuring." This is employed
to combine or group diverse "elements" into simpler and more manageable
groups.

A *tradeoff* is involved in this task. Suppose a particular situation has 100
major elements. Each could be addressed individually, but that would be
time-consuming and expensive. Conversely, the 100 elements could be
combined into, say, five groups, within which the elements are as similar as
possible. These would be much simpler and more manageable, but some
groups might contain elements that were quite different from each other.
Some potentially important differences might be glossed over. The tradeoff
therefore is between *simplicity* and *homogeneity*.

Situation structuring is based on the work of George Kelly, a psychologist, and more recently by Mildred Shaw in her book *On Becoming a Personal
Scientist* (1980). The QCQ version of their process has four main stages:

1. Identification of the major elements (people, physical items, emotions, etc.) in the situation;
2. Through "triangulation," identification of important "dimensions" (e.g., personal-impersonal, new-old, healthy-sick) inherent in the situation;
3. Rating of each element on each dimension; and
4. Statistical grouping of the elements on the dimensions to find the optimum balance between simplicity (few groups) and homogeneity (similarity of elements within the groups).

The result should be a better understanding of the situation and its component parts.

The first stage is to itemize the major elements in the situation being considered. For this DCCS employed the list of 14 variables in Table 6.3. These were based in part on the subject word list in CyberQuest (see Section 6.1).

The next major step was to input dimensions. These are polar opposite descriptors or adjectives like "new-old." There are three ways to make such inputs. The first is "triangulation." QCQ draws and displays three of the elements at random. The DCCS team then is asked to find the two that are most similar to each other and decide how they differ from the remaining one. For example, the two similar ones may relate to "long term effect," while the third may be the opposite—"short term effect." This process is continued until no substantially "new" dimensions arise.

TABLE 6.3 Selected Elements for Situation Structuring

Topic: CO Concentrations in U.S. Urban Areas
Date: 10/22/2013
Case: C:\Users\John\Documents\Qcq\QCQ-AfterBreak Redundancy code\Cases–Tri

CO Concentration
Vehicle Emissions
Atmospheric Conditions
Vehicle Ownership
Emission Controls
Government Expenditure
Regulations
Increased Driving
Air Chemistry
Plant Coverage
Time
Geographic Spread
Industrial Sources
Sunlight

The second way is to take descriptor pairs from the CyberQuest list (see Section 6.1). The third approach is to allow the team to add some of its *own* dimensions.

Eight dimensions were added altogether (Table 6.4).

The third step involves scoring of each element on each dimension (Table 6.5). If the element is considered completely to the "left side," it is

TABLE 6.4 List of Dimensions

Topic: CO Concentrations in U.S. Urban Areas
Date: 10/22/2013
Case: C:\Users\John\Documents\Qcq\QCQ-AfterBreak Redundancy code\Cases–Tri

CO Production–CO Concentration
Long-Term Effect–Short-Term Effect
Fast Absorbtion–Slow Absorbtion
Public Responsibility–Private Responsibility
High-Density Area–Low-Density Area
Natural Emissions–Human-Made Emissions
Spending–Regulation
Physical Change–Economic Change

TABLE 6.5 Scoring Instructions and Example for One Element

Enter/Edit Scores for Each Element and Dimension

Return Print Edit Format Help

Instructions for Putting in the Score –
[1] Go to the Desired Dimension/Element Cell.
[2] Enter a Number Between 0.0 and 10.0
   0.0 Element is Closest to Far Left of Dimension
   10.0 Element is Closest to Far Right of Dimension
   5.0 Element is In Between (or Not Applicable)
[3] Make Sure a Score is Entered in Each Cell.

Situation: Carbon Monoxide Concentrations in Urban Areas

N8	0.3	
0.0<= Dimension/Element Score <=10	CO Concentration	Vehicle
CO Production–CO Consumption	2.5	
Long Term Effect–Short Term Effect	4.2	
Fast Absorbtion–Slow Absorbtion	1.5	
Public Responsibility–Private Responsibility	1.0	
High Density Area–Low Density Area	0.5	
Natural Emissions–Human Made Emissions	4.2	
Spending–Regulation	3.0	
Physical Change–Economic Change	0.4	

given a score of "0"; completely to the "right side" a "5"; and anywhere in between a correspondingly-scaled value (to the nearest tenth). The mid-scale value (2.5) is utilized if the combination is "not applicable." As an example, the score assigned to the first element—CO concentration—on the dimension "long term effect<>short term effect" was 4.2, implying that the concentration of CO was a phenomenon that occurred predominantly in a small time frame.

In the last step QCQ groups the elements statistically (Table 6.6). This is done starting with each element in its own group (i.e., by itself). Under this condition there is maximum homogeneity (similarity) of elements within each group. A measure of this is the "G-Score," which has a value of 1.00 at that point. Elements then are combined sequentially into smaller numbers of groups (while maintaining the maximum G-Score at each stage) until only one group remains. At this juncture the G-Score is 0.00 since all the disparate elements have been combined into one big, heterogeneous group.

TABLE 6.6 | **Grouping of Elements**

Topic: CO Concentrations in U.S. Urban Areas
Date: 10/22/2013
Case: C:\Users\John\Documents\Qcq\QCQ-AfterBreak Redundancy code\Cases–Tri

---

G-Score: .7337397

    Group 1   Vehicle Emissions/Control
        CO Concentration
        Vehicle Emissions
    Group 2   Atmospheric Buildup/Diffusion
        Atmospheric Conditions
        Air Chemistry
        Time
        Geographic Spread
    Group 3   Human Emission Production Causes
        Vehicle Ownership
        Increased Driving
        Industrial Sources
    Group 4   Government Intervention Mechanisms
        Emission Controls
    Group 5   Government Expenditures/Regulations
        Government Expenditure
        Regulations
    Group 6   Photosynthesis-Related Factors
        Plant Coverage
        Sunlight

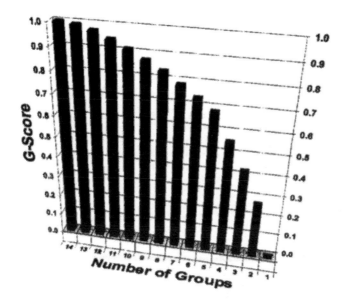

Figure 6.1 Sequential grouping of elements and associated G-score.

As shown in Figure 6.1, there is a steady decline in the G-Score as groups are put together. There also is an "elbow" in the graph where the G-Score drops off more precipitously than before. This point (or one close thereto) is taken as the best location in the tradeoff between simplicity (few groups) and similarity or homogeneity of elements within the groups (G-Score). This "elbow" occurs with a "grouping" of six groups and G = 0.734. There thus is a loss of about 27% of the homogeneity in the elements in exchange for the simplicity of using only six groups. QCQ now asked the DCCS team to pinpoint the *stage* that represented the best grouping. Following the preceding logic, this was stage "8" (with 6 groups).

Next the team was requested to interpret these six entities and give each a name. The last one, for instance, was a combination of plants and sunlight, so it was called "Photosynthesis-related factors." The full list of resultant names is shown in Table 6.7. They help in identifying major categories of variables that should be considered in the AIRPOL model.

6.6 Cull the List of Variables and Theories

The result of the preceding three tasks will be a list of variables that seem to be active (or potentially active in the future) in the situation under study. In

---

TABLE 6.7 **List of Assigned Group Names**

Topic: CO Concentrations in U.S. Urban Areas
Date: 10/22/2013
Case: C:\Users\John\Documents\Qcq\QCQ-AfterBreak Redundancy code\Cases–Tri

Group 1	Vehicle Emissions/Control
Group 2	Atmospheric Buildup/Diffusion
Group 3	Human Emission Production Causes
Group 4	Government Intervention Mechanisms
Group 5	Government Expenditures/Regulations
Group 6	Photosynthesis-Related Factors

TABLE 6.8 **List of Culled Variables**

Federal air pollution control expenditures (PE)
Time (YEAR)
Population (POP)
Gross domestic product (GNP)
Vehicle miles of travel (VMT)
Carbon monoxide concentrations (CO)

---

practice these variables will be fairly specific and many will be more technical than described here. Let us assume that the consequent, rather small list for the AIRPOL model is that in Table 6.8. These variables, taken together, will be considered (at least for the moment) to be the *domain* for the AIRPOL model. All other variables will be excluded, primarily for reasons of simplicity.

6.7 Recapitulation

The techniques presented in this and the previous chapter have allowed what initially was a vague, fuzzy situation to be clarified considerably to the point where a small number of relevant variables and theologues have been identified. In the beginning the only known factor in the AIRPOL case was the goal of reducing carbon monoxide concentrations. In this QCQ step the variety of variables and relationships to be considered first was expanded via:

- Content analysis,
- Review of QCQ's dimensions checklist,
- Searches of theory databases,
- Access to encyclopedias (mainly on CD-ROMs),

- Search of the World Wide Web,
- Use of CyberQuest—problem solving and innovation support system, and
- Use of the Public Administration Genome Project

The list then was condensed using "situation structuring" and the culling procedure.

6.8 An Expanded Learning Case: The New Minivan

Perhaps the most difficult situation for any analyst is when there is no data at all. This would be the case where a possible innovation is being considered. Since an innovation is, by definition, new, there is no direct historical evidence on which to base an analysis like regression. A particular example would be the minivan at the moment before it was put on the market. Since no such thing existed before, how could anybody forecast its likely success?

Surrogate variables can be employed, but there always is the question of how closely a surrogate mimics the desired variable.

Perhaps the best that can be done is to look at the sales trends in "closely similar" vehicles and in the factors that might affect these sales as well as the cost of producing the new vehicle. Some candidates for these are presented in Table 6.9. The station wagon obviously is a "closely similar" entity, as is the Japanese Road Runner and British Land Rover. All of these have been around for some time and thus have a sales history.

TABLE 6.9   Trends Related to Minivan Sales

Station wagon purchases
Baggage taken by families/business people on trips
Dislike of trucks
People going to formal affairs
Multiple use of vehicles (small business + family)
Number of high income families
Long distance travel
Concern for comfort
Legal constraints (e.g., on required car mileage)
Complaints about small cars
Profit margins
Allowable work rules in a new plant
U.S. car market growth
Likelihood of Japanese to produce quickly
Sales for British Land Rover and Japanese Road Runner
Costs of production—new machinery and plant

One reason for the potential attractiveness of the proposed minivan presumably is that it can carry more people and/or baggage on long trips than a station wagon. Trends in these factors can be established from surveys done over a period of years. On the production side, past experience with development of new manufacturing plants might show that new technology and work rules would reduce labor costs considerably.

The net upshot of a review of these relevant trends for which past data were available would be to confirm that an increasing number of minivans could be sold at good profit margins.

7

Step 3. Theory Development

The main objective in this stage is to complete the identification of relevant variables and their relationships for the model in the AIRPOL case. Involved are the actions for specifying variables and catalysts, showing the causal links between and among them, and indicating the structure and timing of the relationships. The result should be an exhaustive theory, otherwise referred to as a "conceptual model," of the phenomena under study.

7.1 The Theory Development Process

The main steps in the theory or model development process are presented in Table 7.1. First, the set of culled variables identified in the previous step (Table 6.8) can be both expanded and made more specific. The general factor "Population," for example, might become "U.S. Resident Population." The recursive questioning process, also introduced in that step, then can be employed in full to make the actual connections in the potential links diagram (see Figure 5.1). In the process each variable needs to be categorized into one of several very specific classes—client strategy, external, intermediate, and goal. If the resultant model is intended to be dynamic

Supernumerary Intelligence, pages 95–108
Copyright © 2015 by Information Age Publishing
All rights of reproduction in any form reserved.

TABLE 7.1   Substeps in QCQ Step 3: Theory Development

Identify specific variables
Identify possible links between the variables
Classify the variables (as external, goal, etc.)
Specify relationships in more detail
    Determine type of mathematical structure
    Undertake cause/effect analysis
    Undertake necessary and sufficient analysis
    Specify time affinities
    Incorporate catalysis and catalysts
    Identify exact theories, assumptions, etc.
    Recognize situational constraints
    Detail related experience and confidence

(changing with time), then a "time clock" (day, month, year, etc.) variable has to be recognized, and there also may be some corresponding reaction times to take into account.

The next step involves a closer investigation of the individual $Y:X_j$ relationships. This starts with the selection of the appropriate mathematical structure (e.g., if the relationship has been assigned a "positive" [direct] or "negative" [inverse] one). A cause-effect analysis then can be undertaken by responding to the six major questions on the topic in Table 7.2.

If the model being developed is intended to be dynamic, then the time affinity for each $Y:X_j$ relationship needs investigation. There may be an associated nonzero reaction (delay) or "preaction" (anticipation) time. Moreover, this time may be increasing or decreasing, in which case it becomes another type of variable ("pre/reaction"), and it will have its own set of affecting factors (called "catalysts," after the chemical concept).

The last set of steps involves a closer look at the theories or analogues (otherwise called "theologues") behind both the individual $Y:X_j$ relationship and that for Y versus *all* its corresponding X's. Documentation is

TABLE 7.2   QCQ Central Questions Asked on Cause and Effect

Is there an identifiable "agent" in X that "causes" Y?
Is there a close spatial proximity between X and Y?
Is there a close time proximity between X and Y?
Does X (or its anticipation) occur *before* Y?
If X were manipulated (all else constant), would Y change?
Is there a transfer of "energy" from X to Y?

---

requested for the associated theologue; any notable anomalies, paradoxes, and extreme examples; and relevant experience with, and situational constraints inherent in, the relationship.

In most cases it is necessary to return to QCQ Step 2 or go forward to Step 4 (usually to enter definitions, measures, and data for variables) to make the model more comprehensive and comprehendible.

7.2 Identify Specific Variables

The activities in Step 2 ended with an initial set of variables (re-created in Table 7.3) and possibly some relevant theories to connect them. This list most likely is incomplete, so some additional thinking is necessary. This involves the explicit and systematic application of the recursive (expanding and culling) process introduced in Chapter 5.

The first task in that recursive process is to identify those factors that are possible "direct" or "immediate" causes (X variables) for the goal variable(s), which in the AIRPOL model is just COC. Experience might indicate, for example, that COC is influenced by population growth (POP). Yet that may not be considered "direct," since POP first influences VMT, which then affects COC. VMT thus is a "direct" cause, along with federal air pollution control expenditures (PE).

The systematic backward (or "upward") chaining of questions and answers needed in this process is illustrated in Table 7.4.

TABLE 7.3 List of Culled Variables from QCQ Step 2

Federal air pollution control expenditures (PE)
Time (YEAR)
Population (POP)
Gross domestic product per capita (GDPPC)
Vehicle miles of travel (VMT)
Carbon monoxide concentration (COC)

TABLE 7.4 Example of a Chained Set of Questions

Question: What variables directly affect "carbon monoxide concentration" (COC)?
Answer: Total federal pollution control expenditures (PE) and vehicle miles of travel (VMT)

Question: What variables directly affect VMT?
Answer: Population (POP) and gross domestic product per capita (GDPPC)

Question: What variables directly affect POP?
Answer: Time (YEAR)

TABLE 7.5 **Direct Effect Variables Stopping at Invariate**

Question: What variables directly affect "carbon monoxide concentration" (COC)?
Answer: Total federal pollution control expenditures (PE) and vehicle miles of travel (VMT)

Question: What variables directly affect PE?
Answer: Continuing federal air pollution control expenditures (FPE) and additional federal air pollution control expenditures (APE).

Question: What variables directly affect FPE?
Answer: Gross domestic product per capita (GDPPC)

Question: What variables directly affect GDPPC?
Answer: Time (YEAR)

As can be seen in Table 7.5, this process continues until an invariate (e.g., "Time" or "YEAR") or strategy is reached.

When more than one variable affects another, the influences of the others also must be traced. What about PE's effect on COC, for instance?

The theory here is that there always will be an underlying growth in pollution control expenditures (called "FPE"), with the amount depending on the GDPPC (which in turn depends solely on the YEAR). EPA and Congress—the immediate clients—are probably most interested in the impacts of *additions* or *subtractions* (APE) to those ongoing amounts (FPE). The *total* expenditure (PE) then can be derived simply by summation through an "accounting" equation: PE = FPE + APE.

Note that part of the recursive path for PE goes back once more to an invariate (YEAR again). This is necessary because, in any relationship (with a dependent variable Y vs. one or more independent X's), the independent variables *also* have to be forecast. This means that they too become dependents in yet other relationships. Where does it all end? Hopefully with variables for which accurate forecasts can be made—the invariates (which below are categorized as "externals").

The story is not complete, however. Another recursive branch for PE stops with a *client strategy* variable (see Figure 5.1), which is "additional federal pollution control expenditures" (APE). The general conclusion, then, is that *any path that leads to a goal variable should start from an invariate (external) or client strategy.*

It may seem that the preceding recursive process for identifying variables and constructing connections between them is strictly mechanical—done once and then finished. As our own experience and that from the field of artificial intelligence (AI) demonstrates, that view is far from the reality. In AI much effort has gone into investigating the role of "knowledge engineers" in helping professionals in a particular topical field create "expert systems" (a type of model) to capture their proficiency (Knowledge Engineering for Expert Systems, 1988).

As a general finding, even some of the seemingly "simple" processes take much more time and effort to document than anticipated. Much of this is due to the constant need to go back, rethink, and redo. This finding closely resembles Clausewitz's description of "friction" in war. He said that in war, friction is "the force that makes the apparently easy so difficult and the difficult seemingly impossible" (Clausewitz, 1832/1984). Influencing variables are added, deleted, and changed after further thought and conversations uncover previously unappreciated aspects of the situation at hand. The resulting full set of variables and interconnections (as illustrated in Figure 5.1) is called the problem, situation, or system "domain." This can be imagined as a cordon line that differentiates the items of concern from "the rest of the world."

Two questions, which long have daunted systems analysts, arise in creating this domain:

1. How far should the domain boundaries be stretched to include variables and relationships currently *outside* the domain? Why, for example, should GDPPC be taken only as a function of time (YEAR)? There are hundreds of variables (trade balance, inflation, etc.) that influence GDPPC. Why not take them into account?

2. How much and what kind of detail should be included *within* the domain? It would have been possible, for instance, to create a simple model that had COC as a function of just YEAR and APE. This, however, would not have done much to satisfy our innate desire to understand "why?" On the other hand, a model with thousands of variables would be overwhelming.

Unfortunately, QCQ does not offer any direct answers to these questions. Indirectly, however, are the concerns for the client and for available study resources (both identified in Step 1). The (hypothetical) client in the AIRPOL case is the Environmental Protection Agency, which presumably has only passing interest in the GDPPC. Moreover, if time and resources are short, then it simply is impossible to develop a model with much detail. The focus must go directly to the client and the client's associated issues (goals and strategies).

Two general principles also help in answering the questions. The first is the easy-to-forget concept of *eliminating redundancy*—both in variables and in relationships. An obvious case would arise in the AIRPOL model if, say, the variable (and corresponding relationship) of "motorized kilometers of trip-making" (MKT) also were included. This would be almost exactly the same as VMT ("vehicle miles of travel") and thus offer no new information of value.

Redundancy can be much more subtle, however. Should both POP and GDPPC be included in the AIRPOL model, for instance? While they obviously are quite different entities—human beings versus money—they also might be seen as representing a common underlying factor or theme of "size" or "growth" of the nation. So either one (or a combination) might take the place of the two to capture that notion.

The second principle has to do with *maintaining "balance"* in the "force field" (Lewin, 1943) of a relationship. This can be demonstrated with the COC versus POP, PE and VMT association. There is at least one "force"—PE—trying to push down COC and at least one other "force"—VMT—(and POP) trying to push it up. The resultant COC level thus comes about as an *equilibrium balance* between these two competitive pressures.

If there were no offsetting force in one direction, the dependent variable presumably would zoom off without any constraint. What, for instance, is keeping VMT from doing this? Both of the latter are pushing it to increase. Why should VMT not go immediately to infinity? An appropriate version of this relationship would include some other force (like, say, the price of travel) that would offset the upward pressure of POP and GDPPC.

7.3   Identify Possible Links

The next major phase in QCQ is to relate the variables to each other using identified theories or analogues ("theologues"). In the case where no suitable theologue exists, a new one must be created. The recursive process described in the preceding section is a major prelude to this whole endeavor.

The procedure in this phase entails four interconnected and usually repeated steps. First, the variables are "connected" to show which "dependent" ones are *directly* and *immediately* related to each "independent" one. This is followed by a determination of the "role" (strategy, external, goal, etc.) for each variable and then a detailed cause/effect, necessary-sufficient analysis requiring a response to several questions about the nature of each relationship. Time affinities are specified in the fourth step.

A major philosophical question to be addressed in the first step is "What is meant by 'direct' or 'immediate'?" Why, for instance, does GDPPC "directly" affect VMT, which in turn "directly" affects COC? Why not have GDPPC "directly" affect EMPLOYMENT (another intermediate variable), which "directly" affects VMT then COC? Or why not simplify: drop VMT altogether and have GNP "directly" influence COC?

All these models are possible, especially since there are few clearly established rules or criteria for creating and making a decision among models of different sizes. One criterion to be observed, in keeping with the discussion on situation structuring in Section 6.4, is that of "simplicity," while an opposing one is of "understandability." The tradeoff between these two helps to determine the *number* of intervening variables. The *sequence*, on the other hand, is influenced in great measure by the model developer's view (or the appropriate theologue) of the succession of causality (see Section 7.6). GDPPC affects VMT, which affects COC because that seems to be the corresponding sequence of events in reality—people earn money, so they then can travel, which subsequently creates CO concentrations. In this model, GDPPC does *not* directly or immediately influence COC. Yet, if VMT were eliminated as a variable (for simplicity's sake), GDPPC *could* become a direct or immediate influence on COC (see Table 7.6).

It may even be desirable (although not done here) to develop more than one model to account for the same goal variable(s). For instance, one AIRPOL model may deal with physical conditions (wind, snow, terrain, etc.) that affect COC concentrations and another with legal/political factors (laws, regulations, court decisions, etc.). Most of the variables and relationships in these two models would be quite different. And then there always is the question about the accuracy of just one model.

TABLE 7.6   "Possible Links" Model

Goal:	COC = f(PE, VMT)
Intermediate:	PE = FPE + APE
Intermediate:	FPE = f(GDPPC)
Intermediate:	VMT = f(POP, GDPPC)
External (vs. time):	POP = f(YEAR)
External (vs. time):	GDPPC = f(YEAR)
Client Strategy:	APE
Time Clock:	YEAR
Pre/Reaction Time:	(none specified yet)
Catalyst:	(none specified yet)

7.4 Identify Variable Roles

The next step in this stage of QCQ is to classify each variable into one of the following seven roles. This classification follows from the description of the metamodel in Chapter 1 and is illustrated in Table 7.7.

The identification of client strategy variables at first might seem to be an easy task. Presumably the client or user has complete control over the variable and thus can change it in any way desired. While this may be possible in controlled experiments in a laboratory setting, it generally is not the circumstance outside the lab.

In the AIRPOL case, for example, the initial focus had been on *all* federal funding for air pollution control programs. But the clients—citizens in polluted areas and the EPA —have only partial command over such funding decisions. These mostly come under the control of Congress, the President, and perhaps even the courts. EPA and the citizens can do little more than wishfully beg their case (mainly through the budget making and voting processes).

The other part of the money quests would consist of *additions* or *subtractions* to the stream proposed in budgets by EPA. Thus, with some generality, the originally conceived strategy variable (PE) was divided into one part beyond client control (FPE) and another (APE) within.

TABLE 7.7 Potential Roles for a Variable

Goal: one that represents the ultimate objective in the situation under study. It is affected by, but also can affect, other variables.

Client Strategy: one over which the client has (or possibly could have) the power to control. It is assumed to be unaffected by other variables.

Time Clock: a single variable taken to represent the passage of time (in days, months, years, etc.)

External (vs. time): one that is assumed completely beyond the client's power to control and, for simplicity, is assumed to be unaffected by any other variable except the passage of time (i.e., the time clock).

External (from data): one that is assumed completely beyond the client's power to control and, for simplicity, is assumed to be unaffected by any other variable. Future values (forecasted data) are supplied from some outside source (e.g., another organization).

Intermediate: a non-goal that both affects and is affected by other variables.

Pre/Reaction Time: the varying amount of time it takes for one variable (X) to affect another (Y). If Y occurs after X, it is a reaction time (delay). If Y comes before X, it is a "preaction" time—that is, Y is based on the *anticipation* of X.

Invariate: an external variable that is a constant, or at least changes in a very predictable fashion.

Catalyst: a variable that influences the preaction or reaction *time*—that is, the time it takes for a relationship between two variables to occur. It can be influenced by other variables.

For this and other reasons, the theory adopted in the AIRPOL case was that there is a fixed part of the federal funding by Congress, the citizenry, and the courts. The other part would come from a continuous annual stream. This would consist of additions to, or subtractions from the flow. Thus, with some generality, the conceived strategy variable (PE), was divided into one part strategy-related and another part (APE) systematically fixed every year.

With the classification of the AIRPOL variables, the model (at this point a set of generic relationships) now would look like Figure 5.1.

7.5   Determine the Type of Mathematical Structure

The next task is to provide more specifics on each individual relationship. This starts with the identification of the generic mathematical structure that best suits the theory for each $Y:X_j$ pair. Some examples are provided in Table 7.8 for the situation where both Y and $X_j \geq 0$. Most associations seem to fall into the "monotonic" categories. That between VMT and POP, for instance, is an obvious candidate for "monotonically increasing"—the more people there are in the country, all other things being equal, the more travel there will be. Similar reasoning would hold for VMT versus GNP.

If the VMT versus POP example is stretched quite far, however, we might imagine a situation where the country (i.e., the set of urban areas) becomes so crowded, and resultant congestion is so great, that people cut back on their travel. This would be an instance of an "optimum maximum."

A "duotonic" structure is not found often, but an "open left" version might manifest itself in, say, the COC versus PE association. Generally, with more governmental expenditure (PE), we would expect the top part of the curve to hold true. On the other hand, if an attempt were made to spend too much money, it may overwhelm the administrative capacity to do so. The result may be that less money actually gets spent and that it is squandered so haphazardly that the situation in fact gets worse (that is, COC concentrations *increase*).

TABLE 7.8   Some Types of Mathematical Structures

Monotonic: Y always increases (decreases) steadily as X increases.

Optimum: Y reaches a maximum or minimum somewhere in the range of X.

Duotonic: There is a maximum (minimum) limit to X somewhere in the Y range.

Cyclical Stationary: Y varies periodically above and below its mean value.

Don't Know: There is insufficient knowledge about the relationship between Y and X.

Still another possible structure is "cyclical stationary." There is periodic or recurrent variation above and below a constant (mean) value of Y. An example might arise if average annual rainfall (AAR) were taken as an external (vs. time) variable influencing COC concentrations. The relationship of AAR to YEAR might be imagined as having a cyclical stationary structure since rainfall numbers vary up and down over time.

From these examples it is clear that different structures might apply given different circumstances. Again, a theory or analogue is helpful in making the selection. Another guiding factor is the horizon time, specified in QCQ Step 1 (see Section 4.1). If that time period is short, there is much less chance of bumping into odd situations. The "overpopulated country" scenario used as an illustration immediately preceding, for instance, is highly unlikely to occur by the year 2020 (the stipulated horizon year in the AIRPOL model) and thus can be safely ignored in that case.

A major predicament occurs when there is neither a good theologue nor any relevant experiences available to use as a basis for selecting the appropriate structure. To illustrate: suppose that average wind speed (AWS) were employed as a variable affecting COC. To our knowledge no data have been collected, much less a study made, of annual average wind speeds for the U.S. as a whole. It is easy to imagine, however, that winds can cause changes in COC concentrations. A first guess probably would be that if there were more winds, they would blow out and dilute the concentrations. Still, there could be circumstances where the winds would blow the CO emissions *into* relatively enclosed areas (like building "canyons") and thereby *increase* concentrations.

Which circumstance holds? Nobody really has any evidence, so the "don't know" structure in Figure 7.1 is selected. The predicament suggested above arises when, in QCQ Step 5 regression is employed to calibrate the equation and in the process produces a sign for the parameter (coefficient) for AWS as an output. There is a natural tendency to conclude that this is the correct sign. It may be, but the COC versus VMT example brought out in Figure 11.4 (where regression erroneously showed COC as decreasing with increased VMT) highlights the fact that such a conclusion can be entirely wrong.

7.6 Undertake Cause/Effect Analysis

The next step in the QCQ process is to take a closer look at the cause/effect relation for each goal, intermediate, and pre/reaction time variable (i.e., each possible type of dependent variable). This is undertaken to verify the causality implied in the respective relationship.

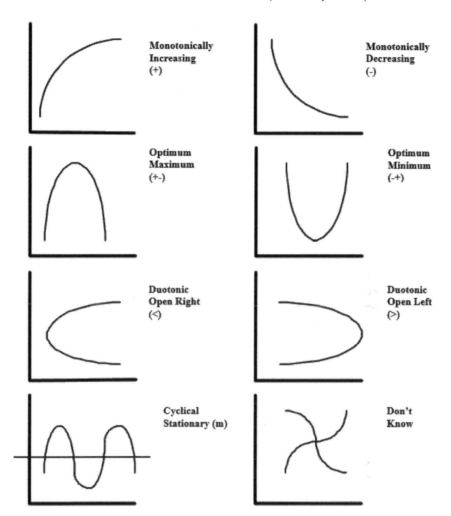

Figure 7.1 Varieties of mathematical structures.

Dr. Robert Shulman and we have undertaken an in-depth study—from Plato to Hume to modern day thinkers—on the nature of cause and effect. This analysis is summarized in Appendix D. We, of course, make no claim that we understand completely what has perplexed philosophers for millennia. Yet we feel that substantial improvements have been made over various types of so-called "causal analyses" that offer no guidance whatsoever on the nature of the topic (Ching & Chih, 2008).

As can be seen in Appendix D, there are quite a few characteristics that need to be assessed to help establish causality. These are divided into ten categories (see Table 7.9) Most of these are addressed in various stages of QCQ. Examples are in Table 7.10. This seems to leave six major questions to be addressed at this point in QCQ Step 3.

The "anticipation" part of the fourth question might need explanation. Human beings appear to be unique in that they plan and base decisions in part on what they *anticipate* will happen (as well as on what *has* happened). In fact, that is the major reason for the existence of QCQ in the first place—people want forecasts on which to base current decisions. Hence, in "real" time, some "causes" actually will occur *after* the effect.

For the relationship between COC (the Y variable) and PE (the X variable), the responses to these questions might look like those in Table 7.11.

There is not sufficient understanding yet on our part to know how many (and which) "Yes" answers are needed to declare an "official" causal relation. The preceding example, for instance, produced four "Yes" responses out of six. A "Yes" on the fifth question is particularly crucial since that query reflects the standard scientific experimental paradigm. As a result, most people, we feel, would consider the above relationship to be "causal."

Another aspect of cause/effect analysis involves looking at *sets* of variables as being causal. Often it is not one but several variables together that are both necessary and sufficient from a causal standpoint (Babbie, 2012). A "necessary" cause (or set of causes) is one that (generally) must be present for the effect to occur. For example, it is necessary to have people (POP)

TABLE 7.9 **Characteristics Needed to Assess Cause and Effect**

A "client" for whom the explanation is being given.
An "agent" to carry out the cause.
A clear definition of the proposed "cause" (X variable).
A subject or "receptacle" to receive the "effect" of X.
A clear definition of the proposed "effect" (Y factor).
A scenario showing the main sets of variables.
A clear definition of the proposed mode of relationship between X and Y.
A measure of the "strength" of relationship between X and Y.
A measure of the "truth" of the X factor.
A measure of the "truth" of the relationship between X and Y.

TABLE 7.10 **Characteristics Addressed by QCQ**

The "client" is identified in Step 1.
Definitions and measures of X and Y are entered in Step 4.
"Strengths" and "truths" of relationships are established in Step 5 and evaluated in Step 6.

TABLE 7.11 Example Likely Responses to Six Cause Questions

Question: Is there an identifiable "agent" in X that causes Y?
Answer: Yes. Federal government agencies (the "agents") start programs (like for emission control) that reduce COC.

Question: Is there a close spatial proximity between X and Y?
Answer: No. The agencies may be in Washington, DC but COC is all over the country (and in the atmosphere).

Question: Is there a close temporal proximity between X and Y?
Answer: No. It can take anywhere from two to ten years for the government programs to be initiated and to start having an effect.

Question: Does X (or its anticipation) occur *before* Y?
Answer: Yes. The program spending must take place before COC can be reduced because of PE.

Question: If X were manipulated, all else constant, would Y change?
Answer: Yes. For example, state government auto emissions testing programs show directly the impact on COC.

Question: Is there a transfer of "energy" from X to Y?
Answer: Yes. Federal money flows ("energy") to state and local governments, who work (use up "energy") to spend it properly.

to have travel (VMT). If there were no people, there would be no travel. But people have to have money (GDPPC) in order to pay for the travel. So POP by itself is not sufficient.

A "sufficient" cause (or set of causes) is one that generally guarantees that the effect will occur (Babbie, 2012). Car ownership usually is sufficient to ensure travel (VMT), but it is not necessary (trucks, buses, motorcycles, and the like also can be utilized).

Much more discussion on necessary and sufficient conditions can be found in Appendix E. The implications of such conditions are made manifest in the choice of intercepts, which occurs in QCQ Step 5, as described in Chapter 8.

One benefit of the causal questioning is that it helps avoid mistaking symptoms (a change in normal function indicating a disorder) for causes. To take a rather stretched example, if there were more travel (VMT), there should be more formal education (EDU) being completed (part of the travel is getting to school). But there also should be more COC, so there might be a nice correlation between EDU and CO.

Does EDU "cause" COC? The answers to all six of the above questions probably would be "No," thereby signaling an overall "No" response. Still, because of the correlation, a change in EDU might be taken by some analysts as a *symptom* of COC.

7.7   Recapitulation

In this chapter we have dealt with many of the concepts behind the building of a model to represent the situation under scrutiny. It may be that a good model already exists, so little work is required here. But if this is not the case, it will be necessary to develop a new (at least partially) model (i.e., theory). So this step in QCQ is called "theory development," or perhaps "local theory development," signaling the fact that nothing of this nature exists in the study area at the moment.

The model developers then must deal not only with such common topics as data availabilities, types of mathematical structures, and time affinities. They also must consider any cause and effect situational constraints.

7.8   An Expanded Learning Case: Boyle's Law

Almost any introductory chemistry course introduces the student to Boyle's law for a gas in a pressurized container (like an automobile tire)

$$PV/T = c \tag{7.1}$$

where P = pressure, V = volume, T = temperature, and c is a constant.

The curious aspect of this formula is that there is no specific dependent variable. It is an *implicit* equation. The issue, then, is what to take as the "Y" variable for regression purposes.

The more general version is:

$$(P^{\wedge}a)*(V^{\wedge}b)*(T^{\wedge}\text{-}d) = c \tag{7.2}$$

There are two approaches to calibrating this relationship. One is to treat the constant as the dependent variable. The other is to select the desired variable (say, V) as the dependent and regress it against the remainder:

$$V = c*(T^{\wedge}d)/(P^{\wedge}\text{-}a) \tag{7.3}$$

There is no mathematical difficulty here, just conceptual.

8

Step 3. Theory Development (Continued)

This chapter follows the previous one in helping to examine any currently available, relevant models (theories) and, where needed locally, to address weaknesses that might exist. Particular attention is given the timing relationships, assumptions and anomalies, and extreme examples (perhaps attributed to paradoxes).

8.1 Specify Time Affinities

The *timing* (or, more precisely, the *sequence*) of events connecting Y and X is an important aspect of the cause/effect determination. In most cases people expect Y to be a fairly immediate *reaction* to X in order to assign "causality" to X. A time-varying or *dynamic* model thus would seem to be the norm.

For many reasons (e.g., lack of available data), many modeling projects are *not* concerned with variables and relationships that change over time (i.e., the models are static or cross-sectional in nature). If that is the case, this step can be skipped. If not, it is necessary to specify any reaction times (delays) or "preaction" times (anticipations) that may be relevant for each $Y:X_j$ pair (see Table 8.1).

Supernumerary Intelligence, pages 109–118
109

TABLE 8.1   Types of Time Affinities

Delay (Reaction): the number of time periods between the start of X to when the full effect of Y occurs.

Anticipation (Preaction): the number of time periods in the future between the expectation of X and when the full effect on Y occurs.

To illustrate, we might find in the AIRPOL model that it was taking about two years between the point when Congress appropriated new air pollution control funds (APE) and programs were put in place for their use. A similar time period might elapse before the impact of the new and continuing funding together (total = PE = APE + FPE) on COC were felt. Time delays of this magnitude thus can be incorporated in the model.

As mentioned, another time-related characteristic to be considered is the opposite of delay—anticipation (Rosen, 1985). To illustrate, people might (and do) base their current car buying decisions (which reflect in turn on COC) on what they *anticipate* their incomes (GDPPC) will be in the future, not on what they have earned in the past.

Anticipation is a strong human characteristic and really is a main reason for using QCQ itself. An important assumption here is that the future is not *just* a repetition of the past (history may repeat itself in some circumstances, but not all). It also can be, at the least, an extrapolation of the past and, at the most, a whole new and different world.

If time is an integral part of the model, then it stands to reason that the reaction or preaction times themselves may be variables and possibly even dependent on other variables. This logic leads to the notions of catalysis and catalysts. The former is:

> a phenomenon in which a relatively small amount of foreign material called a "catalyst," augments the rate of a chemical reaction without itself being consumed. (Parker, 1982, p. 304)

In a chemical reaction, catalysis makes a reaction happen at a faster rate, often over a million fold (Gilbert, 1992). It is, in fact, a basis of life—we could not live without it. Secondly, the catalyst is regenerated. There is, however, no known biological case where more than one catalyst works in a particular reaction.

The concept of catalysis has not been employed frequently in social science methodology. In fact, it is not even mentioned in one of the prominent texts (Babbie, 2012). Yet there are many instances where it obviously is at work, as, for example, in the speeding of social interaction through improved communications and faster transportation.

The social science analogy may not be complete, however. There is some question here about the meaning of the "consumed" or "regeneration" aspect of catalysis, for example. And, as the communications/transportation illustration shows, in a social situation there may be more than one catalyst acting in a given relationship.

In QCQ a catalyst is seen as affecting the reaction or preaction times (i.e., the amount of delays or anticipations) in a relationship. The "foreign material" is simply another variable (or variables). No direct attention is given in the definition to the phenomenon of the "catalyst not being consumed itself," although in some cases it appears that this is so.

In theory the impacts of catalysts can get very complicated. A catalyst can be affected by other variables, whose rate of reaction can be influenced by other (or the original) catalysts. QCQ simply requests that the user "keep it simple" since QCQ has not been tested extensively with these kinds of complexities.

Catalysis can be specified in the same way as any other relationship. A catalyst can be any strategy, external, intermediate, goal, or even a time clock variable. The affected pre/reaction time becomes simply another dependent variable. The only difference with any other relationship is that the catalytic process has to be affiliated with a Y:X *connection* whose reaction or preaction time it enlivens.

Two examples of catalysis can be found in the causal diagram in Figure 8.1. The associated symbol looks like a house lying on its side. Imagine in the AIRPOL case that the model developers have taken a close look at the time affinities involved in various relationships (see the beginning of this section). In so doing, they have found that the situation is made even more complex by the fact that some delays (reactions) are decreasing over the years.

There are speedups, for instance, in federal administrative (paper handling and coordination) processes (FPI), catalyzed by communications and transportation improvements (represented generically by GDPPC). These speedups allow additional federal air pollution control expenditures (APE) approved by Congress to be incorporated in programs more rapidly. Similarly, federal budgetary process enhancements (FBPS—seen simply as a function of YEAR) are reducing the time taken to expend the funds and thereby have a more immediate impact on carbon monoxide concentrations.

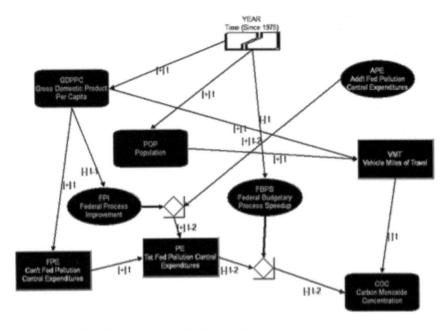

Figure 8.1   The (beta) model including catalysts.

The two new relationships thus are:

1. Reaction Time: FPI = f(GDPPC), which is associated with the delay in the PE versus APE connection, and
2. Reaction Time: FBPS = f(YEAR), which is associated with the delay in the COC versus PE connection.

A further extension of thinking on temporal relationships like these would envision the reaction (or preaction) time as having a *distribution*. In other words, while the average (mean) time for, say, FPI is decreasing (as a function of GDPPC) from four to two years, the range at any point in time may be from one to six years. Some additional funds (APE) approved in 2010, for instance, may go through the paperwork process in one year while others may take up to six years to make it through.

It should be mentioned that we have not found data on reaction (and particularly preaction) times to be readily available. This makes inclusion of such variables a difficult and questionable task.

8.2   Identify Exact Theories, Assumptions, Etc.

The spotlight in QCQ now focuses on the theoretical background for the variables and relationship used for each influenced variable being addressed (e.g., for COC vs. VMT [vehicle miles of travel] and PE [total governmental air pollution control expenditures]). Three sets of related concepts are defined in Table 8.2.

Some associated definitions are provided in Table 8.3.

To illustrate some of these concepts: for the VMT variable, microeconomic supply and demand theory would help "explain" the connection to both POP and GDPPC. This is portrayed in Figure 8.2, where the X axis is the quantity (annual VMT) and the Y axis is the corresponding unit cost ($ per vehicle mile of travel). Each demand curve (actually a straight line) shows how the quantity of travel increases as the cost goes down. In a somewhat opposite fashion, the supply curve shows that travel gets more expensive (e.g., in terms of the time lost due to congestion) as VMT increases.

For a given price of travel (horizontal dotted line), if population increases, there obviously will be more travel (the demand curve shifts outward). Similarly, if people have more income (GDPPC), they can travel more for the same price. Again, the demand curve shifts outward.

TABLE 8.2   Basic Definitions I

Theory/Analogue ("Theologue"): theory or analogue used to "explain" the overall relationship.

Assumption: major explanation made regarding the above theory or analogy.

Anomaly/Paradox/Extreme Example ("APEs"): anomalies, paradoxes, and extreme examples that should be addressed to make the above "theologue" useful.

TABLE 8.3   Some Basic Definitions

Theory: A plausible or scientifically accepted general principle offered to explain observed fact.

Analogue: Something that is similar to something else in two or more respects and thus may be similar in many other respects.

Assumption: A statement taken for granted but not proven.

Paradox: A statement that seems contrary to common sense and yet is perhaps true.

Anomaly: An irregularity.

Extreme Example: An illustration that goes to great lengths or beyond normal limits.

Note: All definitions are based on those given in *The Merriam-Webster Dictionary.*

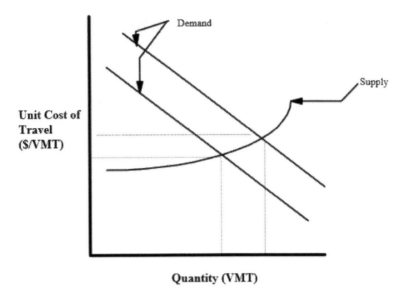

Figure 8.2 Microeconomic theory applied to travel.

An *assumption* would be that telecommuting—at-home use of tele-phone, computer conferencing, interactive TV, and so on—would not sig-nificantly reduce commuting by motorized vehicle.

A *paradox* could be that telecommuting actually will *increase* travel. Peo-ple may see or hear about interesting events or places via computer and want to go there to experience them in person (rather than vicariously on the machine).

Two *anomalies* to be taken into account are the "energy crises" in 1972–1973 and 1979–1980. There were long lines at gas stations and substantial shortages of fuel, yet VMT was slowed only slightly (see the data for the lat-ter time period in the next chapter). Any theory for VMT thus should be able to account for this.

Finally, an extreme example might be use of price *subsidies* by private industry to encourage travel. This takes place, for instance, when gambling casinos underwrite bus fares or car parking costs to attract customers to bet at their establishments.

The theory or analogue as well as the associated calibrated equation (QCQ Step 5) used to relate VMT to POP and GDPPC should be able to encompass the assumptions, paradoxes, anomalies, and extreme examples brought out in this step of QCQ. If not, the apparent reasons should be documented in QCQ Step 6 (evaluation), perhaps providing an opportunity to improve the theory or analogue at that juncture.

If no "theologue" (theory + analogue) is available from the literature and discussions, then one has to be created.

8.3   Recognize Situational Constraints

A situational constraint reflects restrictions and qualifications (usually in the data or definitions) that make it difficult to generalize from the relationship. As defined in QCQ:

> *Situational Constraint:* Description of any limitations in the situation that would reflect on the nature and extent of the relationship being considered.

Looking again at the COC vs. VMT relationship as an illustration, we find that COC is measured in a subset of urban areas across the country whereas VMT is computed from a nationwide sample, and therefore includes rural areas. The AIRPOL model user consequently ought to be aware that the relationship built on these variables could be somewhat misleading.

If, for instance, the *urban* travel component of VMT is increasing at a greater rate than the rural (which it seems to be), then the *forecasted* COC levels probably will be lower than they should be. This is due to the relatively greater preponderance of rural traffic in the *past data* (as opposed to in the *forecast years*).

8.4   Detail Related Experience and Confidence

The conceptualization of most relationships is based on informal and unsystematic experiences that are much broader and more numerous than reflected in the data at hand. These experiences help to lend confidence to the specification of the relationship. At the very least, the formal relationship ought to be able to reproduce the results of the informal experiences.

QCQ offers the opportunity to put in comments related to:

> *Experience & Confidence:* Description of the type and amount of work accrued with the relationship and the resultant feeling of support in it.

Taking the COC versus VMT relationship as an example, we all know that the internal combustion engine is used by millions of people daily. They see exhaust fumes all the time and know that carbon monoxide, although invisible, is a component of them. Exhausts obviously lead to concentrations (note the need for some simple logic here to make the connection).

Similarly, many states have pollution control device inspections where, again, the connection between COC and VMT can be derived through a combination of demonstration and simple logic. These millions of daily experiences can lend a degree of credibility to the relationship far beyond the relatively few data points used to calibrate the relationship.

8.5 Avoid Errors

It is possible (and not too difficult) to make various kinds of errors when entering the variables and their linkages. A common error, for instance, is to forget to input any influencing condition for an intermediate, goal, or pre/reaction time variable. QCQ will check for many of these problems.

Particularly when there is a large number of variables and interconnections, it is difficult to keep track of all the linkages. Any hand-drawn diagram, done say on butcher paper, gets to look like spaghetti. Worse, there is no guarantee that all the relevant connections have been made. There thus is a need to "despaghettitize" the relationships.

A listing like that ahead in Chapter 9, Table 9.1, helps in this regard. First, the variables are divided by role (external, client strategy, etc.). Second, the number of variables *influenced by* a particular variable is shown on the left. If any of these numbers is 0 (aside, possibly, for a goal variable), there most likely is a problem—the variable is not shown as affecting any other (although it may be kept in QCQ simply to maintain any associated information and data in case it is needed in the future).

Third, shown underneath each intermediate, goal, and pre/reaction time variable are those other variables that *affect it.* Again, if there are none, much suspicion should be aroused. Last shown is any pre/reaction time variable associated with a given $Y:X_j$ relationship. QCQ thus has neatly summarized and tabulated all of the variables and connections and enabled both the developer and user to peruse the overall model and find omissions or mistaken connections fairly quickly.

8.6 Recapitulation

The purpose of this step in QCQ has been to expand on, and add much greater detail to, the initial set of variables, connections, and associated theories emanating from Step 2. This is done in preparation for the specification and entry of data in Step 4.

In reality these three steps are highly interconnected, usually with much jumping back and forth. There can be several "chicken or egg" dilemmas. It might be necessary, for instance, to have a measure and data for a variable (Step 4) before a decision can be reached on whether to include it as an influencing factor (Step 3). And it may be necessary to make this decision before a search is made for a relevant theory or analogue (Step 2). Or maybe if a good theory were found, it would help in making the connections and collecting data.

Whatever the actual sequence of events, it is necessary to go through most of the actions in Step 3. This starts with creating a complete list of variables, making the possible connections between them, and classifying them into roles (strategy, external, etc.). At this point a cause/effect analysis can be undertaken.

Finally, the relationships are thought out in detail. This starts with specification of the theories, assumptions, paradoxes, anomalies, and extreme examples behind the relationships. At this point it is possible to start to identify the general mathematical structure of each relationship as well as its time affinity. If appropriate, catalysis can be incorporated to take into account changes in reaction and/or preaction times due to certain influencing variables. The effort in this step then can be wrapped up by recognizing situational constraints and detailing relevant experiences with, and confidence in, the relationship.

8.7 An Expanded Learning Case: The Agricultural Plots Experiment Case

Most of the examples so far have dealt with non-experimental situations—the developer/modeler has no control over the factors being considered. Presumably, if some control could be exerted over certain variables, with the rest either constant or randomized, it would be possible to make some more concrete conclusions about causes and effects as well as the strength of such.

A good, simple example involves an agricultural experiment in which the aim is to determine the effect of a certain level of fertilizer on growth of wheat. Imagine a plot of land that has been divided into a large number of subplots. Half are selected at random for the fertilizer application, the other half for none. The wheat then is planted and measurements made at harvest time of, say, the average height of stalk in each plot. The difference between the average heights in the fertilized versus the unfertilized plots then would represent the effect of the fertilizer.

First note that several factors may be constant. The soil, for instance, may all be clay. The plot may be located in a very rainy area, and so on. The conclusions thus can hold only for these restricted conditions (which should be explicitly reported). This brings into question forecast validity or volatility. To save time and future research expenditures, it would be nice to be able to expand the conclusions to, say, medium rainfall situations. But this would be risky.

Second, note that, while other factors are randomized, they occur at certain average levels. The amount of nitrogen in the soil, as an example, may, because of the randomization process, be about the same average level in the fertilized versus unfertilized soil, but it may be much less than found in normal circumstances elsewhere. So the conclusions again would be risky to apply in other places.

Imagine now that a tornado strikes and completely wipes out the wheat in all the subplots. What conclusion might be reached? That the difference brought about by the fertilizer is 0? The experiment obviously must be considered null and void. What then if the tornado only struck half of the plot? A portion of one subplot? What if some bug infested a small number of subplots? These questions beg the question of when a "null and void" label ought to be applied. Obviously, even in a laboratory situation, there can be hundreds of external, uncontrollable variables that come in to play. But when are they considered "critical"?

The main point here is that controlled experiments also have limitations, some of which may not be intuitively apparent.

This case brought out some of the pitfalls that await the "controlled" experiment. There is little that can be done, of course, after a major unexpected event interrupts the experiment, except perhaps to start over again (meanwhile trying to find a way to keep the same type of occurrence from happening again).

The main question here, though, is how to handle the other, non-major events that can affect the integrity of the experiment. Obviously this is a matter of judgment. Perhaps the best that can be done is to record the more important of these unexpected externalities and describe their possible implications so that future users can make useful interpretations for their own situations.

9

Step 3. Theory Development (Continued Again)

At this point in the process, the first action should be to make sure that all the relevant data and intellectual materials are collected and divided into discernible "piles" (that is, categories or classes). These should reflect the findings from all steps in the development of the case (i.e., "goals" from QCQ Step 1, "important variables" from Step 2, "interrelations" from Step 3, "data and sources thereof" from Step 4, and so on). An important output from the efforts in this chapter thus is a revised version of the main model. Another set of outputs would come from the use of that model for categorizing variables, exploring connectivity and minimum time paths, and creating and using graphics for complex problems.

9.1 Review the Main Model

Figure 9.1 is a graphic replica of the first (alpha) AIRPOL model proposed by our hypothetical consultants—Data Cruncher Computer Services (DCCS) (see Figure 5.1). Table 9.1 is a tabular replica. They show all

Supernumerary Intelligence, pages 119–138
Copyright © 2015 by Information Age Publishing
All rights of reproduction in any form reserved.

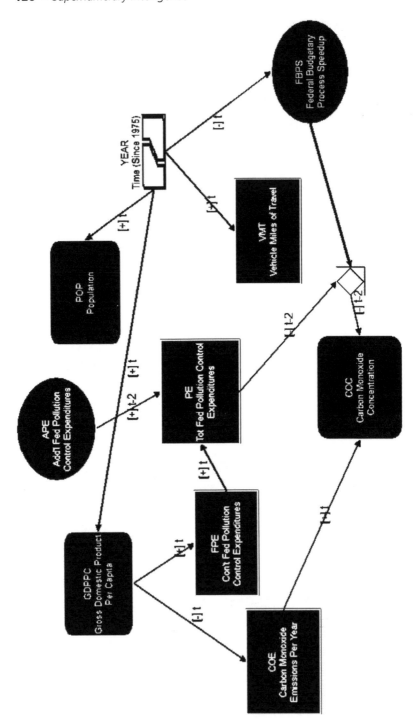

Figure 9.1 Original (incomplete) (alpha) model for U.S. carbon monoxide levels.

TABLE 9.1   Original (Alpha) Model with Variables Along With Influences

CASE: Airpolly—Update 2010–2020 vs. Time Ver2. Table G.2. Main Factors Used to
Determine Warrants (Con't -1)an 12, 2014

DATE: 03-09-2013   TIME: 23:21:23

===

ID CODE and DESCRIPTION (Subject and Action/Status)

===

       UNSPECIFIED VARIABLES

"""

       CLIENT STRATEGY VARIABLES

----

* 1* APE Additional Fed Pollution Control Expenditures

"""

       TIME CLOCK VARIABLE

----

4 YEAR TIME (Since 1975)

"""

       INTERMEDIATE VARIABLES

----

* 1* COE Carbon Monoxide Emissions per Year
    {-}[t] (0) GDPPC Gross Domestic Product Per Capita
* 1* FPE Continued Fed Pollution Control Expenditures
    {+}[t](0) GDPPC Gross Domestic Product Per Capita
* 1* PE Tot Fed Pollution Control Expenditures
    {+}[t-2](0) APE Additional Fed Pollution Control Expenditures
    {+}[t](0) FPE Continued Fed Pollution Control Expenditures
* 0* VMT Vehicle Miles of Travel
    {+}[t](0) GDPPC Gross Domestic Product Per Capita

"""

       GOAL VARIABLES

----

* 0* COC Carbon Monoxide Concentration
    {+}[t](0) COE Carbon Monoxide Emissions per Year
    {-}[t-2](0) PE Tot Fed Pollution Control Expenditures
    <C> FBPS Federal Budgetary Process Speedup

"""

       RE/PRE ACTION TIME VARIABLES

----

* 0* FBPS Federal Budgetary Process Speedup
    {-}[t](0) YEAR Time (Since 1975)

"""

       EXTERNAL [f(Time)] VARIABLES

----

2 GDPPC Gross Domestic Product Per Capita
    {+}[t] (0) YEAR Time (Since 1975)
* 0 * POP Population
    {+}[t](0) YEAR Time (Since 1975)

"""

(continued)

TABLE 9.1 Original (Alpha) Model with Variables Along With Influences (continued)

EXTERNAL [Data] VARIABLES

Note: LEGEND
   xx   Number of Other Variables Directly Influenced by that Variable
   {xx}   Type of Relationship (e.g., {+ } is Monotonically Increasing)
   [xx]   Time Relationship (e.g., [t-2] is a Delay of 2 Time Periods)
   (xx)   Number of Cause–Effect Questions Answered Positively (Out of 6)
   <C>   Catalyst (Affects the Reaction Time of the Relationship)

the variables and relationships thought to be important on the first run through. But times can change, often quickly. So a review of the model found that there were two main changes needed: the connection of POP (population) to VMT (vehicle miles of travel) and then VMT to COC (carbon monoxide concentrations). These actions led to a model that followed one of the main rules in Chapter 2: namely that every variable should connect with at least one goal. Table 9.2 shows a description of one of the originally under-represented variables (POP), and Table 9.3 and Figure 9.2 portray the completed revised model.

9.2 Categorize Variables

After a model has been developed and is considered to be complete, or at least have most of the variables entered, it may be helpful to classify them in a way that is desirable to the user. This may help the client to better understand the situation at hand and make any needed additions or other changes that shape the model to be as close as possible to the reality being faced. Note that the process to be followed here and the product that results are somewhat different than those associated with a situation structuring exercise (Section 6.5), so it may be worthwhile to do both.

The apparatus for carrying out this classification process is shown in Figure 9.3. To illustrate: all the variables in the case at hand are listed in the top right hand box. They can be dragged into the desired categories in the upper left box. These categories can be anything that the user desires, but an appeal is made to make them consistent with those already established for QCQ as well as the PAGP.

The variables already committed to a given category are shown in the bottom left box, while the latest variable to be accessed is portrayed, along with its relevant categories, in the lower right box.

TABLE 9.2 Description of the Components of a Variable (POP) in the Original Model

ID CODE: POP
DESCRIPTION: U. S. Population
ROLE: EXTERNAL [f(Time)]
===
DEFINITION: Total U.S. population
SHORT MEASURE: millions of people
FULL MEASURE: Millions of people in the total U.S. population, including armed forces and civilian federal employees living abroad. Illegal immigrants and others temporarily in the U.S. are not included.
As of July 1 of each year.
===
CATEGORY MEMBERSHIP
===
DIRECTLY INFLUENCING VARIABLES/CATALYSTS
===
{+}[t 0](0) YEAR Time (Since 1975)
===
VARIABLES/CATALYSTS DIRECTLY INFLUENCED BY THIS ONE
===
    None
===
    LEGEND FOR INFLUENCING/INFLUENCED VARIABLES:
    {xx} Relation Type (e.g., {+ } is Monotonically Increasing)
    [xx] Time Relation (e.g., [t-2] is Delay of 2 Time Periods)
    (xx) # of Cause-Effect Questions Answered Positively (max=6)
    <T> The Pre/Reaction Time Variable in the Relationship
===

===
VARIABLE PERVASIVENESS MEASURES:
===
0 Goal Variables Are Influenced Out of a Total of 1 (0%)
0 Relatable (Dependent) Variables Influenced Out of a Total of 6 (0%)
0 Relationships Are Influenced Out of a Total of 12 (0%)

TABLE 9.3 Model (Chi) Variables Along with Influences

CASE: Airpolly—Complete Update 2010-2020 vs. Time Ver 2
DATE: 04-23-2013 + TIME: +14:43:23
===
ID CODE and DESCRIPTION (Subject and Action/Status)
===
        UNSPECIFIED VARIABLES

»»»
        CLIENT STRATEGY VARIABLES
----
* 1* APE Additional Fed Pollution Control Expenditures
»»»

(continued)

TABLE 9.3   Model (Chi) Variables Along with Influences (continued)

TIME CLOCK VARIABLE

----

* 3* YEAR Time (Since 1975)

„„

INTERMEDIATE VARIABLES

----

* 1* COE Carbon Monoxide Emissions per Year
    {-}[t] (0) GDPPC Gross Domestic Product Per Capita
* 1* FPE Continued Fed Pollution Control Expenditures
    {+}[t] (0) GDPPC Gross Domestic Product Per Capita
* 1* PE Tot Fed Pollution Control Expenditures
    {+}[t-2] (0) APE Additional Fed Pollution Control Expenditures
    {+}[t] (0) FPE Continued Fed Pollution Control Expenditures
* 1* VMT Vehicle Miles of Travel
    {+}[t] (0) POP Population

„„

GOAL VARIABLES

----

* 0* COC Carbon Monoxide Concentration
    {+}[t] (0) COE Carbon Monoxide Emissions per Year
    {-}[t-2] (0) PE Tot Fed Pollution Control Expenditures
    <C> FBPS Federal Budgetary Process Speedup
    {+}[t] (0) VMT Vehicle Miles of Travel

„„

RE/PRE ACTION TIME VARIABLES

----

* 0* FBPS Federal Budgetary Process Speedup
    {-}[t] (0) YEAR Time (Since 1975)

„„

EXTERNAL [f(Time)] VARIABLES

----

* 2* GDPPC Gross Domestic Product Per Capita
    {+}[t] (0) YEAR Time (Since 1975)
* 1* POP Population
    {+}[t] (0) YEAR Time (Since 1975)

„„

EXTERNAL [Data] VARIABLES

Note: See Table 9.1 for legend.

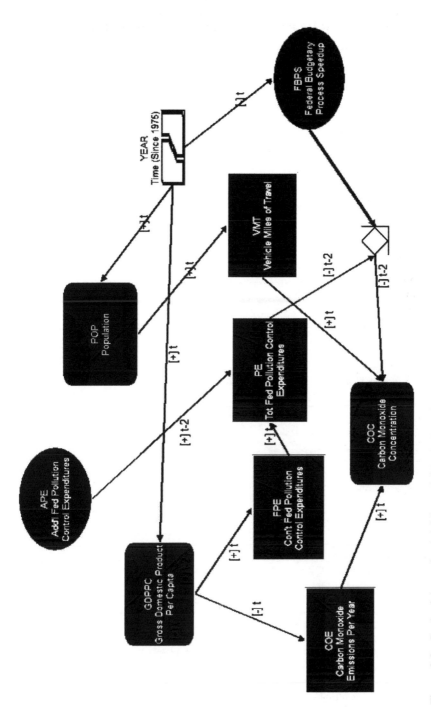

Figure 9.2 Revised (complete) (chi) model for U.S. carbon monoxide levels.

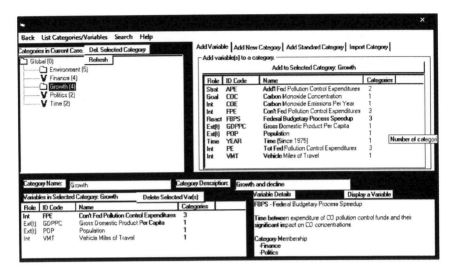

Figure 9.3   Layout of the classification scheme for combining variables in a case.

9.3   Explore Connections

A second worthwhile subproject that can be undertaken, particularly when it is thought that all the desired and proper bivariate relationships have been entered in the database, is to check for connectivity. This is done in QCQ using a version of Moore's Algorithm (1957) for finding minimum time (or variable) paths in a network.

A sample of the output is presented in Figure 9.4. On the upper left is the list of all the variables in the case. The user can pick one of these as a starting point, then select another one, in the upper right box, as the "destination" (or just scroll through the listing to get a feel for how richly connected the starting variable is). The bottom box gives the full account of the sequence of connections of the two chosen variables. Note that there can be many connections (and therefore paths) between given variables in a large, dense network. The choice of which ones to display then may be arbitrary (and unseen).

9.4   Determine Minimum Time (Variables) Paths

When a case has a time dimension, especially with various degrees of delays among the variables, it is just a relatively small extra effort to find the minimum time paths from one variable to another. This means the path of minimum total delay between the two. This feature is captured in the upper

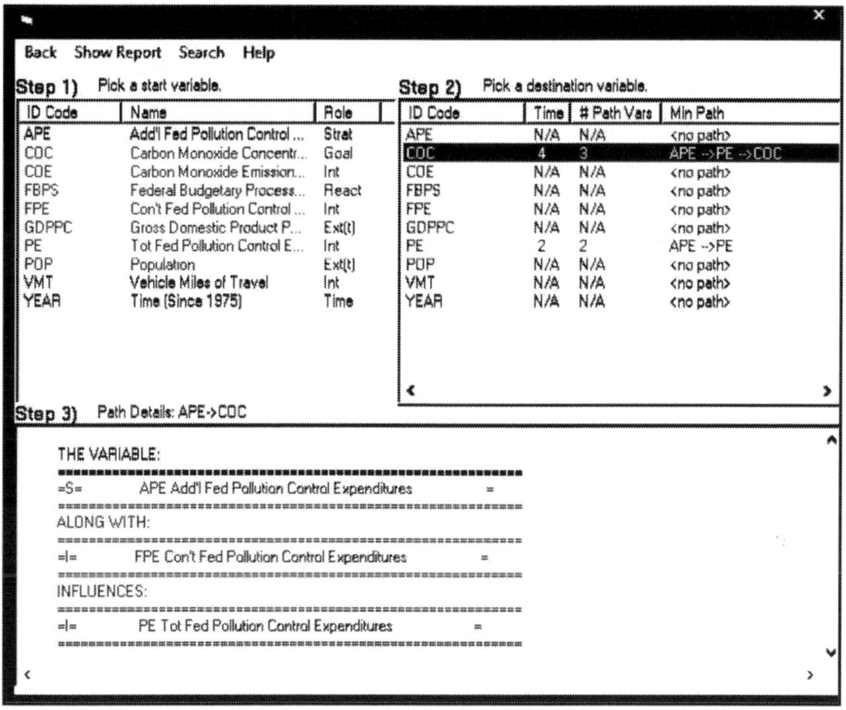

Figure 9.4 Display of the connections between the variables APE and COC.

right box in Figure 9.4 where, for example, the minimum time path from APE (additional federal pollution control expenditures) and COC (carbon monoxide concentration) is through PE (total federal pollution control expenditures). The total delay is four years, on a path of three variables. A condensation of the resulting printout can be found in Table 9.4.

9.5 Check on Meeting Goals

The preceding procedures (algorithms) also can be very helpful in, for instance, checking to see that each goal is affected by at least one strategy and, conversely, that each strategy affects at least one goal variable. An illustration of one exercise in this realm, in Table 9.5, shows that APE (the single strategy) is definitely related to the single goal (COC)—see the end of the table.

TABLE 9.4   Partial Output of Exercise to Get a Minimum Time Path

THE VARIABLE:

===
=S=   APE Additional Fed Pollution Control Expenditures
===

ALONG WITH:

===
=I=   FPE Continued Fed Pollution Control Expenditures
===

INFLUENCES:

===
=I=   PE Tot Fed Pollution Control Expenditures
===

Min Time = 2 Variables on Min Time Path = 2 Min Time Path Sign = +

WHICH, ALONG WITH:

===
=I=   COE Carbon Monoxide Emissions per Year
=I=   VMT Vehicle Miles of Travel
===

INFLUENCES:

===
=G=   COC Carbon Monoxide Concentration
===

Min Time = 4 Variables on Min Time Path = 3 Min Time Path Sign = -

Note: If a relationship has no specified time affinity, then it is taken as 0.

TABLE 9.5   Sample Output of a Variable Description (in a Goals Check)

ID CODE: APE
DESCRIPTION: Additional Fed Pollution Control Expenditures
ROLE: CLIENT STRATEGY

===
DEFINITION: Additional (above continuing, generally increasing) yearly appropriation of
   Federal funds for CO pollution control.
SHORT MEASURE: $billion-current$
FULL MEASURE: Additional Federal outlays for Natural Resources and Environment $
   billions—current$
===

CATEGORY MEMBERSHIP

Environment Finance

===
DIRECTLY INFLUENCING VARIABLES/CATALYSTS
===

<Not Applicable>

===
VARIABLES/CATALYSTS DIRECTLY INFLUENCED BY THIS ONE
===

{+}[t-2] (0) PE Tot Fed Pollution Control Expenditures
===

(continued)

TABLE 9.5   Sample Output of a Variable Description (in a Goals Check) (continued)

VARIABLE PERVASIVENESS MEASURES:

===

1 Goal Variable Is Influenced Out of a Total of 1 (100%)

2 Relatable (Dependent) Variables Are Influenced Out of a Total of 6 (33%)

2 Relationships Are Influenced Out of a Total of 13 (15%)

===

GOAL MINIMUM TIME PATH MEASURES:

===

Goal   [MinTime, MinTimeVars, MinTimeSign]

===

COC Carbon Monoxide Concentration   [4 3 -]

Note: Legend:
MinTime: Minimum Time for a Change in APE to Influence a Goal
MinTimeVars: Number of Variables on Minimum Time Path (MTP)
MinTimeSign: Resultant Sign of Cumulative Influences of Variables on MTP

9.6   Develop Graphics

Life is fairly easy when you only have a few variables and relations with which to deal. Life can get more complex, though, in a hurry when the situation is much richer. This truism is demonstrated in Figure 9.5. This obviously points to a high degree of complexity in the case, even to the point where the names of the variables cannot be read. Of course, we could make the chart bigger.

But this case (dealing with university institutional capacity building in Malawi) has "only" 29 variables. There are other cases, for example dealing with the fallout from Hurricane Katrina, in 2005 in the U.S. Gulf Coast area, that have almost 2,000 variables and over that number of relationships. In these cases use of QCQ generally focuses on finding paths through a usually very fragmented "network." So a study of connectivity is the order of the day, and the graphics used are of the type of Figure 9.4 and a similar kind of output for the Malawi case (exemplified in Figure 9.6 and seen in tabular form in Table 9.6).

9.7   Recapitulation

This chapter starts to show how a finished (or close thereto) model can be used to help understand the situation at hand. Such help can come from setting up a tabular output, as in Figure 9.2; improving the classification system; tracking each non-goal to at least one goal; and making sure that each goal can be "reached" by at least one strategy or external variable. Help

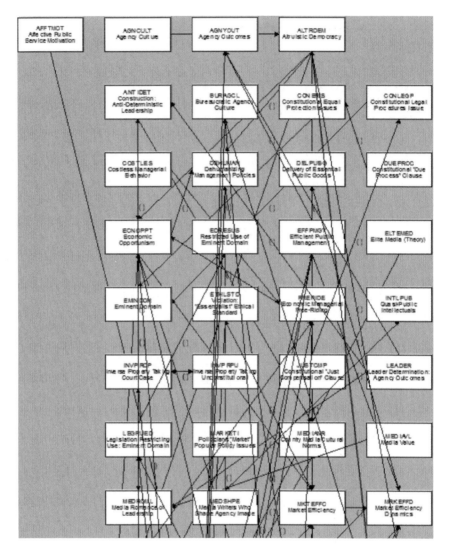

Figure 9.5 A more complex case dealing with university capacity building in Malawi (top part of interrelationship diagram).

also can be provided for models that have a time variable to calculate minimum times of reactions. Now all that is needed for a good statistical analysis is a proper set of data, a feature that is discussed in the next chapter.

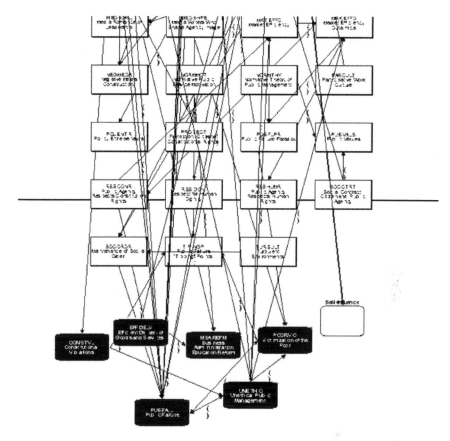

Figure 9.6 A more complex case dealing with university capacity building in Malawi (lower part of interrelationship diagram).

TABLE 9.6 Report on Sample Exploration of Paths in a Model

DESCRIPTION OF A SELECTED PATH IN THE MODEL

```
===============================================================================
```

CASE: PA Genome Project\Tlou Josiah\University Institutional Capacity Building—Malawi

DATE: 5/5/2013

```
===============================================================================
```

THE VARIABLE:

```
===============================================================================
```

=S=   UPICSTR UPIC Project Starts

```
===============================================================================
```

ALONG WITH:

```
===============================================================================
```

==   SANCTPT Sanctioning Selection: College Participants

```
===============================================================================
```

(continued)

TABLE 9.6   Report on Sample Exploration of Paths in a Model (continued)

INFLUENCES:
==
==   HOSTPST Host Project Site for In-Country Training
==
ALONG WITH:
==
==   STUDYLV Grant of Study Leave to Candidates
==
INFLUENCES:
==
==   TRAINIC In-Country Training for Master's Candidates
==
INFLUENCES:
==
==   TRAINMS Master's Degree Candidates Trained
==
INFLUENCES:
==
==   MEDGRAD M.Ed Candidates Graduated
==
INFLUENCES:
==
MEDATDC   M.Ed Graduates Working at Project Site

Note: If a relationship has no special time affinity, then it is taken as 0.

9.8   An Expanded Learning Case: Travel Time among Three Points (Two Link)

The case example involves a situation almost everyone has faced—estimating the travel time for a given trip. In this case, to highlight an awkward point, the X (independent) variables are the distances and speeds, respectively, on two links connecting three points:

A   B   C

The objective is to estimate the overall travel time from A to C. Data are available for this but (as a slight variation) *not* for travel times on the individual links. The full set of data (which is completely fictional) is displayed in Table 9.7.

A typical multiple regression run with these data leads to the equation:

$$TAC = 0.533*DAB - 0.0741*SAB + 0.353*DBC - 0.270*SBC + 0.889 \qquad (9.1)$$

TABLE 9.7 Distances, Speeds, and Travel Times

Travel Time A to C (TAC)	Distance A to B (DAB)	Speed A to B (SAB)	Distance B to C (DBC)	Speed B to C (SBC)
1.90	3	2	2	5
5.00	3	2	7	2
1.45	5	4	1	5
2.27	5	3	3	5
1.08	2	25	5	5
1.52	4	15	5	4
1.67	2	4	7	6
6.20	6	5	5	1
1.09	4	4	1	11

with the corresponding statistics of MAD = 1.38, MAPD = 56.5%, MAE = 1.08, MAPE = 139.0%, and R^2 = 0.78.

By traditional social science measures, Equation 9.1 is a good one. The R^2 is high and the signs are in the "right" directions since TAC is shown to increase as the distances increase (+ signs) and as the speeds decrease (– signs). A closer look reveals some problems, however. First, the mean absolute error (MAE) represents a reduction of only about 22% from the MAD. This is very small. Second, the MAPE *is over twice as large the MAPD*. This is due in large measure to the estimated value for the last case of 0.10, which leads to a percentage error of 100*(1.09 – 0.10)/0.10 = 990%. This certainly highlights the potential disadvantage of using a regression procedure to maximize R^2 if the concern is to reduce big errors on small numbers.

Another major problem with the equation is that the overall travel time (TAC) will *not* be 0 in the case where both distances are 0. Further, TAC is not infinite when both speeds are 0. Moreover, if the speeds are relatively high compared to the distances, it is quite possible to get a negative travel time.

We may be tempted to say that, while these revelations are true, they deal with extreme situations. As long as the independent variables are kept within the ranges wherein they were measured, all should work out acceptably. Unfortunately, this is not necessarily true, as demonstrated by the following substitutions of in-range values:

$$TAC = 0.533*(2) – 0.0741*(25) + 0.353*(1) – 0.270*(11) + 0.889 = –1.63$$

A negative travel time obviously is meaningless (unless you are going backwards).

Nor should there necessarily be a restriction to these ranges, anyway. Many forecasting exercises require inputs that are outside the calibration range [INT-23 V'Yugin, Calibration Errors]. For instance, we might want to use the equation that results from this analysis to forecast travel times with quite diverse inputs (e.g., on long trips from New York to San Francisco as well as short ones from Oakland to San Francisco).

A further point of interest in Equation 9.1 is that some of the independent variables are intercorrelated (Belsley, Kuh, & Welsch, 1980). In particular, SBC and DBC have a correlation of 0.55 (not substantial, but still big enough for our example here). The standard approach in multiple linear regression is to drop out one of these two variables because they essentially are "the same" (or "collinear"). This would leave an equation like:

$$TAC = 0.188*DAB \qquad (9.2)$$

In addition to the strange feature of leaving out a variable everyone knows is integral to the situation, it turns out that the R^2 is only somewhat lower (0.70). So we have a case where fewer variables are almost as good.

The solution to the overall problem is to use as the independent variables the *ratios* of the distances and speeds on each link, respectively. In other words, the problem should be broken into components. A multiple linear regression run on these gives simply:

$$TAC = 1.00*(DAB/SAB) + 1.00*(DBC/SBC) \qquad (9.3)$$

which has, as expected, a MAE = 0, MAPE = 0%, and R^2 = 1.00. This shows that "proper" specification of the form(s) of the independent variables can lead to the best goodness of fit results. (Note, however, that if the two ratios happened to be highly intercorrelated—which they are not in this case— the traditional "fix" would require that one ratio be eliminated.)

Now let us look at this case in a different way. We first get the ranges for the variables (Table 9.8). The calibration data ranges are much different from the conceivable, so the operational ranges all are taken to be from 0 to +∞.

The important feature of this case is the division into like elements (the two links) and their recombination later. We start by asking the question of whether the situation is composed of essentially similar parts. This obviously is the condition here, so we can select one of the parts (say the link from A to B) and work with that first.

TABLE 9.8   Two Link Problem Information

Aim: Determine the total travel time over two links connecting three points.

Goal Variable: Travel time over two links: TAC

External Variables: Distance on link from A to B: DAB
Speed on link from A to B: SAB
Distance on link from B to C: DBC
Speed on link from B to C: SBC

Possible Links Diagram:

```
      +                +
DAB --------    TAC <--------------- DBC
        _        ^        _
SAB ---------------->| |<------------------- SB
```

Universe: all points on the globe.

Population: all points in the U.S.

Sample: 9 cases (made up), not sampled in any formal way.

Measurement Error: assumed 0.

All external variables are obtained as current values (no forecasts needed).

The task now is to look at each independent variable with respect to the dependent. Two approaches are possible. In the first we ask if there is any existing theory available. There is, of course, in the form of the common definition:

$$\text{Speed} = \text{Distance}/\text{Time} \qquad (9.4)$$

or, in this case:

$$SAB = DAB/TAB \qquad (9.5)$$

which can be rearranged to give:

$$TAB = DAB/SAB \qquad (9.6)$$

The right hand side of this becomes the new variable, along with its counterpart of DBC/SBC.

At this point the relationship could be viewed strictly as an "accounting" one. The travel time from A to C simply is the sum of the times from A to B and from B to C:

$$TAC = TAB + TBC \qquad (9.7)$$

TABLE 9.9   Two Link Problem Range Information

Ranges:		Calibration		
Variable	Role	Data Range	Conceivable	Operational
TAC	Goal	1.08 to 6.20	0 to large	0 to +∞
DAB	External	2 to 6	0 to 8000	0 to +∞
SAB	External	2 to 25	0 to 100	0 to +∞
DBC	External	1 to 7	0 to 800	0 to +∞
SBC	External	1 to 11	0 to 100	0 to +∞
TAB	Intermediate	0.27 to 1.67	0 to large	0 to +∞
TBC	Intermediate	0.09 to 5.00	0 to large	0 to +∞

Alternately, if we still wanted to undertake regression, we would ask questions about the ranges of TAB and TBC (see bottom of Table 9.9) and their intercepts. Both of the latter could be greater than 0, of course, since TAC would not necessarily be 0 if either TAB or TBC were 0.

A multiple linear format thus is an eligible pre-equation:

$$TAC <=> a*TAB + b* TBC \qquad (9.8)$$

Regression leads to the obvious result that $a = b = 1$.

If, for some reason, the theory embodied in the definition in Equation 9.4 were unknown, then the process would be similar to that used in Section 12.16 to derive the gravity model. But first we must ask if there are any constraints, spanning over all the parts, that eventually must be met. This is the circumstance here since, if both distances are 0, then the travel time must be 0 (or, stated another way, if DAB + DBC = 0, then TAC = 0), assuming DAB and DBC $\geq$ 0.

At this point we initiate a search for eligible structures, which involves an exploration of characteristics. We know from any travel experience that, everything else held constant, TAC will increase monotonically with DAB, without any limits on either. We now ask "What would be the value of total trip time (TAC) if DAB = 0?" It may not be 0 since there still will be a time on the BC link. We thus have a situation with a possible nonzero intercept. All this information points to either a linear or exponential form:

Taking the simplest first:

$$TAC <=> a + b*DAB \qquad (9.9)$$

with the constraint (parameter range) that $a \geq 0$.

Looking now at the relationship between TAC and SAB, we know that TAC will decrease monotonically with SAB (the faster we go, the less time we will need to get to our destination). But TAC will have to go to $+\infty$ as SAB approaches zero. The eligible possible forms (see Chapter 12) thus will be hyperbola or power. The simplest of these is:

$$\text{TAC} \iff c/\text{SAB} \tag{9.10}$$

with range limitations of $0 < c < +\infty$.

We now create combinations and make substitutions to generate permutations. We can start by replacing either or both of the two parameters in Equation 9.8 with Equation 9.9, which gives the permutations:

$$\text{TAC} \iff (c/\text{SAB}) + (b*\text{DAB}) \tag{9.11}$$

$$\text{TAC} \iff a + c*\text{DAB}/\text{SAB} \tag{9.12}$$

$$\text{TAC} \iff (c/\text{SAB}) + (c*\text{DAB}/\text{SAB}) \tag{9.13}$$

The next step is to combine the parts, keeping in mind that they must have the same constitution. Remember, too, the overall constraint that TAC must be 0 if both DAB and DBC are 0.

Let us try substituting the part for link BC for parameter c in Equation 9.10:

$$\text{TAC} = (((d/\text{SBC}) + (f* \text{DBC}))/\text{SAB}) + (b*\text{DAB}) \tag{9.14}$$

or, substituting for b,

$$\text{TAC} = (c/\text{SAB}) + ((d/\text{SBC}) + (f*\text{DBC}))*\text{DAB} \tag{9.15}$$

Neither of these permutations are acceptable, first because the parts do not have the same resultant constitution, and second because TAC will not be 0 if both distances are 0. The same would be true if Equation 9.17 were employed instead of 9.15.

The next trial involves substitution in Equation 9.16. The two possible permutations are:

$$TAC = g + h*(DBC/SBC) + d*(DAB/SAB) \qquad (9.16)$$

and

$$TAC = a + (g + h*(DBC/SBC))(DAB/SAB) \qquad (9.17)$$

Both of these meet the preceding constraint if the parameters g and a, respectively, are set to 0. The second, however, is inappropriate because the ratio of DAB/SAB is treated differently than DBC/SBC. Moreover, TAC would equal 0 if DAB were 0 but DBC were not. We thus are left with the permutation in Equation 9.18 (without the g parameter).

Curve fitting with this equation leads to:

$$TAC = 1.00*(DBC/SBC) + 1.00*(DAB/SAB) \qquad (9.18)$$

which is what we expected. The GoF criteria all are perfect (so in this case it really would not have made any difference if we had elected to maximize R^2 or minimize the MAE or MAPE).

10

Step 4. Data Specification and Collection

This step in QCQ is centered on data—its specification, collection, and entry/editing (see Table 10.1). The first step is to review each variable in the model to determine how it is to be defined and measured. If these prove satisfactory, then there are several other characteristics—like accuracy, precision, and sample size—that need to be documented.

The values for some variables can come from calculation rather than data. For this reason it is desirable to identify "accounting" and other "outside" equations that may be relevant. These come either from definitions (e.g., speed is distance divided by time) or from theories (see, for instance, the gravity model, in Section 12.16).

TABLE 10.1   QCQ Step 4: Data Specification and Collection

1. Specify definitions and other information on variables
2. Identify "accounting" and other "outside" equations
3. Enter and edit data in the data base management system
4. Establish the operational range for each variable

Supernumerary Intelligence, pages 139–149
Copyright © 2015 by Information Age Publishing
All rights of reproduction in any form reserved.

Data for the remaining variables must come from primary (surveys) or secondary (e.g., the Census) sources. QCQ has provided a specialized spreadsheet for entering and editing such data as part of a database management system (DBMS).

The last task is to establish the operational range for each variable. This is a prerequisite for the development of the proper mathematical forms and their subsequent calibration in the next step of QCQ.

This fourth step in Quantitative CyberQuest (QCQ) involves the location, specification, collection, and entry of data. While it is not the purpose of QCQ to detail all the steps in survey research (for obtaining data first hand), QCQ does help guide the search of various secondary information sources (like the Internet) for leads in obtaining the data that best suit the variables and relationships identified in the preceding stages. The ultimate aim is to find appropriate quantitative data and get exact definitions and measures of all variables as well as information on other specified characteristics (e.g., the accuracy) of that data.

In some instances the accumulation of data may not be necessary since they can be derived from simple definitions or accounting relationships or possibly computed from an equation based on existing theory. The two former types are referred to as "accounting" equations and the latter as "outside" equations. Both can and should be entered in this stage of QCQ.

10.1 Specify Definitions and Other Information on Variables

Up to this point in the QCQ process, variables have been given only very brief descriptions—enough so that an outline of possible links can be established. It now is important to be much more specific about their nature and characteristics. QCQ thus requests a full definition and description of the measure to be used. In this regard, QCQ provides its own definitions as a guide (See Table 10.2). The first definition is close to what Babbie calls a "nominal" definition. One that includes the measure(s) to be employed would resemble his "operational" definition (Babbie, 2013).

TABLE 10.2 Definition of a Definition and a Measure

Definition: A statement of the meaning of the variable, resting on the basis of the common experience of the people who will be using this study. (Rapoport, 1965)

Measure: A standard unit employed to determine the dimensions, categories, capacity, or amount of a variable. (Babbie, 2013)

We have found that provision of exact definitions and measures is a time consuming, yet extremely important, part of the QCQ process. Without good specification at this stage, there is a considerable chance that the results may be misinterpreted, simply because the client has a concept in mind that is different from that of the model developer.

An example with federal air pollution control expenditures (APE, FPE, and PE) in the AIRPOL model demonstrates the significance. The question is "What comprises an official 'expenditure'?" Is it *approval* of the relevant budget by Congress? Is it an *agreement* by a federal agency to transfer funds to, say, a state? Is it the actual *transfer*? Is it the signing of a *contract* by the state with, say, a builder to construct a testing station? Is it the *completion* of the building and final payment? Perhaps one to ten years can elapse between the first of these events and the last.

The definition obviously will relate to the extent of delay and thus to the magnitude of the expected impact (on CO concentrations) of the expenditure in any year. If an "official" expenditure is defined as that at the time of congressional approval, then the impact may be, say, eight years away. If the final payment for the test station building marks the "official" expenditure, the impact ought to come very soon thereafter. In either case, the AIRPOL model should reflect the actual reaction time accurately.

A definition generally should describe who, what, where, when, and possibly also why. The measure should reflect the "how" question. The "population" variable in the AIRPOL model, as an illustration, might be defined simply as: "The total number of people in the United States in each year." The measure can get fairly complicated, however, as illustrated in Table 10.3.

Presumably the focal point in the AIRPOL model should have been on those people creating the CO concentrations—those of driving age and residing and traveling in the 200 or so urban areas being affected. Instead, for simplicity and because of data availability, the focus was shifted to the total population of citizens of the U.S. (which includes both babies and the

---

TABLE 10.3   Some Characteristics of the Definition of U.S. Population

Are tourists from other countries included (they travel and cause pollution)?

Are illegal immigrants included (they travel and cause pollution)?

Are those citizens working in or visiting other countries included (e.g., those in the military overseas are not traveling here)?

Are those who are born or die in the year included?

At what point in the year is the count made (there can be about a 1% difference in population between the beginning and end of the year)?

elderly, both urban and rural dwellers, and those citizens residing in other countries). Again, an understanding of the definition and measure is of central importance.

The complete set of definitions employed by QCQ in this step is reproduced in Table 10.4, with some examples for the vehicle miles of travel (VMT) variable in Table 10.5. Getting information on each of these characteristics usually is, to repeat, a time consuming and difficult task. Much may not be readily available.

TABLE 10.4   Some Variable-Related Definitions in QCQ

Definition: A statement of the meaning of the variable, resting on the basis of the common experience of the people who will be using this study. (Rapoport, 1965)

Measure: A standard unit employed to determine the dimensions, categories, capacity, or amount of a variable. (Babbie, 2013)

Validity: The extent to which a measure corresponds to the concept it is intended to reflect. (Mannheim & Rich, 1991)

Precision: The degree to which a measurement conforms strictly to a standard.

Accuracy: The extent to which the results of a calculation of the readings of an instrument approach the "true values" of the calculated or measured quantities, and are free from error. (McGraw-Hill Concise Encyclopedia of Science and Technology) (Parker, 1982)

Reliability: The extent to which repeated measures with the same instrument would yield the same result each time. (Babbie, 2013)

Agreement: The extent of harmony or consensus of opinion on the definition and measure.

Potential Sphere of Influence: The population or set of elements (individuals, objects, processes) for which it ultimately would be most desirous for a particular theory or hypothesis to hold.

Population: All elements (individuals, objects, processes) that have a well-defined characteristic (variable). (Dickey & Watts, 1978)

Sample Size/Type: The number of elements that are selected from the population in a well-defined manner (e.g., random, systematic, stratified). (Dickey & Watts, 1978)

Source/Reference

If from a personal discussion, the name of responder, date, address/location, and phone number. If from the literature, the author(s), title, journal name, volume, issue, & date.

Completeness

The spread of the number of observations across the potential range of the variable.

Representativeness

The degree to which a relatively small number of observations resemble every important group, class, or quality from which they are drawn. (Mannheim & Rich, 1991)

Coverage of Extremes

The degree to which possible extreme values (outliers) are covered by the data.

Degrees of Freedom

The difference between the number of observations and the number of parameters used in an equation to estimate them.

(continued)

TABLE 10.4   Some Variable-Related Definitions in QCQ (continued)

Constrained Values

Data representing situations where unusual events or influences prevent the full value of the number from being realized.

Element (Unit of Observation, Unit of Analysis)

The smallest unit of observation (individual, object, process) to be sampled and about which generalizations are to be drawn. (Mannheim & Rich, 1991)

Availability

The relative accessibility and cost of data for a variable.

Sequentiality

The degree to which a variable repeats itself in a cyclic manner over time.

Type of Measurement Scale

Nominal—division of the variable into unique categories. Any number given a category is a label, not implying rank.

Ratio—division of the variable into units that are of equal value. Also, there is an absolute zero point. (Babbie, 2013)

Other Comments

Any major comments that may be useful.

TABLE 10.5   Sample Background Information on a Variable (VMT)

FOR: Vehicle miles of travel (VMT):

Definition: "total miles driven by cars, trucks, buses, and motorcycles on `major' highways."

Measure: Traffic counts using automatic recorders at a selected spot along a given length of roadway. Counting took place from 6 AM to 8 PM on summer weekdays during the particular year.

Element (Unit of Observation): An individual motor vehicle traveling a set distance.

Potential Sphere of Influence: Ultimately it is desired to apply the AIRPOL model to any country in the world, but only U.S. data are available.

Population: The set of all motor vehicle miles driven in the U.S. in a given year (over a 36 year period from 1975–2010).

Sample Type and Size: All motor vehicles using a designated stretch of a random sample of 500 "major" highways in the country in a year.

Precision: One motor vehicle over a given distance of a highway.

Accuracy: Because only "major" highways are considered and because pneumatic tube counters only count axles, not vehicles, the vehicle mile figures may be "off" by 2–5%.

Reliability: Snow and ice on the counters may lead to slightly different readings, but the differences will be very small.

Unit of Analysis: All VMT in the U.S. in a given year.

Constrained Values: some data may come from years (e.g., 1979) when there were fuel shortages.

Note: Some of these descriptions are made up for illustrative purposes.

An example that relates to the characteristic of "accuracy" is the U.S. census. The decennial U.S. population census figure, for example, is thought by many observers to be inaccurate by around 1%, on the low side [INT-20 Population Estimation Accuracy; INT-10 IG Questions Census Accuracy]. This small amount is attributed to success in finding many of the homeless, people living in remote areas, and those who do not want to be counted. But, since nobody really knows how many of these people there are, the U.S. Bureau of the Census does not include them at all.

To make matters more confusing (for model developers, anyway),

a. The population undercount is thought to be getting lower because of increased investigative efforts on the part of the Census Bureau.
b. The population count *between* each 10-year census is based on a very small sample, which makes sampling error a characteristic of concern.

The net upshot of these kinds of discoveries may be to get the user to look at the quantitative figures with a fuller appreciation of their breadth and with somewhat greater skepticism.

10.2   Identify "Accounting" and "Outside" Equations

"Accounting" variables, and their corresponding relationships, are ones derived, by definition, from simple sums, differences, or ratios of variables. No statistical regression is needed to get the equation.

For example, the relationship for PE (total federal air pollution control expenditures) is an "accounting" one. PE is, by definition, the simple sum of FPE (*continuing* federal air pollution control expenditures) and APE (*additional* federal air pollution control expenditures):

$$PE = FPE + APE \qquad (10.1)$$

There thus is no need to calibrate this equation.

"Outside" equations are those obtained from previous research efforts and incorporated into the current model. They may be linear, as in Equation 10.1, or another form completely. There are none in the AIRPOL model, but the "Speed = Distance/Time" example in the two link travel time case (Chapter 9) is a good illustration. QCQ currently will accept any relationship for an "outside" equation that can be employed in a spreadsheet.

This feature of QCQ—to be able to incorporate pre-existing equations—is an important one that cannot be accomplished readily in, say, statistical packages. The importance comes from not having to repeat all of what may have been considerable investigation and analysis that went into development of the pre-existing equation.

A potential problem can arise when the user inadvertently enters an "outside" equation that can violate the limits of a Y (dependent) variable (see Section 10.4). Suppose, as an illustration, COC were just a function of PE and the user entered the "outside" linear equation of:

$$COC(t) = 15.16 - 0.464*PE(t) \qquad (10.2)$$

This happens to fit the data quite well ($R^2 = 0.934$), but if PE exceeds 32.67, COC becomes negative. This, of course, is nonsensical and does not make for good forecasting.

An inappropriate "outside" equation can make the situation even worse. If, say, the equation gives negative values when such are not possible, and these numbers then are used as input to help calibrate a subsequent equation, the calibration calculations may lead to very strange and unacceptable results (like a correlation coefficient greater than 1).

10.3 Enter/Edit Data in a Database Management System

A search now has to be made for readily available data, that is, those from secondary sources. Fortunately, in the AIRPOL case, yearly time series information on most of the identified variables was found in various issues of the *Statistical Abstract of the U.S.* (see Appendix F).

As noted in other sections, data on reaction (and particularly preaction) times may not be readily available (those for FPI and FPBS in Appendix F are "guesstimates"). This makes inclusion of such variables a questionable task.

10.4 Establish Operational Range for Each Variable

Two questions now have to be answered for each variable in the model—one about the upper limit and the other about the lower. Together these form the variable's *operational range*. This information plays a crucial role in the calibration process (QCQ Step 5, described in the next chapter) because the form of the resultant equation will depend upon the limits. For example, if a dependent (Y) variable has both upper and lower limits, a linear relationship (form) with any X variable will be inappropriate since it ultimately will violate the limits on Y at some point.

The *lowest* value the upper limit of a variable (X) can take is slightly greater than (or equal to) the largest value of X in the data set. Otherwise X must be "essentially unbounded" (+ infinity). What is meant by "slightly greater" is that it is possible that the conceivable limit may be reached within the horizon period specified in the situation description in QCQ Step 1 (see also Chapter 4). Similar thinking applies to the lower boundary.

Many times such boundaries are not readily apparent. For this reason the chart in Table 10.6 may be of assistance. It is a checklist that gives examples of possible limits under each of the 12 dimensions brought out earlier in QCQ steps one and two. Review of these dimensions and examples may stimulate thoughts about constraints directly pertinent to the situation at hand.

More specifically for the AIRPOL model, the task involved in getting the "operational range" of each variable (X) required (1) determining the highest and lowest values of X in the calibration data set (the "outside limits"), and (2) comparing these to the "conceivable" limits. For instance, for the population (POP) variable (see Appendix F) the outside limits range from 215.9 to 313.9 million, and the conceivable limits could range from 0 to many billions.

The question now is if the upper and lower conceivable limits are substantially different from their respective outside limits, which in this case is true. The lower conceivable boundary of 0 is much less than the 215.9 million, and the upper limit is essentially infinite compared to the outside limit of 313.9 million (and whatever values possibly could occur during the horizon time period—to the year 2020). As a result, the "operational" limits are set equal to the respective conceivable ones. Table 10.7 summarizes the results for some of the other variables.

10.5   Recapitulation

Development of a good quantified equation is much more difficult than may be imagined. For instance, we reject almost without question one that has been derived by simply dropping the data into a linear regression program and using the resulting equation verbatim. There is too much room for criticism about, for example, the "reachability" of the equation. See the next chapter for a rundown on this and kindred issues.

10.6   An Expanded Learning Case: The Gasoline Tax Model

About 35 years ago Dickey developed a model to help Virginia's Division of Motor Vehicles forecast the amount of annual revenue that would accrue from taxes charged at the gas pump on motor vehicle fuels. Part of that ef-

TABLE 10.6   Examples of Possible Limits for Each Dimension

1. *Technological*
   Speed of light
   Hours in a day (by definition)
   Statistical confidence limits
2. *Economic*
   Spending restricted by income
   Import controls
   Capacity to store inventory
3. *Managerial*
   Span of control (# of people that can be managed at once)
   Ability to fire government workers
   Budgets (money and personnel)
4. *Political*
   Majority of votes needed to get elected
   Rights granted by constitution
   Required responsibilities of office
5. *Social*
   Conforming behavior requirements
   Getting older
   Gender
   Race
6. *Cultural*
   Prohibitions
   Standard practices
   Adherence to words of elders/experienced people
7. *Intellectual*
   Knowledge absorption rate
   Highest degree obtainable
   Knowledge dissemination rate
8. *Religious/Ethical*
   Proscribed behavior (e.g., the Ten Commandments)
   Accepted beliefs/doctrines
9. *Ecological*
   Land holding capacity
   Air pollution saturation point
   Rate of evolution
10. *Health*
    Athletic records of long standing age pain
11. *Sensual*
    Smells that make a person sick
    Human environmental limits (e.g., exterior temperature)
    Hearing range
12. *Legal*
    Workplace regulations
    Restriction of free speech

TABLE 10.7   Limits for Selected Variables in the AIRPOL Case

Limit Var	YEAR	POP	GDPPC	VMT	FPE	COC
Lower Outside	0	215.9	20,034	1.330	2.5	5.89
Upper Outside	38	313.9	37,691	2.946	10.8	1.80
Lower Conceivable	-big	0	0	0	0	0
Upper Conceivable	+big	+big	+big	+big	+big	+big
Lower Operational	-inf	0	0	0	0	0
Upper Operational	+inf	+inf	+inf	+inf	+inf	+inf

Note: "inf" = "infinity"

fort involved forecasting the number of new cars purchased per household each year. The data used at the time is plotted in Figure 10.1.

Four years stood out as being completely separate from (and much lower than) the rest. Curiously, they occurred every year from 1967 to 1970. After some telephone calls, he discovered that there were major auto production strikes in those years. New cars thus were not available to be bought for much of the time.

The problem here is whether to include the four strike years in the regression analysis. Obviously the data for these times are substantial "outliers," being "constrained" by the strikes. Generally speaking, if these outliers

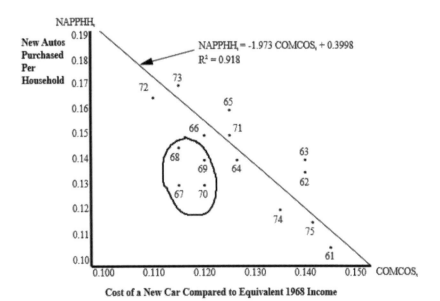

Figure 10.1   New car purchases versus costs.

are "substantial," they simply can be ignored. The rationale for doing such should be recorded, however. This can be done in QCQ under the heading of "data representativeness."

11

Step 5. Individual Relationship Development

This step is central to QCQ—it involves the creation of quantitative relationships from the connections conceptualized in Steps 1 through 3, using the data identified in Step 4. Various tools can be employed in the process, with QCQ asking questions and directing the user in deciding which resulting equations are the most logical and reasonable. In the end a relationship needs to be calibrated for each external (function of time), intermediate, goal, and pre/reaction time variable in the possible links diagram developed mainly in Step 3. More detail on these actions is presented in Table 11.1.

In terms of the AIRPOL case, note that, as our hypothetical story progresses, the DCCS has, as should be expected, continuously made some changes from the "possible links" (alpha) model in Chapter 5 through the beta in Chapter 8 to the chi in Chapter 9. Now suppose, after some further thought, changes have been put in place by DCCS, as demonstrated in the latest model (delta) in Figure 11.1. The main differences from the chi

Supernumerary Intelligence, pages 151–164
Copyright © 2015 by Information Age Publishing
151

TABLE 11.1 Tasks in Developing Individual Relationships

1. Identify the operational range for each variable (done in Step 4).
2. Determine if the relationship needs calibration or is an "accounting" or an "outside" one already derived from a theory (entered in Step 4).
3. Specify the goodness of fit criterion to be optimized for the relationship.
4. Identify the type of intercept and warrant for the relationship.
5. Determine if "reachability" is desired and possible.
6. Undertake the "pre-equalization" calibration process.
7. Generate and select the best of the eligible pre-equalities.

---

version are that (1) COC is now dependent on VMT, (see new arrow at bottom right in Figure 11.1) as well as before on PE and COE (2) there is only one catalyst (FBPS); and (3) VMT is a function of POP and GDPPC.

Now an equation needs to be created for each Y (dependent) variable—namely VMT, FPE, and COC, along with the external (function of time) variables POP and GDPPC and the reaction time FBPS. To do this requires as inputs:

1. A completed version of the "possible links" diagram showing the pre/reaction variables. Created in Step 3.
2. The selected mathematical structure as well as time affinity of each relationship pair (i.e., each arrow in Figure 11.1). Entered in Step 3.
3. The actual data. Entered in Step 4.
4. The operational range for each variable. Specified in Step 4.

Remember that a calibrated equation is *not* needed for PE (total federal air pollution control expenditures) since its value can be found via an "accounting" equation—that is, simply by adding the *continuing* expenditures (FPE) to the *additional* ones (APE).

Before getting started on this journey, however, we think it is important to recognize that regression will be the main tool to be employed and it has many potential drawbacks (and benefits) that are not readily recognized. Hence we will spend this chapter going through a variety of examples to demonstrate these issues and will start on the completion of the model in Chapter 12.

Note:
Those who feel they need a little help or a quick refresher in statistics, particularly surrounding regression, should go to Appendix A before proceeding here.

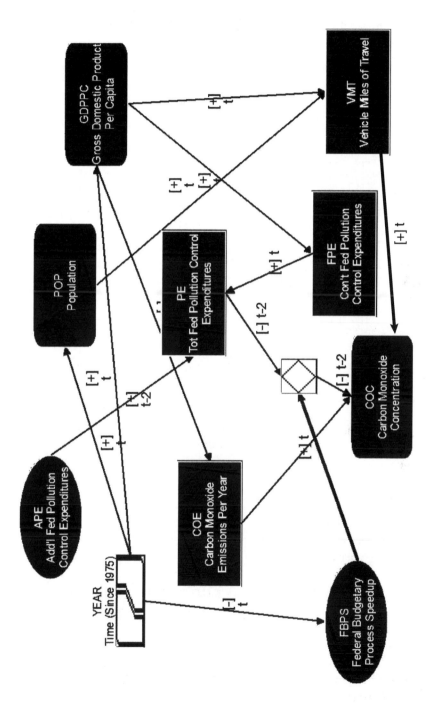

Figure 11.1 Causal model (delta) of a program to reduce U.S. CO concentrations.

11.1 Some Drawbacks to Regression

The focus is on CO concentration (COC) in urban areas across the United States. Data are available for 36 years starting in 1975 (referred to as YEAR=0). Figure 11.2 shows the distribution over time.

11.1.1 Negative Forecasts

A linear regression run between COC and YEAR gives

$$COC = 10.28 - 0.270*YEAR \qquad (11.1)$$

This shows CO concentrations going down as time progresses. The standard GoF measures are quite respectable—for instance, $R^2 = 0.972$ and MAPE = 8.76% (vs. a MAPD of 47.3%). A retrospective estimate for the year 2000 (YEAR=25) gives a COC level of 3.53, but in 2015 the estimate is –0.52, whatever that means. This occurrence highlights the "boundary" problems that some (linear) regression equations can have.

11.1.2 Symmetric and "No Cause" Correlation

An interesting exercise would involve reversing the variables in Equation 11.1—have YEAR be a function of COC. This obviously is silly, but that is the point. With regression, you can develop equations that have no cause-effect meaning whatsoever. Moreover, in this case, the R^2 is high—0.96, which shows that a high correlation and cause-effect do not necessarily go together.

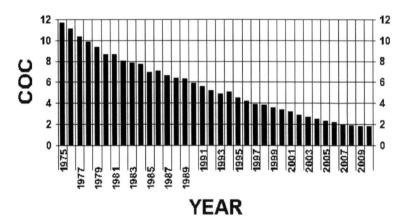

Figure 11.2 U.S. carbon monoxide concentration (COC) by year.

Actually, the causal nature of time (YEAR) in Equation 11.1 might also be questioned. Every action takes time, of course, but in this case if time simply passed with no action (like the driving of a car) being taken by anyone (that is, without any "agent"), it is difficult to imagine any CO concentrations changing.

A curious property of the correlation coefficient (and R^2) is that it is "symmetric." The R values for COC versus YEAR and YEAR versus COC are equal (0.986). This finding casts doubt on the usefulness of a measure that would give the same result no matter which of two variables were selected to be the dependent one.

11.1.3 Lack of Policy/Decision Variables

Another difficulty is that Equation 11.1 does not show how governmental actions or, more specifically, expenditures (PE, in this case taken to be those by the EPA) affect COC, so there is no way to test decisions on, say, different expenditure levels to see how strongly they affect COC. So there should be an equation like:

$$COC = f\ (PE) \tag{11.2}$$

that shows PE, along with the other variables, affecting CO concentration levels (see Figure 11.3).

Scatter Diagram of COC vs PE

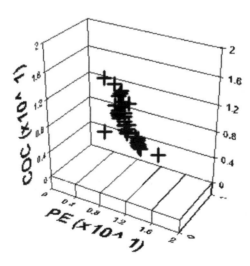

Figure 11.3 COC levels vs. total federal air pollution expenditures by year.

11.1.4   Incorrect Signs

"Governmental expenditures" (PE) are not the only factors influencing COC, however. There is something *creating* it—the mobile sources—or simply vehicle miles of travel (VMT). If COC were related to VMT by itself via a linear regression, the result would be:

$$COC = 15.53 - 4.498 * VMT \tag{11.3}$$

with the relatively good GoF measures of $R^2 = 0.95$, MAPE = 7.58%, and maximum absolute error (MINIMAX, which was optimized) = 2.129.

Interestingly, this equation, and the scattergram in Figure 11.4 show that as travel *increases*, COC *decreases*. The implication is that we can help the air environment by driving *more*. This outcome is an example of a good-fitting regression that, taken alone, is completely contradictory to actuality. It also illustrates that some relationships cannot be built on the basis of data alone. There has to be other knowledge brought to bear. In this case, everyone knows from many daily experiences (and, in some states, from required emission testing) that motor vehicles burn fuel, and that this produces COC. By simple deduction, then, more travel leads to *more* COC. As a result, Equation 11.2 perhaps should read:

$$COC = f\ (PE, VMT) \tag{11.4}$$

Scatter Diagram of COC vs VMT

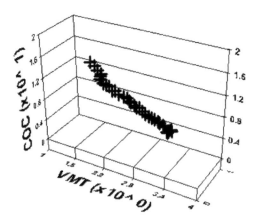

Figure 11.4.   CO concentration levels vs. vehicle miles of travel.

This highlights the importance of *both* PE and VMT. The associated multiple linear regression is:

$$COC = 16.84 - 4.806 * VMT - 0.7472 * PE, \qquad (11.5)$$

which has an R^2 of 0.962 but still has a negative sign for VMT.

This equation points to a potential dilemma with regression. Often it is used as a weapon in a "hunting expedition." Suppose, for a moment, that we had no other worldly evidence about the direction of impact of VMT on COC. If we took the data as given and ran the regression to get Equation 11.5, we would conclude that *more* driving *decreases* COC. This particular hunting expedition obviously would have been seriously misled.

Equation 11.5, in conjunction with Equation 11.3, also demonstrates another characteristic of regression. Addition of another variable *always adds to the R^2* (in this case from 0.86 to 0.91). At first glance this seems highly reasonable—more information should lead to a better explanation (fit). Yet it also would hold for misinformation, disinformation, and information overload.

Another difficulty with Equation 11.3 is that it lacks "balance." The level of most factors in the world is a result of a balance of many forces—some raising the level, some pulling it down. As it stands, Equation 11.3 only has the latter. Yet there must be something that is trying to force COC up; otherwise it would have disappeared completely long ago.

Still another calibrated (nonlinear) version is:

$$COC = 45.63 * e^{(-0.8702*VMT)} * e^{(-0.04672* PE)} \qquad (11.6)$$

This does not have the appropriate sign for VMT. Also, it does not have good "balance" since VMT is forcing COC to decrease while PE is having the same effect. On the other hand, Equation 11.6 has about the same R^2 (0.972) as Equation 11.5. A tradeoff thus still has to be made between proper direction of relationship, balance, and goodness of fit.

11.1.5 Direct and Indirect Influences

To use the preceding equation (Equation 11.6) for *forecasting* requires that we have values for both VMT and PE in the horizon year. These must be obtained via their own equations. VMT might depend most *immediately* or *directly* on, say, gross domestic product per capita (GDPPC) and population (POP). These, in turn, could be influenced by other factors. Where does it all end? None of the preceding individual equations give any clue to either the *sequence* of interrelations or to the *domain boundaries* set to keep from modeling the whole world.

11.1.6 Domains and Goals

Indeed, Table 11.2 contains a list of 39 factors that might influence COC levels (derived in part using a checklist in QCQ). These were obtained with very little thought. Many, many more could be identified. Again, where to stop?

TABLE 11.2   Factors that May Impact on COC Levels

Economic:
  Household income to buy and operate new cars and trucks.
  Interest rates (for car/truck loans).
  Federal spending for pollution control.
  Vehicle miles of travel.
Legal:
  Compatible court decisions.
  Enforcement of emission control regulations.
  Number of localities/states having emission control laws.
Political:
  Amount local political defense of local industry (e.g., auto manufacturing in Detroit).
  State legislator support of environmental laws.
Managerial:
  Number of local governmental personnel dealing with the problem.
  Time needed to produce a required budget.
  Time required to implement an environmental program.
  Personnel with environmental training.
Technological:
  Use of catalytic converters.
  Use of lighter, more fuel efficient cars.
  Use of lower emission fuels.
  Vehicle CO emissions.
  Miles of expressways and arterial streets.
Ecological:
  Heating degree days.
  Area covered by vegetation.
  CO dissipation rates.
  Number of atmospheric inversions per year.
  Wind directions and speeds.
  Terrain.

(continued)

TABLE 11.2 Factors that May Impact on COC Levels (continued)

Sensual:

Degree of "smell" of CO and other exhausts.

Number of days that big buildings can be seen from a given distance.

Social:

Geographic distribution of jobs vs. housing locations.

School segregation (impact on geographic distribution).

Travel behavior (e.g., vehicle miles of travel).

Total population.

Religious/Ethical:

Degree of remorse of drivers about polluting the environment.

Number of the clergy preaching environmental quality.

Intellectual:

Number of studies indicating travel as a polluting factor.

Number of newspaper articles on the topic.

Cultural:

Frequency of automobile advertisements.

People seeing the auto or truck as a symbol of "individual freedom."

Health:

Leaks in catalytic converters.

Mental health of drivers (people drive faster if under a lot of time stress).

Deaths

The factors listed under the "legal" grouping point to an interesting issue for regression analysis. Much of law is based on precedent (a single court decision changes a legal interpretation, which remains that way for a long time). Once a precedent (i.e., value of a variable) is set, then it becomes a constant. Regression currently does not enable such a process.

The last category (health) helps bring out several additional points:

1. The "leaks in catalytic converters" variable obviously did not exist before catalytic converters became available. By extension, this means there probably will be other *new technologies (variables)* that come into play during the *forecast* period.
2. Some variables (like "death") are irreversible, yet regression coefficients cannot be limited to such "one way" relationships.
3. "Two way" causation is possible in the real world but not in a single regression equation. CO can cause deaths, but deaths possibly can cause COC to decrease (e.g., because of the resultant news coverage and more intense investigations). If this two way causation occurs at approximately the same time, the corresponding equations will have to be simultaneous.

4. The question of "What is the 'true' aim of the study?" is broached. Is the objective to reduce CO concentration or to improve health (since CO can kill people)?

11.1.7 *"Accounting" and Deduced Relationships*

To forecast PE, we might imagine that pollution control expenditures might rise in relation to the GDPPC (the more income per capita, the more private, public, and non-profit funds available to fight pollution), but that Congress could add (or subtract) desired increments to this base every year. These additions (APE) would comprise the policy to be tested. PE then would consist of the "normal" increase (FPE), as related to GDPPC, plus the increment (APE):

$$PE = FPE + APE \tag{11.7}$$

Note that regression would be completely inappropriate here. This equation is simply a matter of "accounting"—adding like variables together.

Another place where regression would be inappropriate (actually unneeded) would be where a relationship is derived by substitution (i.e., deduction). For instance, if, as suggested, FPE is a function of GDPPC:

$$FPE = 1.276 + 0.0002539 * GDPPC \tag{11.8}$$

then, by substitution in Equation 11.7:

$$PE = (1.276 + 0.0002539 * GDPPC) + APE \tag{11.9}$$

Regression obviously is not required to create this equation.

11.1.8 *Sign Switching and Coefficient Magnitudes*

Still another difficulty that arises in regression is that the signs of influencing variables can switch as new variables are added. Take, as an example, the VMT versus POP and GDPPC relationship mentioned previously. The individual relationships (linear) are:

$$VMT = -2.770 + 1.929 * POP \tag{11.10}$$

and

$$VMT = -0.4318 + 0.00009248 * GDPPC \qquad (11.11)$$

Both have the desired sign (both positive, since there should be more travel with more people and more income) and both have high GoF measures ($R^2 = 0.974$ and 0.969, respectively).

The resultant multiple linear regression line is:

$$VMT = -1.940 + 0.3569*POP - 0.0005305*GDPPC \qquad (11.12)$$

with an R^2 of 0.976.

Note several aspects of this equation. First, the sign of GDPPC has gone negative, which certainly is counterfactual. One way to overcome this is simply to add Equations 11.10 and 11.11 (which gives 2*VMT), then divide by 2 to get:

$$VMT = -1.313 + 0.1121*POP + 0.0001302*GDPPC \qquad (11.13)$$

The R^2 for this, however, is 0.923, which is less than that for VMT versus POP alone in Equation 11.10.

Second, the coefficient for POP in Equation 11.12 is about *three times as large* as the corresponding one in Equation 11.10. This begs the question of "What is the 'real' amount of influence of POP on VMT?" Third, the R^2 of Equation 11.12 is larger than that for either of the individual regressions, which should make it the best. Again, a good value for the GoF is not necessarily indicative of the most desirable relationship.

Note also that dropping one independent variable out of two changes the regression coefficients substantially. Yet if, say, 100 factors were employed in an analysis, then each one would "contribute" *on average* only 1% (which is very little).

11.1.9   *Controlling*

An advantage mentioned for regression is that the effects of certain variables can be "controlled" to enable analysis of the independent impact of another. The process essentially involves averaging correlations computed at different set levels of the variable being "controlled."

As an example, take the relationship between COC and VMT in Equation 11.13, where $R = -0.926$. The complaint might be made that that correlation is not a "true" indicator of the GoF because the effect of governmental expenditures (PE) has not been held constant (controlled). When this is done statistically, the revised correlation (R) is –0.541. This chart obviously is quite different from the previous one.

The problems are that:

1. R still is negative, which is counterfactual.
2. All the calculations to derive the new chart were based on assumed linear relations between all variables.
3. The new R value is an *average* over different levels of PE, which may not be representative of a particular future policy level (for PE) being considered.
4. The new R value may change again as still other variables are considered and "controlled."

11.1.10   Necessary and Sufficient Conditions

The disturbing prospect from Equation 11.12 is that we cannot use both POP and GDPPC when both really are required. Money (GDPPC) cannot create travel (VMT) if there are no people (POP), and people cannot travel without money. POP and GDPPC both are *necessary* conditions for VMT. They may even be sufficient (although this is doubtful since other factors—like age and household size—may be involved). The point is that regression by itself says nothing at all about necessary and sufficient conditions.

11.1.11   Value of Different Equations for Extrapolation

Another possible difficulty to be addressed is that of significant differences in forecasted values. As an example, suppose VMT is taken as a function of time (YEAR since 1975). A linear regression gives the results:

$$\text{VMT} = 1.491 + 0.03885 * \text{YEAR} \qquad (11.14)$$

with $R^2 = 0.411$.

An exponential equation based on the same data is:

$$\text{VMT} = 1.177 * e \wedge (0.04037 * \text{YEAR}), \qquad (11.15)$$

which has a fairly close R^2 (= 0.366). See also Table 11.3.

The former gives a forecast for the year 2020 (YEAR = 45) of 3.24 trillion miles, while the latter gives an unbelievable 7.24—more than twice

TABLE 11.3   VMT Forecast Results for Two Equations

Type	1975	1980	1990	2000	2010	2020
Actual	1.330	1.521	2.148	2.748	2.945	*****
Linear	1.491	1.685	2.073	2.462	2.851	3.239
Exponential	1.177	1.440	2.155	3.226	4.828	7.239

times higher. Goodness of fit alone, as measured by the coefficient of determination, does not seem to provide much of a clue as to which equation might give a better forecast.

11.1.12   *Extrapolating Percentages*

An alternate approach might be to forecast the *percentage* increase in a given variable rather than the actual value. This percentage then can be employed to make the predictions. Our experience with this was not very good, starting with having some low R's and then having some unusual negative changes. *The F-test of overall significance determines whether the relationship is statistically significant*

11.1.13   *Data Requirements in Time Series*

Another, older experiment showed that either too much or too little time series data may be detrimental. In one experiment the objective was to forecast a known recent value for gross domestic product (GDP) with various amounts of past data, initially with one observation—the most recent, then with the two most recent, then with three, and so on until 15 observations were used. Linear regression was employed throughout. The results can be found in Table 11.4.

Notice first that the R^2's for all the equations are just about perfect. So from the standpoint of goodness of fit, any one could be employed.

Now look at the first row—with one point. The 1990 forecast (the 1989 level repeated) is not that bad ($4,118 vs. the actual of $4,263). Moreover, from a practical standpoint, the value of one point, if that is all that can be obtained, is immense. Some knowledge is better than none at all (as a test of this, ask a friend what the GDP was in 1990 and see if the number is closer than $4,118. Very doubtful). The disadvantage of having just one observation, of course, is that the forecast for succeeding years (e.g., the year 2000) will still be the same—$4,118.

The forecast closest to the actual comes when six observations are employed in the regression. The reason for this is that, with only a little data,

TABLE 11.4 1990 Forecasts with Different Amounts of Data

# of Cases	Slope	Intercept	R^2	GDP (1990)[a]
1	0	4118	(Undefined)	4118
2	101.0	2704	1.00	4219
3	116.5	2492	0.99	4240
4	126.3	2362	0.99	4256
5	127.4	2347	1.00	4258
6	127.9	2340	1.00	4259
7	134.4	2261	1.00	4276
8	145.4	2129	0.99	4309
9	148.4	2094	0.99	4319
...				
15	191.5	1631	0.98	4504

[a] Actual 1990 GDP was $4263 (in billions of current dollars).

unique, localized short term effects with perhaps no longevity sway the forecast. On the other hand, if there is a lot of historical data, the outdated trends will be more numerous and thus hold sway over the more recent, relevant ones.

11.2   Recapitulation

Development of equations, especially using regression, can be a very tricky endeavor. Particularly perplexing is the fact that there can be several completely different equations that can "explain" very well, say, variations in COC over the years. And we can include in them those that are a function of federal monies (APE and FPE) and those that have nothing whatsoever to do with them. So where does that leave DCCS in their analysis? Not that bad, of course, if they can focus on the monies.

12

Step 5. Individual Relationship Development (Continued)

The next task in QCQ is to develop or "calibrate" an equation for each affected (Y) variable (those shown with input arrows in the causal diagram in Figure 11.1). Before getting into the details of what may be a new and different process, let us pick up the story on DCCS, our hypothetical consulting company, which, before taking the first formal step here has checked for all the required input information for a calibration to take place.

For each dependent (Y) variable that they plan to use in the overall model there should be:

1. At least one affecting (X_j) variable that has been identified for each Y (QCQ Step 3).
2. A sign (+ or –) that has been assigned to each (Y and X_j) pair (QCQ Step 3).
3. Sufficient data for all variables involved in the model (QCQ Step 4).

Supernumerary Intelligence, pages 165–200
Copyright © 2015 by Information Age Publishing
All rights of reproduction in any form reserved.

    4. Limits, if any, assigned to all variables involved in the model (QCQ Step 4).

DCCS now was ready to move forward.

12.1   The "Pre-Equalization" Process

The calibration process involves what is called "pre-equalization"—a process to find the eligible mathematical forms of the individual relationships for each Y with each influencing (X_j) variable and subsequently combining and using regression on them.

The "pre-equalization" concept makes itself known when different forms of the relationship for Y are tried temporarily, with a decision on the final equality made at the end. While the intermediate versions all are equations for Y, they are not intended to be equal to each other. Hence the need for terms like "pre-equality" and "pre-equalization." They really describe a process that almost everybody uses (e.g., in developing a multiple linear regression equation) but as far as we know has never been given a name before.

The general calibration procedure for any Y variable starts with the checking of preceding identification of the *form(s)* of relationship with each influencing (X_j) variable, followed by combination of the respective forms over all the X_j's. Each combination then is calibrated as a "pre-equation" and the best is selected as the "final" equation.

The overall procedure and terminology will be illustrated four times: first for the simple case of an external variable (as a function of time); second in a more detailed explanation, using another external variable; third as a more complicated process for the COC versus VMT and PE relationship; and fourth for a case where all variables have both lower and upper limits.

12.2   Example 1: An External Variable (Function of Time)

If a Y variable is an external one, the first question asked is whether it is to be forecasted as a function of time (i.e., YEAR [from 1975]) or, instead, if future values (data) are to be supplied from some outside source. DCCS had decided earlier (Step 3) that U.S. population (POP) needed to be forecast as a function of YEAR (years since 1975) and that DCCS would develop the relevant equation themselves (as opposed to getting the equations or forecasts from another source).

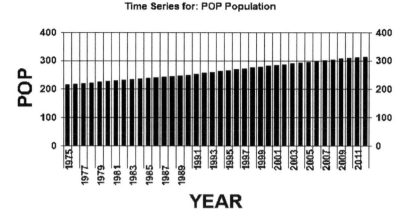

Figure 12.1 U.S. population levels over time.

The graph of POP versus YEAR (Figure 12.1) shows an almost constant trend with YEAR, with very little scatter. So the relationship has a prerequisite rate of growth being relatively invariate with time (if it were not, the top part of the model in Figure 11.1 would have to be given serious reconsideration).

DCCS subsequently went through the preceding QCQ stages and steps and established that:

1. The sign (structure) was set as "+"
2. Both POP and YEAR were established with lower limits of 0 and no (i.e., infinite) upper limits
3. The intercept should be ≥ 0
4. The desired goodness of fit (GoF) measure was the coefficient of determination (R^2).

The question now was "What general *form* of relationship (otherwise known as a 'warrant') between POP and YEAR should be employed?" There were several possibilities (listed in approximate order from the "simplest" to the most complex):

- Linear
- Exponential
- Catenary
- Cosh

The reasonable choice would be to take the simplest one with the highest R^2 value (see the evaluation criteria in the next chapter).

Looking just at the first two, DCCS found the following relationships:

$$POP <=> 212.1 + 2.753 * YEAR \qquad (12.1)$$

and:

$$POP <=> 215.2 * e^{\wedge}(0.0105 * YEAR) \qquad (12.2)$$

with both having an outstanding R^2 value (0.996 and 0.998, respectively). See the calibration report in Table 12.1.

The "<=>"symbol here means "pre-equality." DCCS developed both equations (that is, "pre-equations") for assessment purposes and as a basis for a final choice. There certainly was no intention to equate them to each other, as could be done if they were "real" equations.

The subsequent decision by DCCS was to take the linear form since it was the simplest. It also was expected to have a better record for forecasting purposes (see Chapter 11).

12.3   Example 2: A Simple One But in More Detail

Again the DCCS selected an external variable to illustrate the process. And again the question is asked as to whether the variable is to be forecasted as a function of time (i.e.., YEAR [from 1975]) or, instead, if future values (data) are to be supplied from some outside source. DCCS had responded earlier (Step 3) that gross domestic product per capita (GDPPC) needed to be forecast as a function of YEAR (years since 1975), and that they would take the responsibility to create the relevant equation themselves (as compared to getting it or the data second hand or from forecasting equations from elsewhere).

The graph of GDPPC versus time (YEAR) can be seen in Figure 12.2. Like POP, it shows an almost constant trend with YEAR, with minimal deviations. Hence the relationship has the needed rate of growth, being comparatively invariate with time.

As in the preceding process for POP, DCCS then went through the QCQ stages and steps and established that:

1. The sign (structure) was set as"+"

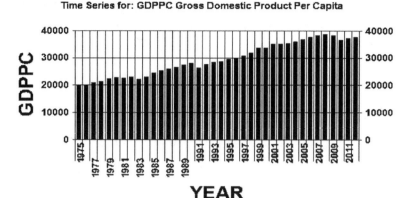

Figure 12.2   Gross domestic product per capita (current $) over time.

2. Both GDPPC and YEAR were established with lower limits of 0 and no (i.e., infinite) upper limits
3. The intercept should be ≥ 0
4. The desired goodness of fit (GoF) measure was the mean absolute percent error (MAPE).

The question now was "What general *form* of relationship (otherwise known as a "warrant") between, say, GDPPC and YEAR should be employed?" There were several possibilities (listed in the preceding section in approximate order from the "simplest" to the "most complex").

DCCS now started on a chart like that in Figure 12.3 to help come up with the best combination of quantified and qualified information to make the needed decisions.

The chart is divided into three steps. But first the focus was on checking, as the team already had done, on the completion of the prerequisite tasks (see the items in the box before the chart). The first step is directed toward finding the most proper *warrant* (that is, mathematical form of relationship) to follow under the circumstances. So, the DCCS principal leader took the first action by clicking on the "Step 1" button. This action brought up the LEGEND (see Table 12.1) in the upper right scroll window. Since the concerns in the LEGEND had already been addressed, the DCCS consultants continued on to QCQ Step 2.

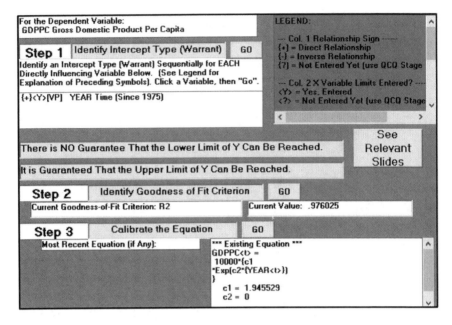

Figure 12.3   Chart to guide 3-step process to calibrate an equation.

TABLE 12.1   Calibration Report for POP versus YEAR

CASE: C:\Users\John Dickey\Documents\Supernumerary
Intelligence Book\QCQ Book\QCQ Book Work In
Progress\Airpolly —Complete Update 2010-2020 vs. Time Ver 2.QCY
DATE: 5/12/2013
===
EQUATION(S) FOR: POP Population
  with 38 Eligible Observations
Where the Objective is to:
  Maximize the Coefficient of Determination (R^2)
BASE STATISTICS
for POP$_{<t>}$

Upper Limit = 1E+38
Lower Limit = 0
Mean = 263.0368
Standard Deviation = 30.65211
Maximum Absolute Deviation (MAXAD) = 50.86316
Maximum Absolute % Deviation (MAXPD) = 19.3369
Mean Absolute Deviation (MAD) = 26.7
Mean Absolute % Deviation (MAPD) = 10.15067

(continued)

TABLE 12.1 Calibration Report for POP versus YEAR (continued)

Maximum Value = 313.9

Minimum Value = 215.9

EXISTING EQUATION

(None Currently)

*** Bivariate (Least Squares) Linear Regressions ***

POP = 2.752819E-02 * YEAR + 2.121097

UNCONSTRAINED LEAST SQUARES LINEAR REGRESSION

$POP<t> = c1+c2*\{YEAR<t>\}$

c1 = 212.109   c2 = 2.75282

Descriptions POP = Population YEAR = Time (Since 1975)

*** Associated Goodness-Of-Fit (GOF) Statistics ***

Standard Error = 1.941762

Maximum Absolute Error (MINIMAX) = 3.849121

Maximum Absolute % Error (MINIMAX%) = 1.755616

Mean Absolute Error (MAE = 1.54852

Mean Absolute % Error (MAPE) = .6231104

Coefficient of Determination (R^2) = 0.9960954

Correlation Coefficient (R) = .9980458

++++ Advantages ++++

Usually Best Goodness Of Fit Value

Linear Usually Best for Forecasting

(If No Other Problems Exist)

Linear Equation Usually Easiest to Understand

Parsimonious (Uses Just 2 Parameters)

All Observed Values of POP<t> Are Reproducible by the Equation

---- Disadvantages ----

Potentially Illogical Situation: This Equation Will Give a Value for POP<t> of 212.109
When All the Independent Variables are 0 (or at Their Corresponding [Usually Lower]
Limits).

This Equation Will Give a Value of No Less Than 212.1096

for POP<t>. This is Higher Than its Lower Limit of 0

*** Bivariate (Least Squares) LnLinear Regressions ***

POP = 1.050016E-02 * f(YEAR) + .7662403

LEAST SQUARES LN LINEAR REGRESSION

$POP<t> = 100*\{c1*Exp(c2*\{YEAR<t>\})\}$

c1 = 2.151662   c2 = 1.050015E-02

Descriptions POP = Population YEAR = Time (Since 1975)

(continued)

TABLE 12.1   Calibration Report for POP versus YEAR (continued)

*** Associated Goodness-Of-Fit (GOF) Statistics ***
    Standard Error = 1.490064
    Maximum Absolute Error (MINIMAX) = 3.421753
    Maximum Absolute % Error (MINIMAX%) = 1.090077
    Mean Absolute Error (MAE) = 1.181567
    Mean Absolute % Error (MAPE) = .4421006
    Coefficient of Determination (R^2) = .9977008   ⇐
    Correlation Coefficient (R) = .9988497
++++ Advantages ++++
Usually Best Goodness of Fit Value
Fairly Good for Forecasting
        (If No Other Problems Exist)
Parsimonious (Uses Just 2 Parameters)
No Violation of Limits
---- Disadvantages ----
Less Easy to Understand Than Linear
This Equation Will Give a Value of No Less Than 859.9135
for POP<t>. This is Higher Than its Lower Limit of 0
There is(are) 0 Observed Value(s) of POP<t>
    too Low to be Reproducible by This Equation

12.4   Warrants

A click on the "YEAR" variable listing in the Step 1 box brought up a screen like that in Figure 12.4. This shows the warranted function (#22) for the conditions specified so far: $X \geq 0$, $Y \geq 0$, no upper limits to X or Y, slope is positive, and function does not have to go through (0,0).

In all there are 72 different warrants. These cover most of the combinations of the possible geometric conditions of limitations. For instance, warrant 55 is an "S-shaped" curve going from lower left to upper right for the situation where there is a positive slope, an upper and lower limitation on Y but none on X, and does not have to go through (0,0). See Appendix G for a full listing of warrants.

Currently there is only one equation associated with each warrant, but there can be several. In addition, because of its relative simplicity and widespread use, a linear function is always run with the warranted one, primarily for comparison purposes. See, for example, the Equation Calibration Report in Table 12.1.

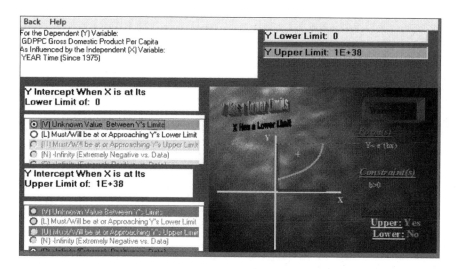

Figure 12.4 Information used to establish a warrant.

12.5 Intercept Types

A strong theme that runs consistently through the preceding chapters of this book is that development of appropriate quantitative relationships requires much more input than just the numbers themselves. In particular, serious consideration must be given to the *limits* on the respective variables as well as how the resulting equations respect (keep within) those limits.

QCQ starts by asking the user to identify the likely character of the *intercept* for each influencing variable. For instance, when both X and Y must be ≥ 0, two intercept possibilities exist for each of the two possible types of signs (monotonic structures "+" and "−"). These are shown in Figures 12.5 and 12.6, respectively.

If, as an example, the sign is "+" (Figure 12.5), the intercept can only be "0" (function (a)) or something greater than or equal to zero (function (b)). In the AIRPOL case at hand, the latter situation would prevail with the relationship between the Y variable of VMT (vehicle miles of travel) and either POP (population) or GDPPC.

Some imagination may be necessary in determining an intercept. For VMT versus GDPPC, for instance, it is necessary to envision the extremely unlikely situation where there is no GDPPC (i.e., no money income). Would there be any travel (VMT)? Maybe not, but there might be bartering, so some means to obtain resources to travel might be possible. This implies an intercept > 0.

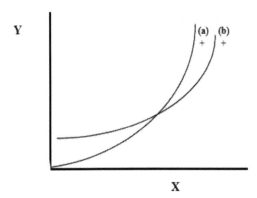

Figure 12.5 Positive monotonic structure.

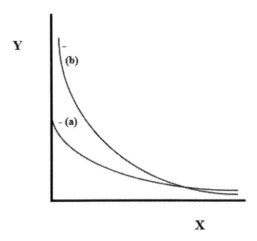

Figure 12.6 Negative monotonic structure.

A similar question may be asked with respect to the VMT versus POP relationship. Presumably, if there are no people, there would be no one to travel, so the intercept should *equal* 0. Of course, we could imagine automatically controlled vehicles, so there could be *vehicular* travel without people on board. All this surmising goes to show that the process of determining the intercept sometimes can be a highly speculative one.

When the sign (structure) is "–" (Figure 12.6), as is true for the COC versus PE relationship, the question is whether the intercept is a (unknown) constant greater than 0 or goes off to infinity. Note that the intercept *cannot* be 0 since (with X and Y both $\geq$ 0) it would not be possible to go "down" from 0.

The situation gets more complex when other types of limits (or lack thereof) on X and Y are considered. Basically, each variable can fall into one of four limit categories:

- An upper limit but not a lower limit,
- A lower limit but not an upper limit,
- Neither an upper nor lower limit, or
- Both a lower and upper limit.

And since there can be two intercepts for some functions as well as a "+" or "–" sign for each of the two functions (one being linear) in each of these domains, there can be 72 possible combinations (or more if, as in Figure 12.5, more than two types of nonlinear functions are provided in each warranted domain).

Perhaps the most complicated case arises when there are both lower and upper limits on both X and Y (see Figure 12.7). This can occur when, say, one performance rating is associated with another (e.g., a gymnastics score vs. a personal appearance rating, both on a scale from 0 to 10). In this case there could be four different intercepts to consider.

Some (but not all) of the intercept possibilities are portrayed in Figure 12.7. There is an intercept on both the X and Y axes as well as on the X and Y limit lines. Functions (a) and (d), for instance, cross the Y = 0 and Y = Limit lines inside the X limits. Meanwhile, function (c) intercepts the X = 0 and X = Limit lines inside the Y limits.

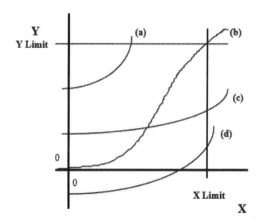

Figure 12.7 Structures with both upper/lower Y limits.

Violations of the upper and lower Y limits are avoided in QCQ simply by not allowing function parameters that would lead to such violations. In other words, there will *always* be a Y value within its limits for each X value within its limits.

The choice then comes down to the two Y intercepts. When the sign is *positive*, as in Figure 12.7, the first question is:

Must/will Y be 0 when X = 0?

and the second is:

Must/will Y = Y Limit when X = X Limit?

If the answer to both of these questions were "Yes," then a function like (b) is employed. If the answer to both were "No," then a function like (c) is appropriate. The two other "Yes/No" combinations would have their own corresponding functions.

The philosophy on choice of intercepts is closely allied to the logical/ mathematical concept of necessary and sufficient conditions. This connection is too intricate to discuss here but is described in Appendix E.

12.6 Determine if "Reachability" is Desired and Possible

Another question to be answered by DCCS was that about "reachability." As can be seen in Figure 12.8, data point 1 (.1) is not "reachable" by either

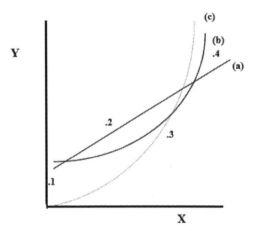

Figure 12.8 The "reachability" of data points.

the linear (a) or nonlinear (b) function. In fact, *no* point below the intercept of either of these functions, respectively, is "reachable." On the other hand, this is not a problem with function (c) (a very faint line) since it goes through (0,0). The tradeoff is that function (c) may not fit the points as well as (a) or (b).

Note that there might be *two* "reachability" questions. Function (c) in Figure 12.7, as an example, reaches neither $Y = 0$ on the left side nor the Y Limit on the right.

The user must decide if "reachability" of the full range of Y should be guaranteed in and of itself. Three considerations that entered into this DCCS decision are:

- The likelihood that *future* values of Y will fall into the "unreachable" range(s),
- The presence of functions of *other* variables that *will* cover the full range of Y, and
- The size of measurement and sampling errors in both the X and Y variables in addition to forecasting errors in the X variable.

Of course, the feeling may be that the variables *left out* of the equation, if included, *would* make the coverage more complete.

An illustration can be drawn from the COC versus PE and VMT relationship in the AIRPOL case. COC presumably goes down as PE (total federal air pollution control expenditures) goes up, so the sign (structure) is "–" (see Figure 12.5). Since COC would *not* be infinite if PE were 0, function (a) (with the intercept ≥ 0) would be the appropriate one.

What, now, if one of the data points for COC were located *above* the intercept? It would not be possible to reproduce or "reach" that point with the derived equation. One approach considered by DCCS would be to use a function like (b) in Figure 12.6. This would cover the full range but may not fit well. A second approach would be to accept the irreproducibility, blaming it on variables not included in the analysis.

The latter tack would pay off if VMT now were included in the equation. COC presumably would increase with VMT, pointing to Figure 12.5. And function (a) would seem to be most appropriate since 0 VMT would imply 0 COC (from mobile sources). The full range of COC thus would be covered (reachable) if VMT were included.

12.7 Specify the Goodness of Fit (GoF) Criterion

The choice of the measure by which to judge how well an equation fits the data on which it is calibrated can make a difference. This is illustrated in Figure 12.9. The Y variable in the diagram is the mean value of owner housing in five census tracts in Roanoke, VA. X is the mean crowding level (fraction of housing units with 1.01 or more people per room). Linear regression equations have been developed under two different sets of GoF criteria (explained below). At the extreme, when crowding is 0, the Y values differ by about 15%!

There are four possible GoF criteria currently recognized in QCQ. The equations for these are presented in Appendix A. The first of these is the coefficient of determination (R^2). This basically is the ratio of the sum of squared deviations "explained" by a regression line compared to the total amount initially (that is, about the mean). It is a *relative* measure.

The correlation coefficient (R) is the square root of the coefficient of determination. For bivariate linear relationships it will have a negative sign when the slope is negative. R also is a *relative* measure.

Both R and R^2 depend on the *square* of the deviation and error (from the mean and regression line, respectively). The origins of this calculation go back at least two centuries (see beginning of Appendix A).

There are other criteria that might be used, and two of these have much common sense appeal. Both employ the *absolute values* of the errors. This tack avoids the situation where a deviation or error that is *two* times as large as another gets counted as *having four times* (the square of 2) as much importance.

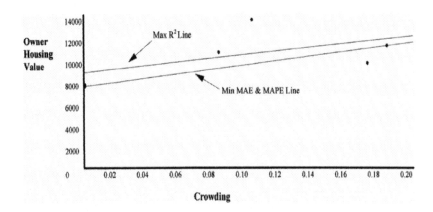

Figure 12.9 Portrayal of differences in best fitting line with different GOF.

The focus of the first alternative is on minimizing the *mean* of the *absolute* errors (MAE, which can be compared with the mean of the absolute deviations about the mean—the MAD). The second alternative is to minimize the *average (mean) absolute percentage error* (MAPE) of points from the regression line. If desired, this can be compared with the equivalent measure—the MAPD—for the deviations about the mean. Note in calculating the MAPE that if an observed value is 0, then that observation is ignored (otherwise the MAPE would be infinite).

The MAPE fits closely to every day experience, where we tend to think of deviations or errors in percentages. For example, supermarket Z's prices are, on the average, 7% less than those at supermarket Q. Or, repeated measures with a cloth tape of the length of a board showed them to be 3% off from the "true" length as measured with a steel tape.

QCQ lets the user select the desired GoF criterion. Some of the thinking behind this selection can be illustrated by returning to the history of the AIRPOL case story. In forecasting COC, the DCCS team felt that the focus should be on the *average magnitude of errors* since they wanted to have consistency and were not overly concerned with those infrequent occasions when the COC error was unusually great or small. The mean absolute error (MAE) thus was chosen as the GoF for that equation.

12.8   Example 3: COC vs. VMT and PE

The preceding example had several but certainly not all of the features of the general process for equation development. In particular, if there is more than one independent variable, there needs to be a way to deal with *combinations* of forms (that is, warrants) for each. This was demonstrated by DCCS with the COC versus VMT and PE relationship.

By way of background review:

- All three variables have a lower limit of 0, with no upper limit.
- The selected GoF is the mean absolute error (MAE)
- COC versus PE (See Figure 12.10)
- COC assumedly would decrease as PE increased (a "–"sign).
- There should be a constant intercept since there would be some (but not infinite) COC if there were no PE.
- COC versus VMT (See Figure 12.11)
- COC assumedly would increase as VMT increases (a "+" sign)
- There should be an intercept of 0 since there would be no CO (from mobile sources) if there were no VMT.

Limits and desired goodness of fit measure

DCCS now determined the *eligible forms*, in approximate order of simplicity:

COC vs. VMT	COC vs. PE
Linear	Linear
Power	Exponential
Catenary	Csch
Cosh	Tractrix
	Inverse Tangent

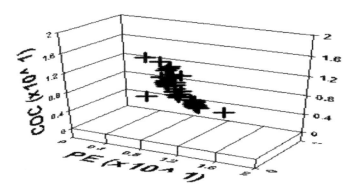

Figure 12.10   COC (Y) vs. PE (X).

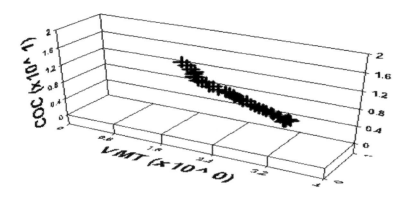

Figure 12.11   COC (Y) vs. VMT (X).

The sign (structure) and intercept type determined their eligibility. For example, if the sign were "+" and the intercept "0," then a linear (through 0), power, or other appropriate warrant could be tried. The linear form (Warrant 1, not shown) would be:

$$Y <=> b*X, \quad \text{with } b > 0 \tag{12.3}$$

while the power would be Warrant 21:

$$Y <=> b*(X^c), \quad \text{with } b,c > 0 \tag{12.4}$$

On the other hand, if the intercept were "> 0," then both a linear and exponential form could be investigated (Warrants still the same):

$$Y <=> a + b*X, \quad \text{with } a,b > 0 \tag{12.5}$$

and

$$Y <=> b*e^{\wedge}(c*X), \quad \text{with } b,c > 0 \tag{12.6}$$

Note that the "+" structure is the only one where a *linear* form is appropriate (and, if there is more than one influencing variable, only when *all of them* can have a nonzero intercept. Otherwise, a linear equation could lead to negative Y values). To illustrate, given the "+" sign for COC versus VMT and the "−" for COC versus PE, a multivariate linear regression would look like:

$$COC = a + b_1 * VMT - b_2 * PE \tag{12.7}$$

So, if PE were large compared to $a + b_1 * VMT$, then COC would be negative, which is not appropriate. The linear form in Equation 12.7 thus is unacceptable.

The next step in the process involved *combining* forms. The first step was to develop a mixed list of forms:

Combination of	COC vs. VMT with	COC vs. PE
1	Linear	Exponential
2	Power	Exponential
3	Linear	Csch
4	Power	Csch
5	Linear	

This list, like that for the individual forms, was ordered by simplicity. Here, for instance, the linear form is the simplest for COC versus VMT and the exponential for COC versus PE.

The initial forms thus were COC <=> a*VMT (linear through 0,0) and COC <=> b*e^(c*PE) (exponential), where "<=>" again is the "pre-equalization" symbol. The forms were *multiplied together* to ensure that COC would be 0 whenever VMT was 0 (no matter the value of PE).

The process then continued to the calibration phase, where curve fitting was applied to get the best values of the parameters for estimating COC. In other words, an attempt was made to find the values of b and c in

$$COC <=> b * VMT*e^{(c*PE)} \tag{12.8}$$

such that the mean of the absolute differences (MAE) between the actual and estimated values of COC was minimized.

The optimization was carried out on an Excel® spreadsheet using the Analysis ToolPak and Solver Add-in, with the constraints that $0 \leq COC < +inf$; the first parameter (b) must be > 0; and the second (c) < 0. This led to the calibrated pre-equality of:

$$COC <=> 24.11 * VMT*e^{(-0.1168*PE)} \tag{12.9}$$

The resultant MAE was 0.64 (with an R^2 of 0.70 and a MAPE of 8.4%).

The scene now was set for DCCS to check the calibration data set for sufficient degrees of freedom. That set contained 36 observations, which were aggregate U.S. figures for the years from 1975 to 2010 (see Appendix F). Since there were only two parameters in the equation (Equation 12.9), this left an adequate 36 − 2 = 34 degrees of freedom.

Trial with another combination of forms: COC <=> d*(VMT^f) (power) and COC <=> b*(e^c*PE) (exponential) eventually led (see the script in Table 12.2) to the calibrated pre-equality of:

$$COC <=> 15.628*(VMT^{0.1973})*e^{(-0.0507*PE)}, \tag{12.10}$$

which turned out to have a slightly better MAE of 0.61 (along with an R^2 of 0.82 an d a MAPE of 7.6%).

After further combinations of variable forms were investigated, Equation 12.10 turned out to be the best. It thus was assigned an equal sign, indicating its stature as the "final" equation.

TABLE 12.2 Sample Script for Investigating Another Combination

Combine the Power Form for VMT:

$\quad$ COC<=>d*(VMT^f)

With the Exponential Form for PE:

$\quad$ COC<=>b*(e^(c*PE)).

To get:

$\quad$ COC<=>b*(e^(c*PE))*(VMT^f)

See if any more X's left for this Y:

$\quad$ No. COC has been equated to a combination of forms for VMT and PE, the only X variables.

Check for sufficient degrees of freedom (df):

$\quad$ The COC data is for 36 years, and there are three parameters in the pre-equality. This leaves an adequate $36 - 3 = 33$ df.

Calibrate the pre-equality:

$\quad$ COC<=>15.628*(VMT^0.1973)*e^(–0.0507*PE)

$\quad$ when MAE is minimized with the constraints that 0<=COC<+inf; the first parameter must be >0; the second >0; and the third <0. The resultant MAE = 0.61 (with a R^2 of 0.82 and a MAPE of 7.6%).

Compare "fit" to that of previous equations:

$\quad$ The MAE of 0.61 was somewhat better than that of 0.64 for Equation 12.5. Moreover, the error for YEAR 9 was only 0.6, while the largest error was only 1.38 (in YEAR 0, or 1975).

Determine if equation is acceptable:

$\quad$ The equation was acceptable since it seemed to do well on all the criteria. It was, however, less simple than Eqn. 12.5 since it had three parameters compared to two.

12.9 Curve Fitting with S-Shaped Structures

If a dependent variable has an upper conceivable limit that is finite, QCQ will automatically treat its structure as either "++" or "--." It will run an unlimited regression on the data first, then a Gompertz (S-Shaped) regression on the results from that.

Suppose for the moment that in the VMT versus POP and GDPPC QCQ relationship that vehicle miles of travel in the U.S. (VMT) were going to be limited for some reason (say, an oil shortage) to 3.0 trillion.

The base equation is the same as would be derived in the process described immediately above, but with a slight variation:

$$\text{est!} = 1 * (\text{POP}^{0.00781}) * e^{(0.000157*\text{GDPPC})} \qquad (12.11)$$

and this est! (estimate) subsequently is used as input to the Gompertz formula. The resultant calibrated equation is:

$$\text{VMT} = 3 * (0.02886 \wedge (0.3385 \wedge \text{est!})) \qquad (12.12)$$

This will guarantee that VMT can approach but never get above 3.00.

Notice that the MAPE for this new equation is 4.47% (compared to 3.77% for Equation 12.11). The imposition of the limit on VMT in this case makes for a looser "fit."

12.10 Handling "Outside" Equations

The use of "outside" equations—those obtained from other sources—is possible under many circumstances. These also have to be calibrated. This will be illustrated here with the "accounting" equation for PE (total federal pollution control expenditures):

$$\text{PE}(t) = \text{APE}(t{-}2) + \text{FPE}(t) \qquad (12.13)$$

where FPE is the ongoing federal government expenditures and APE is the additional ones. The "(t–2)" associated with APE reflects the fact that it takes two years, on average, for programs involving "new" money (APE) to be implemented and joined with funds for existing programs (FPE).

The resulting calibrated equation is:

$$\text{PE}{<}t{>} = c1 + c2*\text{APE}{<}t{-}2{>} + c3*\{\text{FPE}{<}t{>}[/10]\} \qquad (12.14)$$

where:

$$c1 = 8.100\text{E-}05$$

$$c2 = 0.9999$$

$$c3 = 9.999$$

with a GoF criterion, $R^2 = 1.00$. Since, essentially, $c1 = 0$, $c2 = 1$, and $c3 = 10$, the two equations can be seen as identical.

12.11 Example 4: Grade Point Average

It is necessary to change examples at this point to demonstrate the most general process (which, interestingly, comes from the most restricted situ-

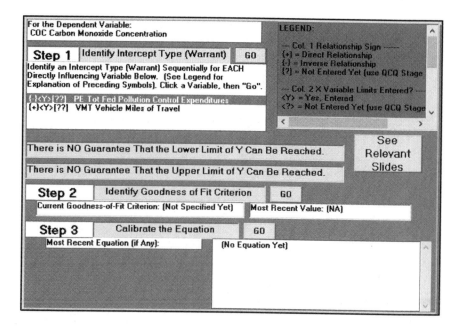

Figure 12.12 Sample chart used to determine variable limits and desired Goodness-of-Fit measure.

ation). This new example has to do with grade point averages (GPA) obtained by secondary school students and has been altered somewhat for illustrative purposes from a study by List (1995). The general relationship is:

$$GPA = f(Math, Reading, Live, SchCurr) \qquad (12.15)$$

where:

GPA(Y) = grade point average (from 0–14)

Math(X_1) = score on standardized math test (from 0–25)

Reading(X_2) = score on standardized reading test (from 0–20)

Live(X_3) = whether student's father lived at home (0=Y, 1=N)

SchCurr(X_4) = school curriculum (0=Academic, 1=Other)

Use will be made of the Warrants Table in Appendix G

As can be seen, all of the variables in this case have both lower and upper bounds. GPA is expected to increase as Math and Reading increase ("+" sign) and decrease as Live and SchCurr increase ("–" sign).

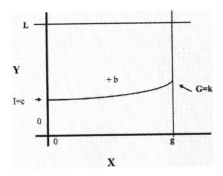

Figure 12.13 Conceptualization of upper and lower limits on both X and Y variables.

The first issue to be addressed is that of intercepts. This can be better understood with the help of the schematic shown in Figure 12.13. It illustrates a general "+" relationship between any Y and X variables where both have lower and upper limits. Without loss of generality, the lower limit can always be made 0 (although such is not necessary in the case at hand). In the chart:

I = Intercept on the Y axis (shown at point c)

L = Upper limit on Y

g = Upper limit on X

G = Intercept on the X = g axis (shown at point k)

The issue now is about the nature of I and G for each Y:X pair.

Two questions have to be asked. For the "+" sign case:

Should/will Y = 0 if X = 0? and Should/will Y = L if X = g?

while for the "−" sign case:

Should/will Y = L if X = 0? and Should/will Y = 0 if X = g?

Take GPA versus Math ("+" sign) as an example. A scan of the Warrants Table (Appendix G) shows that there are four eligible warrants (65 to 68)—ones that cover the situation where both the Y and X variables have both upper and lower limits and the sign is "+." Which one of these warrants should apply (and hence which form should be adopted)? Two questions need to be answered:

Q: Should/will GPA = 0 if Math = 0?
A: No (getting the lowest GPA does not depend just on Math).
So I = c.

Q: Should/will GPA = 14 (its limit) if Math = 25 (its limit)?
A: No (getting the highest GPA does not depend just on Math).
So G = k.

These answers indicate that Warrant 68 is the appropriate one and that neither the bottom or top limits for GPA are necessarily reachable using the Math variable.

Take now GPA versus Reading. The same four warrants (65 to 68) are eligible, but to get the most suitable one, we need to ask the two questions:

Q: Should/will GPA = 0 if Reading = 0?
A: Yes (without any Reading capability, it is impossible to pass any course). So I = 0.

Q: Should/will GPA = 14 (its limit) if Reading = 20 (its limit)?
A: No (getting the highest GPA does not depend just on Reading).
So G = k.

Warrant 66 thus is most appropriate because it does show lower (but not upper) reachability as guaranteed.

Similar questions about the relationship of GPA with Live and SchCurr ("–" signs) reveal no reason why either *have to* go through either (0,L) or (g,0). Warrant 72 therefore is the best for both of these variables.

A "reachabilty" review now is in order. The Reading variable *requires* that the lowest value of GPA (= 0) will be reached, but none of the X variable intercepts necessarily must/will give a GPA value equal to its *upper* limit. As things stand, then, there is no guarantee that the relationship to be derived with the four X variables can possibly lead to the highest GPA. The subsequent question is whether to *enforce* this in some manner.

One rationale in favor would be that, under the right conditions, a given combination of the four X's *would* show a perfect GPA. Hence the derived function somehow should cover this circumstance. A rationale against would be that other important factors (like study habits, time availability, etc.) have not been included, and only with these would a perfect GPA be possible. Let us assume here that the first argument wins out. One way to accomplish this is to expand the GPA versus Reading relationship to cover the full range. This implies that Warrant 65 be used instead of 66.

The next step is to take the forms associated with the final warrant for each X variable and *combine* them. For instance, Warrant 68 for the Math variable (X_1) and Warrant 65 for the Reading variable (X_2) have the associated forms:

$$a_1*(\text{Math}/(25+h_1))^{\wedge}b_1$$

$$(\text{Reading}/20)^{\wedge}b_2$$

while those for Live and SchCurr (X_3 and X_4, respectively) are:

$$a_3*((1\text{-Live})/(1+h_3))^{\wedge}b_3 \text{ and } a_4*((1\text{-SchCurr})/(1+h_4))^{\wedge}b_4$$

where the a's, b's, and h's are parameters to be determined in the calibration process.

Meanwhile, the dependent variable, GPA, should be re-specified by dividing by its range: (= GPA/14).

The combination process is guided by the "AddMult" field in the Warrants Table (Appendix G). Starting with the Math variable, we find that the corresponding warrant (68) has "Add" in that field. The first term for GPA thus reads:

$$(\text{GPA}/14) <=> a_0 + a_1*(\text{Math}/(25+h_1))^{\wedge}b_1 \tag{12.16}$$

where a_0 is a constant appended to the first "Add" form.

Next comes the Reading variable, which has "Mult" associated with its warrant. This means "place the corresponding form in front of whatever exists and multiply accordingly." Thus:

$$(\text{GPA}/14) <=> [(\text{Reading}/20)^{\wedge}b_2][a_0 + a_1*(\text{Math}/(25+h_1))^{\wedge}b_1] \tag{12.17}$$

Now comes the form for the "Live" variable. It has an associated "Add" notation, which means "add the corresponding form to the end of whatever exists so far." The result here is:

$$(\text{GPA}/14) <=> [(\text{Reading}/20)^{\wedge}b_2]*[a_0 + a_1*(\text{Math}/(25+h_1))^{\wedge}b_1 +$$
$$a_3*((1\text{-Live})/(1+h_3))^{\wedge}b_3] \tag{12.18}$$

Last comes the "SchCurr" variable, which also has an "Add" associated with its warrant. The final pre-equation thus is:

$$(GPA/14) <=> [(Reading/20)^{\wedge}b_2]*[a_0 + a_1*(Math/(25+h_1))^{\wedge}b_1 +$$
$$a_3*((1\text{-}Live)/(1+h_3))^{\wedge}b_3 + a_4((1\text{-}SchCurr)/(1+h_4))^{\wedge}b_4] \qquad (12.19)$$

Since there are no other combinations to consider, this pre-equation becomes the final equation.

The task at this point is to find the values of the a's, b's, and h's that maximize R (the chosen GoF) for the given set of data (on 20 students). This optimization is done subject to range constraints on the parameters:

$$a's \geq 0; \quad b's \geq 0; \quad h's \geq 0; \quad a_0 + a_1 + a_3 + a_4 = 1$$

The results were:

$$a_0 = 0.2497; a_1 = 0.1581; a_3 = 0.0525; a_4 = 0.5397$$
$$b_1 = 0.7903; b_2 = 0.2447; b_3 = 1.527; b_4 = 1.253$$
$$h_1 = 0.39; h_3 = 0.009; h_4 = 0.407$$

where the maximum R = 0.69.

12.12   Incorrect Signs (Again)

A second situation comes up when one or more of the intended independent (influencing) variables in a relationship is given a coefficient sign in the regression process opposite to that originally specified. In other words, a variable initially thought to have, say, a negative sign was given a positive one (or vice-versa) in the regression process. This seemingly small problem actually can point to what may be major theoretical and conceptual issues.

12.12.1   Example: COC vs. VMT

In Section 11.1.4 it was shown that in a bivariate regression COC was going *down* as VMT *increased* (see Figure 11.4). This obviously is incorrect since it would mean *reduced* carbon monoxide concentrations with *greater* travel. The wrong sign also emerges when PE is included as an additional variable (and when the GoF is R^2 and a two year delay in PE's impact on COC is incorporated). The resultant equation, which can be compared later on to Equation 12.21, is:

$$COC[t] = 15.97*(VMT[t]^{-0.7858})*e^{(-0.02070*PE[t-2])} \quad (12.20)$$

QCQ checks for inconsistencies like this by using a special procedure in which the regression parameters are compared to the desired sign in the suggested structure.

When the desired and actual signs do not match, QCQ computes the individual (bivariate) regression in hopes that it can be deployed as described in the next section. But, as mentioned in the preceding paragraph and shown in Figure 11.4 the resultant equation also has a negative slope (coefficient). So there is no help available from that approach.

There are several ways left to respond to this situation:

1. Review the definitions and measures for the X and Y variables. They may not be what was first imagined.
2. Reconstitute the X and/or Y variable (e.g., to or from a percentage to an absolute value).
3. Change the desired sign to that reported in the regression (thereby accepting a new theory).
4. Drop the "offending" variable(s).
5. Employ other X variables, especially those that reflect significant underlying forces that counterbalance the "offending" ones.
6. Search for a whole new theory/analogue (theologue).

As can be seen, some of these approaches require the model developer to question much of the basis for the whole relationship.

The strategy adopted by the DCCS was a combination of several of the above approaches, developed over a series of trials. Initially, importance was given to maintaining the VMT variable since it was difficult to imagine COC *not* being related to traffic volumes in some fashion. Perhaps a different measure for this factor would have been appropriate, but VMT had the overwhelming advantage of data availability at the national level for a period of many years. Alternately, perhaps the measure could have been expressed as a percentage. But of what?

The possibility of changing the sign to correspond to that from the regression also was considered. This made little sense, however, since no one could think of a good reason why COC should go down as VMT increased. Outside experience on this was overwhelming. Almost everyone drives and can watch the fuel gauge go down with miles driven. And obviously, the more fuel being consumed, the more CO released. Moreover, many states have exhaust inspection programs which verify this. (Of course, there may not be such substantial, uncontroversial evidence as this for *other* relationships, so that a sign change may be acceptable for them).

A trial now was attempted with VMT combined with miles per gallon (MPG) to give VMT/MPG (that is, gallons of fuel used—per year). This approach still gave the wrong sign.

Next, the question was proffered "What factors have been reducing COC at an even faster rate than VMT is increasing it?" One response was "technology," in the form of catalytic converters; smaller, lighter vehicles; better fuels; and the like. One way to capture the influence of all of these (and others) as a group was to focus on "emissions," on a per vehicle mile basis. Thus the variable COE/VMT was created.

A trial subsequently was undertaken to calibrate the pre-equation: COC versus COE/VMT, VMT, and PE. But VMT still ended up with a negative sign.

In the next trial VMT (as its own variable) was eliminated from the preceding pre-equation. The calibrated result was:

$$COC[t] <=> 1.492 * (COE/VMT[t]^{\wedge}0.4628) * e^{\wedge}(-0.01181 * PE[t-2]) \quad (12.21)$$

with an acceptable MAPE of 3.38%. This then was taken as the final equation.

The story behind all these trials demonstrates the iterative nature of most model building exercises. Rarely will the first conceptualization or theory be acceptable. In fact, the preceding story still is not complete since the *factors influencing COE/VMT* now have to be identified and the corresponding equation(s) calibrated. The final causal diagram can be found in Figure 13.1 and the set of equations in Table 13.1.

12.12.2 *Example: VMT vs. POP and GDPPC*

Another kind of problem with incorrect signs was presented in Section 11.1.4 and alluded to above. The individual *bivariate* linear regressions for VMT versus POP and VMT versus GDPPC both give signs that are appropriate:

$$VMT = -2.770 + 0.005655 * POP \quad (12.22)$$

and

$$VMT = 0.4318 + 0.0009248 * GDPPC \quad (12.23)$$

Yet a multiple linear regression with VMT versus POP and GDPPC together reversed the sign for GDPPC.

The solution employed in QCQ was simply to add the two equations and divide by 2 to get:

$$VMT = 0.225 + 0.002827*POP + 0.00004566*GDPPC \qquad (12.24)$$

12.12.3 Automatic Checking

Users should check for inconsistencies like those described above by utilizing a special procedure in which the regression parameters are compared to the desired sign in the suggested warrant. The first trial should entail an unconstrained regression using all the identified independent variables. If, for COC, there were just VMT and PE, Equation 12.23 demonstrates that this obviously would not be productive. QCQ subsequently computes the individual (bivariate) regression for COC versus VMT in hopes that it can be deployed as described in the next section. As reported in the preceding paragraph, this also has a negative slope (coefficient). So there is no help available from that approach.

12.13 Simultaneity

Simultaneity was addressed already, although rather indirectly, in the preceding section on grade point averages, so here we will just present an opportunity to solve a made up problem. Suppose in the AIRPOL case DCCS hypothesized two relationships as follows:

$$POP(t) = a_0 + a_1*GDPPC(t) + a_2*YEAR$$
$$GDPPC(t) = b_0 + b_1*POP(t)$$

Using the data in Appendix F, find the values of the five parameters, then estimate the levels of POP and GDPPC in YEAR = 38.

12.14 Delays, Anticipations, Catalysts, and Pre/Reaction Times

A review of the causal diagram going back to Figure 8.1 shows two time-related features that QCQ addresses—*reaction times (delays)* and *catalysts*. No time *anticipations ("preaction" times)* were incorporated in the AIRPOL model, but they represent a possible third such feature.

The model in Figure 8.1 contains a delay of two years between the appropriation of additional air pollution control money by Congress (APE) and its inclusion with the ongoing money (FPE). This particular *reaction time* represents the period between congressional appropriation of the money and its expenditure by EPA. Call this interval the federal process improvement reaction time (FPI). This time reportedly is shrinking owing to process improvements, which are influenced by the *catalyst* of GDPPC (the theory is that a greater gross domestic product per capita means more money available to Congress and federal agencies to speed up their interconnected bureaucratic processes).

The situation is made even more complicated by a delay of one year (fixed value) between the generation of GDPPC and its impact on the reaction time FPI.

A second delay was in the time (FBPS) for the impact of the expenditures (PE), once they had been made, to take place. This was seen simply as a function of time (YEAR). This delay initially had been assigned a constant value of two years, but now was viewed as decreasing over the time (so in this instance the "passage of time" or "time clock" was a "catalyst").

Calibration with varying reaction or preaction times can be complex. The number of observations that can be employed in calibrating an equation depends on the maximum delay (d) and maximum anticipation (a) times over all the variables influencing a particular dependent variable. The "a" and "d" parameters subsequently may be a function of the catalytic variables.

As an illustration, suppose that FPI currently involved a delay of two years but had been as high as three in the past. Similarly suppose (hypothetically) that another reaction time actually involved an *anticipation* or *preaction time* and that its maximum historical value was two years. The maximum gap then would be $3 + 2 = 5$ years. If there were 36 observations, it only would be possible to use 31 ($36 - 5$) fully in the calibration process.

12.15   Recapitulation

The process for developing an individual equation can be relatively complicated. The simplest case usually involves calibration for an external (as a function of time) variable. In this situation there is only one independent variable—the passage of time. With intermediate, goal, and pre/reaction time variables, there may be several X factors, each with different types of limits and time affinities. Careful consideration thus must be given to the (1) mathematical forms that respect these limits, (2) manner in which pre/reaction times are incorporated, and (3) way in which eligible forms can be combined. "Pre-equations" are created and calibrated from the various combinations. The one that gives the best value for the selected goodness of fit criterion then is usually selected as the "final" equation.

12.16 An Expanded Learning Case: Newton's Gravity Model

One of the incentives for us to try to improve on traditional regression was a statement by a colleague of ours that "it was a good thing that multiple linear regression was not around when Newton developed the 'law' (model) of gravity." The colleague had in mind a nightmare in which Newton dropped some data into an equation of the form:

$$F_{ij} = a* M_i + b* M_j + c* D_{ij} + d \qquad (12.25)$$

where F_{ij} = force of gravity between two bodies i and j

M_i = mass of body i
M_j = mass of body j
D_{ij} = distance between body i and body j.

instead of creating the well-known equation:

$$F_{ij} = a*M_i* M_j/(D_{ij}{}^{\wedge}2) \qquad (12.26)$$

Certainly if regression is to have any value, it should help in coming up with this "law," which perhaps has had the longest "staying power" of any model known—over 400 years (although it obviously does not work well by itself if gravity is overcome by some other force, say magnetism; Randall, 2005).

Some made up data for masses and distances are presented in Table 12.3. The "force" data were calculated from Equation 12.26 where,

TABLE 12.3 Sample Data for the Gravity Model

Force F_{ij}	Mass i M_i	Mass j M_j	Distance D_{ij}
12	3	2	1
3	2	3	2
4	4	2	2
6	3	9	3
6	3	1	1
24	4	27	3

for simplicity, the "a" parameter was taken as 2. The four cases above the dashed line are the calibration data; the two below are test data.

A multiple linear regression run on the calibration data resulted in the equation:

$$F_{ij} = 1.42\ M_i + 1.83\ M_j - 9.42\ D_{ij} + 13.5 \qquad (12.27)$$

with MAD = 3.0; MAPD = 46.0%; MAE = 0; MAPE = 0%; and R^2 = 1.00.

The GoF of this equation certainly is "perfect" by all three measures, so by all rights we (and Newton, if he had had these data) could stop here and be completely satisfied with the results.

There are, of course, several problems. The most obvious one is that we have left no "degrees of freedom." A straight line always fits two points perfectly; a plane always fits three points perfectly; and, in our case, a four

---

TABLE 12.4   Newton's Gravity Model Information

Stage 1: Situation Description
Aim: Determine the relationship between the force of gravity and other factors.
Client: Newton, scientists.
User: JWDickey
Budget: small
Time Available: 6 months
Goal Variable: Force of gravity: F_{ij}

Stage 2: Theory Search
External (from data) Variables: Mass of body i: M_i
Mass of body j: M_j
Distance from i to j: D_{ij}

Stage 3: Specific Theory Development
Possible Links (Causal) Diagram:

$$M_i \xrightarrow{+} F_{ij} \xleftarrow{+} M_j$$
$$D_{ij} \text{------}|$$

No time delays are taken into account (note, however, that the force of gravity assumedly cannot move faster than the speed of light).

Stage 4: Data Specification and Collection
Definitions, Measurements, Anomalies, Paradoxes: . . .
Universe(?): the Universe
Population: the Universe
Sample: 4 cases (made up), not sampled in any formal way.
Measurement Error: assumed 0.
All external variables are obtained as current values (no forecast needed for them).

dimensional hyperplane always fits four points perfectly. It is "unfair," although certainly possible mathematically in traditional regression, to have a low number of degrees of freedom.

Next, notice that if either one of the masses were 0, the equation still would show a nonzero force—an obvious impossibility. In fact, if *both* masses were 0, there still could be a force (possibly even negative, whatever that would mean).

Second, the coefficients for M_i and M_j are different, yet they should be equal since the two variables are interchangeable (it does not make any difference which mass is considered M_i and which M_j).

Lastly, some of the independent variables have high intercorrelations so that, according to traditional practice, some should be eliminated. This naturally would be totally inappropriate.

Individual graphs of F_{ij} versus M_i, M_j, and D_{ij} are shown in Figure 12.14. Two lessons can be gleaned from these. The first two graphs display a degree of scatter. The very disturbing lesson here is that it may not be possible to tell if an independent variable will *ultimately* make a good contribution to a relationship based solely on its *individual* relationship with the dependent variable (both M_i and M_j obviously will be needed eventually).

The second lesson is almost the opposite of the first—a good fit between a single independent variable and the dependent one should not be grounds for stopping further investigation. The graph of F_{ij} versus D_{ij} will not show much error if a nonlinear form is contemplated. For instance, the equation:

$$F_{ij} = 0.91*(D_{ij} \wedge -5.32)\ (e \wedge 2.58*D_{ij}) \tag{12.28}$$

has a quite good fit (MAE = 0.25, MAPE = 6.4%, and R^2 = 0.98).

While, by all statistical measures, the GoF is high, Equation 12.27 has some serious problems. In accordance with the data (third graph in Figure 12.14), F_{ij} first falls with D_{ij}, then rises. What physical phenomenon possibly could be in back of this? Moreover, independent checking with the test data (two cases at the bottom of Table 12.3) give F_{ij} values of 12.00 and 6.05, respectively. These obviously are not that close to the corresponding actual values of 6 and 24.

The two findings from the graphs in Table 12.3 bring a real conundrum. Some regressions can look bad individually but eventually produce good results, whereas another can be just the opposite. Apparently, not all

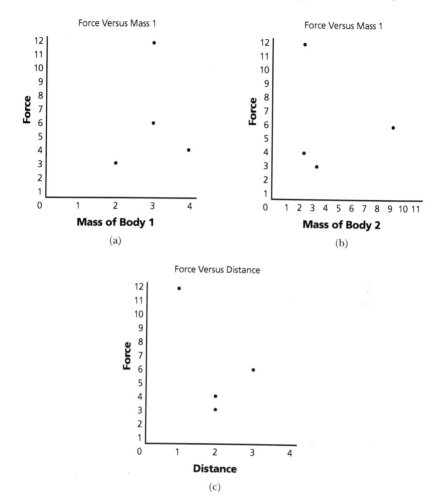

Figure 12.14 Masses and distances for gravity model calibration.

can be told unless *all* the necessary and sufficient variables are included *and* the right form of relationship specified.

A curious related issue is that all of the equations for F (Equations 12.25 through 12.28) are just that—equalities. So if they all equal F_{ij}, then they all should equal each other!! This is not what we mean in this circumstance, however. Each "equation" is what might be called a "pre-equality." It is being "tried out" before the "final" or "true" equality is selected.

We now will take a different approach—following instead the steps in QCQ. Our main concern here will be for the manner in which the equation is derived in Step 5.

TABLE 12.5   Variable Types, Ranges, and Warrants

Variable	Type	Calibration Data	Limits Conceivable	Limits Operational	Warrant
F_{ij}	Goal	3 to 12	0 to $+\infty$	0 to $+\infty$	21
M_i	External	2 to 4	0 to $+\infty$	0 to $+\infty$	21
M_j	External	2 to 9	0 to $+\infty$	0 to $+\infty$	21
D_{ij}	External	1 to 3	>0 to $+\infty$	>0 to $+\infty$	21

We start that step by looking at the ranges associated with each variable. The data ranges are very small compared to the possible values (the infinite universe), so the operational limits are taken from 0 to $+\infty$. Further thought, however, reveals that the distance (D_{ij}) cannot be 0, simply because two bodies cannot physically occupy the same place at the same time. Still, the range union of F_{ij} with the other variables (all of which are external) is the upper right hand (positive) quadrant.

We now ask what warrants (and corresponding pre-equalization forms) would be eligible to represent the relationship between F_{ij} and the other variables. We would expect F_{ij} to increase (monotonically) if either M_i or M_j increased and to decrease (monotonically) as D_{ij} increased. For M_i and M_j the intercept is known. If there is no mass for one of the two bodies, there will be no force. So F_{ij} must be 0 if either M_i or M_j is 0.

These characteristics point to eligible warrants for each F_{ij} versus X relationship. In order of simplicity, for F_{ij} versus M_i or M_j, the possible pre-equalities are linear (with an intercept of 0) and power. For F_{ij} versus D_{ij} it is the hyperbola (a linear form is not possible because [1] it has an intercept when $D_{ij} = 0$ and [2] it eventually will make F_{ij} go negative as D_{ij} increases). Consider, though, that the both the linear (through 0,0) and the hyperbola are just special cases of the power curve:

$$\text{Power: } Y = a \ (X \wedge b) \tag{12.29}$$

$$\text{Linear: } Y = a \ (X \wedge 1) \tag{12.30}$$

$$\text{Hyperbola: } Y = a \ (X \wedge b) \text{ where b is negative} \tag{12.31}$$

So the power form (Warrant 21) can be employed for all the independent variables.

Next note that the only way to meet the constraint that F_{ij} be 0 when either M_i or M_j is 0 is to multiply all the forms together. So the resultant (and only) pre-equality is:

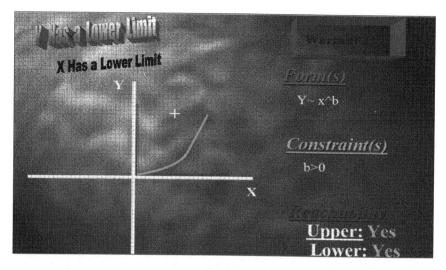

Figure 12.15 Warrant for gravity model variable.

$$F_{ij} <=> a*(M_i \wedge b)*(M_j \wedge c)*(D_{ij} \wedge d) \qquad (12.32)$$

The next step is to try this possibility against the data. We elect to attempt to maximize R^2 (perhaps because Newton did end up squaring distances). This leads to:

$$F_{ij} = 2.0*(M_i \wedge 1.0)*(M_j \wedge 1.0)*(D_{ij} \wedge -2.0) \qquad (12.33)$$

or the more familiar:

$$F_{ij} = 2.0* M_i * M_j/(D_{ij} \wedge 2) \qquad (12.34)$$

(remembering that we made the first constant 2.0 to keep our illustration simple). The correlation, of course, is a perfect 1.00 and the MAE and MAPE both surely equal 0.

Note, too, that the equation meets the rule that M_i and M_j have to be interchangeable (have the same forms and parameter values). This happened "automatically" here but can be forced under less fortuitous circumstances.

It would be natural to stop here since the resulting function is desirable not only in terms of R^2 but also the other evaluation criteria (see Step 6—Relationship Evaluation). It also gives perfect estimates vis-à-vis the two test cases at the bottom of Table 12.3:

$$\mathbf{F}_{ij} = 2.0(3)(1)/(1 \wedge 2.0) = 6 \text{ (perfect)}$$
$$\mathbf{F}_{ij} = 2.0(4)(27)/(3 \wedge 2.0) = 24 \text{ (perfect)}.$$

13

Step 6. Relationship Evaluation

An evaluation of each equation in the overall model now can be undertaken. This assessment can be both *quantitative* and *qualitative*.

Part of the information for the *quantitative* part already has been supplied in the preceding QCQ step—a goodness of fit (GoF) criterion has been selected and the equation calibrated with the optimization of that criterion as an objective. In this step a further assessment can be made by looking at the distribution of the "errors" between actual and estimated values.

The *qualitative* assessment is based on such factors as logical consistency, confirmability, novelty, resolution of paradoxes, and even beauty and harmony. These are some of the criteria that have been found to be operative in the work of many of the most famous scientists (e.g., Nobel Prize winners; Root-Bernstein, 1989).

13.1   The Set of Equations

The main product that ended up being created by DCCS in Step 5 was a set of equations that covered the types of variables and relations (i.e., the

Supernumerary Intelligence, pages 201–219
Copyright © 2015 by Information Age Publishing
All rights of reproduction in any form reserved.

model) under discovery and examination (see Figure 13.1 and Table 13.1). In all there were 11 of the former and 14 of the latter. Two of the variables (APE, a strategy, and YEAR were assumed to be unaffected). The resulting causal diagram was somewhat different than what the DCCS was considering at the end of the previous QCQ step (see Figure 11.1). And therein lies the basis and necessity for the types of evaluations described next.

The main focus of attention still was the fact that, if the fast-increasing vehicle miles of travel (VMT) were included in the model, it would have the strange effect of *reducing* emissions and concentrations. After some hard thinking, the DCCS consultants came up with the thought that the VMT somehow would have to appear in the denominator of the appropriate equation(s) rather than the numerator. And they also felt that technology (as it was part of the development of products and programs for reducing air pollutants) probably was a major contributor to overcoming the effects of greater travel.

An initial pass at this latter possibility was to characterize "technologic impact" as:

$$\text{TECHNOL}(t) = \text{COE}(t)/\text{VMT}(t) \tag{13.1}$$

where, if CO emissions were high and VMT were low, that would signal a very undesirable situation. Whereas, if emissions were low, even on a large volume of travel, that would signal a much more attractive outcome. The difference, of course, would be seen as a result of technology.

Several different models had to be created under this general rubric, perhaps because of a lingering dissatisfaction with the numerator of the above equation. In some sense it felt strange that the impact of technology did not depend on the downward *change* in emissions rather than the level at any one time. So, still another measure was developed:

$$\text{TECHNOL}(t) = (\text{COE}(t\text{-}1) - \text{COE}(t))/\text{VMT}(t) \tag{13.2}$$

where the COE in the preceding period was taken first because emissions generally were higher in the past than now (which leads to an easier-to-work-with positive number).

Some further thought concerned the seeming assumption in Equation 13.2 that most technological innovations can be imagined, produced, sold, and used to some degree in a one year period. This obviously is not possible, but nobody seemed to have a convincing alternative, except for the idea that the average age of a car on the road is about six years old. So, the

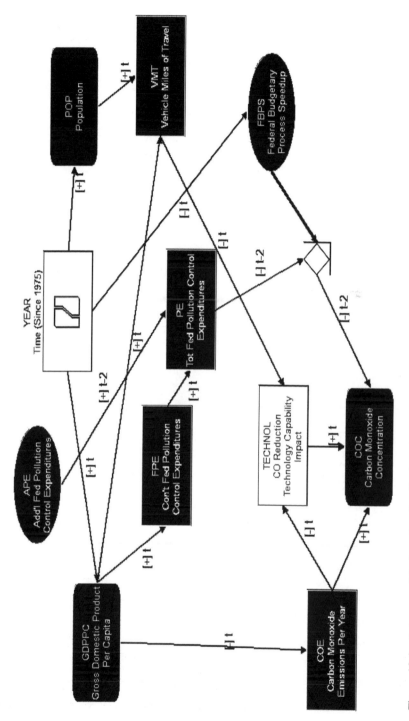

Figure 13.1 Latest graphical version (epsilon) of the COC AIRPOL model.

TABLE 13.1   List of Equations in the Latest Model (June 15, 2013)

Variable: APE Add'l Fed Pollution Control Expenditures
  ROLE: CLIENT STRATEGY
Variable: COC Carbon Monoxide Concentration
  $COC<t> = c1*Exp\ (c2*\{COE<t>[/10]\})*Exp\ (c3*\{PE<t-2>[/10]\})* Exp\ (c4*\{TECHNOL<t>\})$
  $c1 = 0.6334$ $c2 = 0.3313$ $c3 = -0.02572$ $c4 = -0.04591$
Goodness-of-Fit (GOF) Criterion: R^2 Value: .934
Varying Pre/Reaction Time is: FBPS Federal Budgetary Process Speedup
==
Variable: COE Carbon Monoxide Emissions per Year,
  $COE<t> = 10*\{c1*Exp\ (c2*\{GDPPC<t>[/10000]\})\}$
  $c1 = 20.867$ $c2 = -.44627$
Goodness-of-Fit (GOF) Criterion: R^2 Value: .8991396
==
Variable: FBPS Federal Budgetary Process Speedup
  $FBPS<t> = c1*Exp\ (c2*\{YEAR<t>\})$
  $c1 = 2.260$ $c2 = -3.114E-02$
  Note: All Pre/Reaction Equations Are Shown with Positive Values
Goodness-of-Fit (GOF) Criterion: R^2 Value: .9228393
==
Variable: FPE Con't Fed Pollution Control Expenditures
  $FPE<t> = 10*\{c1*\{GDPPC<t>[/10000]\}^\wedge c2\}$
  $c1 = .30640$ $c2 = 1.8434$
Goodness-of-Fit (GOF) Criterion: R^2 Value: .8672172
==
Variable: GDPPC Gross Domestic Product Per Capita
  $GDPPC<t> = c1+c2*\{YEAR<t>\}$
  $c1 = 19294$ $c2 = 549.2$
Goodness-of-Fit (GOF) Criterion: R^2 Value: .9865469
==
Variable: PE Tot Fed Pollution Control Expenditures
  $PE<t> = c1+c2*APE<t-2> + c3*\{FPE<t>[/10]\}$
  $c1 = 8.1004E-05$ $c2 = 0.9999$ $c3 = 9.9999$
Goodness-of-Fit (GOF) Criterion: R^2 Value: 1
==
Variable: POP Population
  $POP<t> = c1 + c2*\{YEAR<t>\}$
  $c1 = 215.46$ $c2 = 2.3566$
Goodness-of-Fit (GOF) Criterion: R Value: .9993293
==
Variable: TECHNOL CO Reduction Technology Capability Impact
  ROLE: Unspecified
  $TECHNOL<t> = -(COE<t> - COE<t-6>)/VMT<t>$
Goodness-of-Fit (GOF) Criterion: R^2 Value: 1
==

(continued)

TABLE 13.1   List of Equations in the Latest Model (June 15, 2013) (continued)

Variable: VMT Vehicle Miles of Travel

$\quad$ VMT<t> = c1*Exp(c2*{GDPPC<t>[/10000]})*{POP<t>[/100]}^c3

$\quad$ c1 = .2377702   c2 = .2939521   c3 = 1.521844

Goodness-of-Fit (GOF) Criterion: R^2 Value: .990272

===

Variable: YEAR Time (Since 1975)

$\quad$ ROLE: TIME CLOCK

latest (and, as it turned out, the last) version of the technology variable looked like:

$$TECHNOL(t) = (COE(t\text{-}6) - COE(t))/VMT(t) \qquad (13.3)$$

The next issue was how to perceive the direct impact, of TECHNOL with other variables, on the concentration of CO (that is, on COC(t)). A happy result was agreement on the use of COE (emissions) and PE (federal pollution control funds) along with TECHNOL. The feeling seemed to be that these three covered the waterfront, with COE being the basic cause of the "problem," PE being a source of funding to fight the problem, and TECHNOL representing the amount and use of technology tools to be used in the battle.

The last decision at this point concerned the equation to use to represent the influence of the three variables on COC. There were several options, but the two most prominent ones were (a) a straight multi-linear regression and (b) a nonlinear one based on the warrants of the variables involved.

The resulting information from the calibration of the multi-linear one was as follows:

Variable: COC carbon monoxide concentration

$$COC<t> \iff c1+c2*\{COE<t>[/10]\}+c3*\{PE<t\text{-}2>[/10]\} + c4*\{TECHNOL<t>\}$$

$\quad$ c1 = −1.566 c2 = 1.299 c3 = −1.586 c4 = −0.2521

Goodness of fit criterion: R^2 value = .893

Varying pre/reaction time is: FBPS federal budgetary process speedup

The R^2 was fairly high (0.893) but not as much as that for the nonlinear (0.934). Still, the former was thought to be more understandable. The DCCS team ended up successfully backing the nonlinear version, though, mainly because:

> COC(t) could end up being a large negative number. The equation could give negative values as much as −1.56 if all the independent variables were located at certain select levels.

The sign of TECHNOL in the linear model is not the same as specified, which could cause theoretical and forecasting problems.

13.2 Undertake Quantitative Evaluation

The quantitative assessment of each calibrated equation developed in the QCQ process is intended to follow many of the standard statistical practices. Some of the traditional queries addressed include those in Table 13.2.

Note that several of these questions are resolved before reaching this stage in QCQ. For the first, for example, the GoF is computed during calibration in QCQ Step 5. If this were unacceptable, presumably there would be no desire on the part of the user to proceed to this next step.

The answer to the second question also is addressed in the preceding step. The user can make a choice on whether the full range of Y should be guaranteed as "reachable." If so, the resulting equation automatically will make it possible to replicate all observed values (the Y_i's).

If the user makes the choice against guaranteed "reachability" (usually for reasons of better fit), it still may turn out (and frequently does) that all the observed values can be replicated with the resulting calibrated equation. In any case, the DCCS QCQ team checks (in this step) whether this happy circumstance actually has occurred or not.

TABLE 13.2 Possible Questions to Ask in a Quantitative Assessment

How good is the GoF value?

Can all the Y_i's be replicated?

Will Y stay within its operational range?

Are there any substantial outliers?

Are there any mistakes ("human errors") to be corrected?

Do the estimates match other known (external) Y values?

Will the equation give estimates that match the values in the test data set (if any)?

Are the resultant parameters and the GoF (assuming R^2) significantly different from 0?

The third question above is somewhat rhetorical because the calibration decision made in QCQ Step 5 may insure that Y will keep within its range.

The question about "outliers" can be given a good deal of attention in this step of QCQ. For example, a traditional comparison of actual and estimated values can be made, in this case for the nonlinear equation developed for COC. The associated diagrams can be seen in Figures 13.2 to 13.4.

These are somewhat different than normal, however. In the first, any point representing a substantial deviation from a 45 degree line signifies a possibly important outlier and should be investigated. The two points at the bottom left look suspicious, but after an in-depth investigation it was found that the data for the two were entered incorrectly! So such a chart turns out to have benefits in more than one way.

A second way that the DCCS team used QCQ to look at and check the data was through a chart like that in Figure 13.3. This shows the error (actual yearly value—estimated) for each COC yearly data point. As might be expected, the chart shows some cyclical ups and downs (positives and negatives) but nothing too outlandish. Hence, the response is "to proceed."

Interestingly, the chart in Figure 13.4 seems to tell an entirely different story, with all the differences being negative! How could this come about? The story again is one of mistakes by the developer. He/she was found to have utilized the wrong equation—a much earlier and inappropriate version—to compute the estimated values. So again the analyses undertaken at this point help to serve several purposes.

The choice that remains for the user/developer after reviewing all the quantitative (and some qualitative) assessment evidence is whether or not

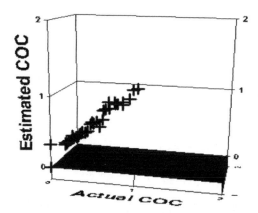

Figure 13.2   Estimated vs. actual values of COC.

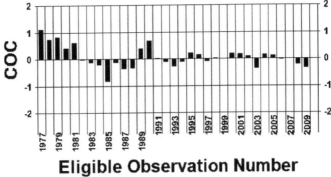

Figure 13.3 Estimation errors (actual values-estimated) for COC by year.

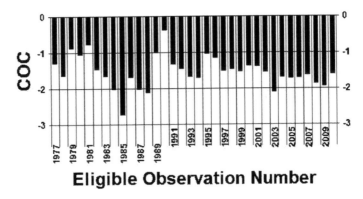

Figure 13.4 Estimation errors (-actual values-estimated) for COC by year.

to proceed with the particular equation. It may turn out, for instance, that if one or more substantial outlier points wew found, that would signal a serious flaw in the equation and to the associated theory or analogue that underlies it. In that case, a return has to be made to preceding steps in QCQ to construct another version. On the other hand, the outlier may be considered a highly unusual event that has little likelihood of happening again.

13.3 Undertake Qualitative Evaluation

The next step in this stage of QCQ is to check the relationship against various qualitative criteria. These are based, with some adaptation, on the remarkable research by Root-Bernstein (1989) on the characteristics and behavior of outstanding scientists (e.g., those who have won Nobel Prizes). Of particular relevance here is his inquiry into the criteria these scientists use to evaluate both their own work and that of others.

The criteria are too numerous to discuss in detail, but they can be divided into five major categories (see Table 13.3). From these, five summary questions can be posed (see Table 13.4).

Perhaps what is so beneficial about the criteria that have been developed from Root-Bernstein's (1989) work is that they highlight a much wider world of considerations than just the traditional statistical measures.

TABLE 13.3   Some Possible Qualification Evaluation Criteria

1. *Logical*
   Offers unifying idea that postulates nothing unnecessary
   Is logically consistent internally
   Is conceivably refutable
   Is explicitly bounded in application
   Is consistent with previously established laws and theories
2. *Empirical*
   Makes observationally confirmable predictions/retrodictions
   Confirming observations are reproducible by skeptics
   Provides criteria for interpretation of observations as fact, artifact, or anomaly
3. *Sociological*
   Resolves problems, paradoxes, or anomalies recognized by the scientific/user community
   Posits problem solving model (paradigm) for related problems
   Poses new problems
   Changes how scientists/analysts/decision makers think about and perform their work
   Changes textbooks and training
4. *Historical*
   Demonstrates novelty in history of the field
   Meets or surpasses criteria set by predecessors or demonstrates they are artifactual
   Incorporates history of testing of previous theories or observations
5. *Aesthetics*
   Displays beauty and harmony
   Demonstrates technical skill in experimentation and communication of results
   Requires interpretation

Note: After Root-Bernstein, 1989, p. 229.

TABLE 13.4   Summary Questions for Qualitative Analysis

Is the equation logical—consistent internally and with other established theories?
Does the equation have an empirical basis for confirming and reproducing observations?
Does the equation pose/resolve paradoxes, and change how people think about and use the results?
Does the equation demonstrate novelty and surpass criteria set by predecessors?
Is the equation "aesthetic"—displaying beauty and parsimony?

The question about "novelty," as an example, forces the developer to do the hard work necessary to find out what has been done before so that the wheel is not reinvented. This is important because so much effort and thought may have gone into preceding studies. Conversely, previous efforts may have been problematic. Neither situation should be ignored, as would happen if data were collected and simply "dropped" into a statistical analysis program.

The focus on paradoxes (third question) also is highly instructive. The issues that led to the need for a particular equation rarely are completely settled by that equation. In fact, it is exceptional when all the issues are even *known*. An equation (and all the materials behind it) thus should be a mechanism not only to help explain but also to open up new vistas. This certainly is the case for the COC versus PE and COC/VMT relationship, where the specific role and measurement of "technology" begs further clarification (see Table 13.5). This finding illustrates the incremental way in which science, and understanding in general, expand and improve on the past.

After responses to the five questions have been offered, the remaining task is to decide if the particular equation is acceptable from an overall viewpoint. If not, possible readjustment of the equation and perhaps other model relationships in addition may be needed. This might require a revisitation of one or all of QCQ Steps 2 to 4.

TABLE 13.5 Qualitative Evaluation Questions and Sample Answers

For the COC vs. COE, PE, and TECHNOL equation involving 36 – 4 degrees of freedom.

Q1: Is the equation logical—consistent internally and with other established theories?
A1: PE is important since it is consistent with all theories about government spending. Per mile emissions consistently reflect the influence of a variety of technologies (e.g., in COE from a cross-section of fuel efficient vehicles).

Q2: Does the equation have an empirical basis for confirming and reproducing observations?
A2: The MAPE is very low. There are no widely differing observations.

Q3: Does the equation pose and resolve paradoxes, and change how people think about and use the results?
A3: Decision makers naturally will focus on expenditures as being important. A new problem is how to be specific about technological aspects such as lighter vehicles and better fuels.

Q4: Does the equation demonstrate novelty and surpass criteria set by predecessors?
A4: There are no examples of a model like this in the past but there has been much written on the topic.

Q5: Is the equation "aesthetic"—displaying beauty and parsimony?
A5: Interpretation is needed to understand how expenditures actually flow through the "system" to influence COC. COC/VMT does simplify the technological aspect by pulling all relevant technologies into one variable.

13.4 Another Type of Model

We have been focused almost entirely on producing a quantitative model, yet a quick look at the literature in the field and at the types of conversations being carried out across public administrators would certainly be light on the types of model developments being demonstrated here. A quick look at the case studies in the PAGP (see Chapter 15), for instance, would reveal just a few that were heavy on producing a complete quantitative picture. The case dealing with the impacts of Hurricane Katrina, as an example, is a compilation of almost 2,000 variables and 1,300 relationships garnered from various unconnected newspaper articles, personal interviews, books, TV videos, and web pages. There are just a few statistics and a few numbers here and there.

Now let us unveil another type of model, as seen in Figure 13.5.

There are several aspects to note. First, the variables come from the aid of the same kinds of sources as in the quantitative model ("qt," see Chapters 4 through 7 and Table 13.6). However, and second, this "ql" model is larger than the qt and could have been many times more so. Third, the ql allows for "unattached" variables (on right) and even "attached-unattached" variables (say if MRKSIZE were felt to be influenced by TAXCRED). So the ql model can become a big (probably incomplete) conglomerate of loosely held variables and relations. Such also does life appear.

The downsides, of course, can be substantial. To name three: clarity of definition and measurement can be lost, the relative strengths of impacts of different variables can be more difficult to gauge, and forecasting into

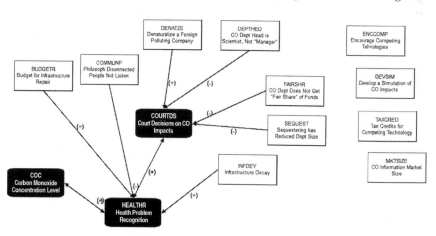

Figure 13.5 One possible alternate non-quantitative COC model.

the future thus is much more "iffy." What to do? We have one suggestion, offered with minimal but seemingly successful experience:

> A certain business magazine would publish forecasts for the economy, like gross national (or domestic) product by quarter (of the year) for up to two years out. They showed the estimates by mathematical model and by expert contacted. Interestingly, no particular model or expert showed a clear-cut advantage. But the mean (average) of all of them together was the closest! So it appears that we need both precise but relatively limited data and a wide scope of experience!

This means that we generally need both types (qt and ql) of QCQ models.

There is still another consideration to take into account—the experience of the expert(s) may be limited for a variety of reasons: they may not have much experience with which to start, and that experience may be an industrial secret and/or government classified.

Those possibilities lead us to a further conceptual subdivision that may prove important in approaching a new problem or opportunity. This subdivision may be imagined in the form of a matrix, as seen previously in Chapter 1 (see Figure 13.6).

		Question	
		Know	Not Know
Answer	Know	Things that you know that you know (You know the question and the answer)	Things that you do not know that you know (You do not know the question but know the answer— Tacit Knowledge
	Not Know	Things that you know that you do not know (You know the question but not the answer)	Things that you do not know that you do not know (You do not know the question or the answer— Unintended Consequences)

Figure 13.6   Categories of knowledge.

We imagine that the consultants (DCCS), at the beginning of this project, sat down and addressed the left hand side of the matrix. Since they assumedly were selected for their expertise in carbon monoxide and related programs, the top-left box ought to contain (from the causal diagram) APE, COC, COE, FPE, PE, and TECHNOL: namely the technical and financial factors. They may have less knowledge of GDPPC, FBPS, and catalysts, but they probably do not know how much they really know about these (bottom left of matrix), which may be a lot, having picked up much in informal ways.

What is missing from the lower left box, however, is "the future." Most likely DCCS would not have been called in had the sponsor known (as least as well as the consultants) what future awaited.

The really interesting aspects come up on the right hand side of the matrix. First, what does DCCS know but they do not know that they know it? For example, let us assume it is POP (U. S. population). But ask anybody on the team for a guess for the year 2010 and he/she probably would say "somewhere between, say, 300 and 310," while the "real" figure is 309.3. Not bad. They really *do* know what they know. We thus can transfer POP into the "Know:Know" upper left box.

Things get really messy, however, when the team tries to do something with the variables and relations in the non-quantitative model presented in Figure 13.5. First, there are those that the members of the team knew that they do not know. One was "sequestering": holding out a fixed percentage of the budget (or positions) from some or all governmental units as a way to reduce the budget. This is a term that the team had never heard before, so it went in the "Not Know:Not Know" box (lower right). It was joined by several other terms. Note, though, that once the team gained more familiarity with the term, it was put in the "Know:Not Know" box and then eventually to "Know:Know."

Any new idea, by definition, starts in the "Not Know:Not Know" box. This would be the case for the variable DENATZE ("denaturalize" any foreign polluting company). Meaning: To "naturalize" a foreign person is to make him/her a citizen. To "denaturalize" him/her is to take away his/her citizenship. Now, since the Supreme Court has ruled that corporations are "people," it stands to reason that they too can be "denaturalized" for certain law-breaking activities. The term subsequently is put into the "Not Know:Not Know" box for some people.

So now "denaturalization" has taken on some meaning and there is likely to be, say, some lawyers checking into it. It may eventually go from "Not Know:Not Know" to "Know:Know." Other variables may progress the same manner, especially if they have enhancing relationships. The objective, it would seem, is to build this kind of supernumerary intelligence (SI) or knowledge to the point where it can be used beneficially to guide appropriate decisions. Two of the advantages of QCQ thus are that it can be employed to (1) aide in the identification of those hidden items on the right side of the "Know-Not Know" Matrix, and to (2) track their movements to the left side so they can be dealt with appropriately.

The qualitative model in Figure 13.5 may not be particularly useful for the first purpose in connection with the AIRPOL model. The reason for this is that the variables were generated more with "interesting!" in mind rather than "applicable." Still, if one variable happens to "click," it would be relatively easy to add complementary variables and relations, as well as to prune all the unnecessary ones.

13.5 Recapitulation

The evaluation stage of QCQ brings out the need to look at both the quantitative and qualitative sides of each relationship as well as the set as a whole. The immediate focus of the former is primarily on various aspects of the "fit" of the equation to the data. A particular concern in this QCQ step is for "outliers"—substantial differences of the observed from estimated values.

The qualitative side of the evaluation helps open up the bigger picture of the roles of, and issues behind, the equations. If, for instance, a *substantial* outlier is found, this may point to the need to expand the theory, and thus the equation, to include a broader set of variables and circumstances. By so doing, the user will be able to transfer more knowledge to the "Know:Know" box, thereby increasing understanding of the phenomena at hand over what it would have been otherwise. Science and practical strategy thus both will have progressed.

13.6 An Expanded Learning Case: The Olympic Gymnastics Performance Model

Rating schemes are used in a wide variety of situations, from judging Olympic skating and gymnastics performances to determining the quality of a paper written for a college course. One type of rating scale is the semantic differential, which may be employed for measuring the "value" of an Olympic performance (see Figure 13.7).

The question to be addressed is of the relationship between performance rating (0 to 10 scale) on, say, the gymnastics high bar and average (mean) hours per day of practice. A coach naturally wants to instruct his

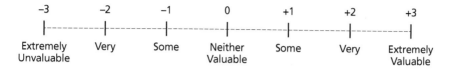

The more typical performance scale is one that goes from 0 to 10:

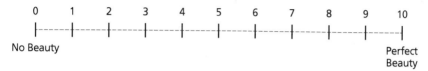

Figure 13.7 Different scales for judging performance.

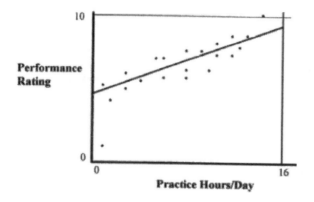

Figure 13.8 Limited performance rating vs. practice time.

or her pupil on how much effort is needed to get the highest score. The (hypothetical) data look like that in Figure 13.8.

The performance scale lacks a little, of course. First, it is subjective— "value (beauty) is in the head (eye) of the beholder." This is why Olympic gymnastics events are judged by a *panel* of people, with the top and bottom scores eliminated. If, for some odd reason, the coach were not aware of this procedure (definition), he might assume, say, that the lowest score by a judge usually was very low and thus tend to underestimate the actual rating his pupil might achieve.

The first issue is that of agreement on the definition and measure of each variable. QCQ asks for a detailed description of these two entities and then asks if there is general (and written) agreement on them. It subsequently asks for similar detail on such characteristics as reliability, accuracy, and precision. These the user can access later when developing relationships, interpreting results, and so on.

In addition, there is much "norming" by judges that goes on over a period of years—for example, a fall while landing from the high bar, it is agreed, automatically deducts 0.5 points. Again, if the coach did not know this part of the definition and measurement of "performance," he might not deduct anything, and thus estimate his pupil's scores to be higher than they would be.

These examples show that regression analyses (as well as any other quantitative or qualitative techniques) can easily be misapplied if a clear definition and measure of the entity under consideration is not supplied. They also show the need for as much *agreement* as possible ahead of time on the *validity* of the definition and measure—does a deduction of 0.5 really represent the "right" amount for a fall on dismount?

Of course, the rating system actually is much more complicated than presented so far (e.g., there are several other types of standard deductions). So they must be spelled out completely for others to understand the analysis (see Table 13.6).

A particular problem with rating data is what might be called "super-achievement." Suppose the coach's pupil is a real prodigy. She has gotten 10's for her performance, which has included a triple somersault at dismount. Now she can do the same thing with a *quintuple* somersault dismount. What rating should she get?

The choice seems to be to change the definition of the performance measure so that a "10" now includes a quintuple somersault or to raise the top score from 10 to something higher. In either case, the measure will be altered such that consistency with past scores is suspect. Are all the points in Figure 13.8 associated with the same definition? Or has the definition changed over time?

TABLE 13.6 Stimulation Source of Variables in Alternate Model

Variable	Stimulus Source	Variable	Stimulus Source
BUDGETR	Discussion with Expert	COC	Given Goal
COMMUNP	Previous Theories	COURTDS	Dimensions Checklist
DENATZE	PA Genome Project	DEPTHED	Dimensions Checklist
DEVSIM	CyberQuest	ENCCOMP	Individual Brainstorming
FAIRSHR	Literature Search	HEALTHR	Given Goal
INFDEY	Possible Links	MKTSIZE	Crowd Source
SEQUEST	Internet Search	TAXCRED	PA Genome Project

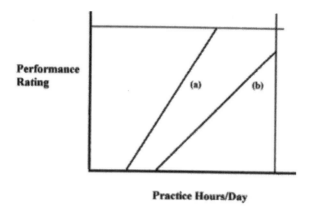

Figure 13.9   Limited performance rating vs. limited coverage.

Another problem inherent in the regression line in Figure 13.8 is that the *predicted* value using the equation can never be 0 or 10. Even if the pupil put in 16 hours a day of practice (assumed to be the maximum to allow for sleeping, eating, etc.), she never will be able to score a 10. This predictive limitation occurs despite the fact that one data point shows a 10 (and another a 0).

Figure 13.9 shows some other problematic equations. Neither line (a) nor (b) covers the *whole range* of X, so it is impossible to know what happens with low levels of practice hours. Line (b), moreover, does not cover the entire range of Y.

A potential solution to the preceding dilemma can be found in Figure 13.10. The equation "connects" at both ends of the spectrums of X and Y. Of course, it is possible that too much practice may be detrimental—not giving the body enough time to recuperate. If so, the maximization curve

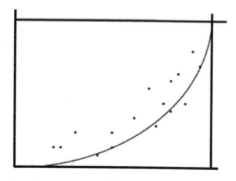

Figure 13.10   Connection at both ends.

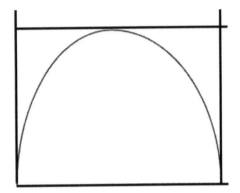

Figure 13.11 Rise and fall.

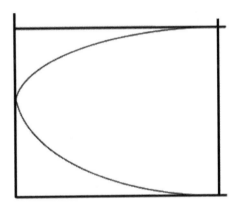

Figure 13.12 Split directions.

in Figure 13.11 might be appropriate, or perhaps the "duotonic" curve in Figure 13.12 fits best. This might imply, for example, that, depending on the total amount of time already expended in training, more could either help (top curve) or hinder (bottom curve).

The point here is that a variety of equation forms, each of which covers the range, might fit a given situation.

Any decent coach also would be checking into some other features of the performance rating system, as in Table 13.7.

TABLE 13.7   Some Questions about a Performance Rating System

(1) Is the measure *reliable*, that is, is the same level of performance getting the same score each time?

(2) Is the measure *accurate*? Is one judge giving a dismount fall deduction if just a knee hits the ground while another gives it only when the whole body does?

(3) What level of *precision* is employed? Is the rating given as "between 4 and 8" or as "7.934582152"? Most people would agree that the former is not specific enough and the latter is far more detailed than is warranted.

14

Step 7. Forecasting

In the last step in the QCQ process the selected system of relationships is employed to make forecasts of goal and other variable levels over the horizon period (identified in Stage 1). These forecasts are made with respect to a set of scenarios involving different levels for the strategy variables and possibly different levels of external variables. The results from these exercises give the client a feel for the likely range of impacts of the strategies on the relevant goals under different circumstances.

If there are no or very few quantitative variables in the situation under study, that still does not mean that nothing can be done to understand it and make some forecasts of value. After all, most of the world runs in this mode every day.

14.1 Develop Scenarios

The initial step in this stage is to create one or more scenarios. If the model is a dynamic one, QCQ starts the scenario building process by asking for the number of time increments in the future to be covered by the forecast.

Supernumerary Intelligence, pages 221–228
Copyright © 2015 by Information Age Publishing
All rights of reproduction in any form reserved.

Usually the response will be in concert with the time horizon specified in QCQ Step 1. In the AIRPOL case the horizon was set at the year 2020 and the data went up to 2010 (except for the APE, which was already known to 2012). The number of time increments thus was set by DCCS for 10.

The next step was to create a "null" or "no change" alternative—one where the client strategy variables are set to 0. This provides a datum by which other, alternate scenarios can be compared. If there are no external (from data) variables, the "blank slate" scenario also *is* the "null." Otherwise, forecast data from the outside source is obtained and entered in the appropriate locations.

DCCS now set up a fully operational, Excel®-compatible spreadsheet (Table 14.1) using the null scenario equations and values. The variables were listed across the top and the 10 columns (for the 10 forecast years) were added to the data rows at the bottom. Note that the year 2010 was coded as the 35th year of data since such started in 1975.

Entry and editing of scenario values and equations was carried out in the same manner as for any spreadsheet.

The "null" alternative new runs (Table 14.1) consisted of entries of 0's (for $0 Billion) in the eight cells (B15 to B22) representing no added federal funds for air pollution projects in the years 2013 to 2020. Just one alternate scenario was investigated (Table 14.2): that with additional air pollution control expenditures of $5 billion in each and every year during the same period.

TABLE 14.1 Spreadsheet with Null Alternative Data and Results

	A	B	C	D	E	F	G	H	I	J	K	L
1	Obs Name	APE	COC	COE	FBPS	FPE	GDPPC	PE	POP	VMT	YEAR	TECHNOL
2	2000	0.9	3.4	50	1	7.2	33746	8.1	282.2	2.748	25	
3	2001	0.7	3.2	49	1.2	7.4	35080	8.1	285	2.776	26	
4	2002	0	2.9	48	1.3	7.5	35102	2.5	287.6	2.851	27	
5	2003	0	2.7	47	0.9	8	35405	8	290.1	2.882	28	
6	2004	0	2.5	46	1	8.3	35976	8.3	292.8	3.01	29	
7	2005	0.2	2.3	45	0.8	7.9	36920	8.1	295.5	3.031	30	1.649621
8	2006	0	2.2	44	0.7	8.3	37701	8.3	298.4	2.964	31	1.68691
9	2007	0	2	42	0.9	8.3	38341	8.3	301.2	2.959	32	2.027712
10	2008	0.6	1.9	43	0.7	7.9	38699	8.5	304.1	2.964	33	1.349528
11	2009	0.4	1.8	43	0.6	8.1	38336	8.5	306.8	2.93	34	1.023891
12	2010	0.5	1.8	42	0.5	11	36676	11.5	309.3	2.945	35	1.018676
13	2011	0.5	1.930396	41	0.7	10.8	37330	11.3	311.6	2.946	36	1.01833
14	2012	0.5	1.941783	38.81274	0.6	7.864989	37691	8.364989	313.9	2.950015	37	1.080422
15	2013	0	1.822765	34.75753	0.691885	8.409208	40163.6	8.409208	316.714	3.108627	38	2.651481
16	2014	0	1.785061	33.91595	0.670665	8.530087	40712.8	8.530087	319.467	3.164421	39	2.870682
17	2015	0	1.723405	33.09475	0.650096	8.650966	41262	8.650966	322.22	3.220996	40	2.764749
18	2016	0	1.664741	32.29343	0.630158	8.771845	41811.2	8.771845	324.973	3.278362	41	2.655767
19	2017	0	1.582844	31.51152	0.610831	8.892724	42360.4	8.892724	327.726	3.336528	42	2.188268
20	2018	0	1.469047	30.74854	0.592097	9.013603	42909.6	9.013603	330.479	3.395505	43	1.180678
21	2019	0	1.425662	30.00403	0.573937	9.134482	43458.8	9.134482	333.232	3.455303	44	1.132152
22	2020	0	1.384516	29.27754	0.556335	9.255361	44008	9.255361	335.985	3.515934	45	1.085689

TABLE 14.2   Spreadsheet with Scenario of APE = $5 B/Yr (2013 to 2020)

	A	B	C	D	E	F	G	H	I	J	K	L
1	Obs Name	APE	COC	COE	FBPS	FPE	GDPPC	PE	POP	VMT	YEAR	TECHNOL
2	2000	0.9	3.4	50	1	7.2	33748	8.1	282.2	2.748	25	
3	2001	0.7	3.2	49	1.2	7.4	35080	8.1	285	2.776	26	
4	2002	0	2.9	48	1.3	7.5	35102	2.5	287.6	2.851	27	
5	2003	0	2.7	47	0.9	8	35405	8	290.1	2.882	28	
6	2004	0	2.5	46	1	8.3	35976	8.3	292.8	3.01	29	
7	2005	0.2	2.3	45	0.8	7.9	36920	8.1	295.5	3.031	30	1.649621
8	2006	0	2.2	44	0.7	8.3	37701	8.3	298.4	2.964	31	1.68691
9	2007	0	2	42	0.9	8.3	38341	8.3	301.2	2.959	32	2.027712
10	2008	0.6	1.9	43	0.7	7.9	38699	8.5	304.1	2.964	33	1.349528
11	2009	0.4	1.8	43	0.6	8.1	38336	8.5	306.8	2.93	34	1.023891
12	2010	0.5	1.8	42	0.5	11	36676	11.5	309.3	2.945	35	1.018676
13	2011	0.5	1.930396	41	0.7	10.8	37330	11.3	311.6	2.946	36	1.01833
14	2012	0.5	1.941783	38.81274	0.6	7.864989	37691	8.364989	313.9	2.950015	37	1.080422
15	2013	5	1.602964	34.75753	0.691885	8.409208	40163.6	13.40921	316.714	3.108627	38	2.651481
16	2014	5	1.569807	33.91595	0.670665	8.530087	40712.8	13.53009	319.467	3.164421	39	2.870682
17	2015	5	1.515586	33.09475	0.650096	8.650096	41262	13.65097	322.22	3.220996	40	2.764749
18	2016	5	1.463996	32.29343	0.630158	8.771845	41811.2	13.77185	324.973	3.278362	41	2.655767
19	2017	5	1.391975	31.51152	0.610831	8.892724	42360.4	13.89272	327.726	3.336528	42	2.188268
20	2018	5	1.2919	30.74854	0.592097	9.013603	42909.6	14.0136	330.479	3.395505	43	1.180678
21	2019	5	1.253747	30.00408	0.573937	9.134482	43458.8	14.13448	333.232	3.455303	44	1.132152
22	2020	5	1.217562	29.27754	0.556335	9.255361	44008	14.25536	335.985	3.515934	45	1.085689

14.2   Make Forecasts

The final task in QCQ is to make forecasts. This is done by employing the "what if" scenarios created in the preceding section. For perspective, both alternatives had the GDPPC growing from $40,163 to $44,008. But, because of preceding technologic history, the null alternative started with a COC of 1.82 ppm compared to 1.60 ppm. The horizon year (2020) comparison was calculated as 1.38 in the null alternative versus 1.22 for the $5 billion per year investment.

The preceding results can be employed to highlight some policy considerations. For example, the client can wonder if spending an extra $40 billion over 10 years to reduce COC from 1.60 to only 1.22 ppm is really worthwhile. This also assumes a moderate economy (reflected in the GDP-PC) does about expected, COC levels will drop, perhaps more than from the impact of additional pollution control expenditures. So one possible policy is to focus on improving the economy, with COC concentrations being taken care of "automatically."

Of course, recognition must be given to the possible forecasting errors involved. The COC equation, when calibrated, had a rather large MAPE of 37.1% (see QCQ Step 6). And this did not include any sampling errors in obtaining the COC data (see QCQ Step 4) or any forecast errors in the *independent* variables (PE and CO/VMT; see QCQ Step 5 again). One of the benefits of QCQ at this point is to be able to quickly access this type of information to help in the interpretation of the forecasts.

14.3   Use Qualitative Models

We concluded the previous chapter by pointing to some possible ways to use quantitative and qualitative models in concert. To see this, let us return to Figure 13.6 in the previous chapter. As noted, this was constructed more for interest purposes than for use. Still, parts of it can relate.

Suppose DCCS were interested in adding some assurance to the forecasts generated for COC. They look back at what may loosely be called a qualitative "model" in Figure 13.6. Some variables in that model can be ignored as not relevant—for example, those four on the right. In addition, we are not dealing with "infrastructure," so that eliminates two more. And we are not interested at this time in being involved in a whole new legal concept ("denaturalization").

Now, since (to bring out a scenario) sequestration was starting to take effect, this means that most managers will be worrying about their future and that of their office, which naturally will detract to some degree from attention to the programs. Maybe, then, a few small but less favorable court decisions might occur and public attention to health might slip a notch. All these events and outcomes are speculative, but the net upshot may be a somewhat noticeable rise in COC from the estimated 2020 level (with 2013 to 2020 APE's = 0 because of efforts to reduce the national budget) of 1.38 ppm to about the 1.5 ppm level.

It might also be reported that the concept of "sequester" has become clearer and maybe raised it to the "Know:Know" status.

14.4   Recapitulation

The "bottom line" for QCQ is its ability to make forecasts under different scenarios while at the same time bringing out a richness of associated qualities. Certainly these end-point capabilities are nothing new, but QCQ, through its spreadsheet feature, can do it very easily and quickly. Complicated scenarios, perhaps involving *sets* of new equations to replicate client strategies, can be developed, entered, and edited with very little effort. Similarly, variations in external conditions can be tested quickly as contingency cases. Then the whole setup can be assessed from both qualitative and quantitative points of view.

This speed and flexibility gives the user the opportunity to test out a wide set of alternatives as well as to go into them in more depth.

14.5   An Expanded Learning Case: The Hamurabi Game

Continuing with the investigation of potential drawbacks of regression, we find it may not represent the actual dynamics of the phenomena under observation. This can be demonstrated with a version of a relatively simple game called "Hammurabi," named after the ruler of ancient Sumeria. His job each year is to decide how many bushels of some unspecified crop (the medium of exchange) to spend on land purchases (or sales), seed for planting, food for the population, and storage for future use. These decisions result in different levels of population, bushels in storage, acres of land, and price of land in the kingdom.

Suppose Hammurabi wanted to develop an equation to forecast next year's population (POPACT) as a function of some of his decisions. One possibility—a multiple linear regression—is:

$$POPACT = 48.08 + 5.052*BISEST - 5.123*BUSHPOP +$$

$$16.47*BSHSEED \qquad (14.1)$$

where:

>   BISEST = Estimated (by Hammurabi) number of bushels in storage (1000's) at the beginning of a given year.

>   BUSHPOP = Number of bushels (1000's) used to feed the population during a given year.

>   BSHSEED = Number of bushels (1000's) used to make seed for planting in a given year.

The R^2 for this equation is 0.66, while the MAPE is 8.1%. These are tolerable, although not great values.

But does this equation represent in any way what "really" happens in Sumeria? The answer (from us, the game's programmers) is "definitely not!"

The first reason goes directly to the negative sign for BUSHPOP. Certainly, throughout the game, if people are fed more, then (all other things being equal) they will *increase* in number.

But the situation is much more complex than that. The schematic in Figure 14.1 helps to explain why. Each year, as brought out above, Hammurabi has to make decisions about the expenditure of bushels. These decisions are to be implemented by the administrators in Sumeria. However, for various reasons, they are not carried out exactly as requested (with random deviations reflecting these variations).

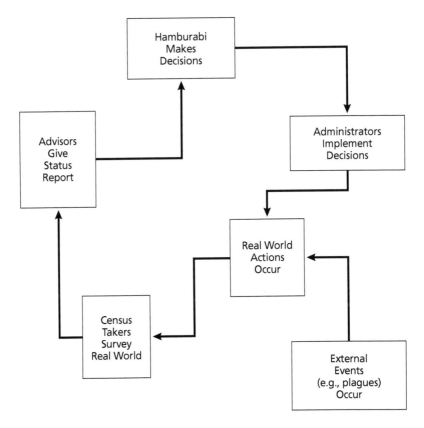

Figure 14.1 Flow chart of basic actions in Hammurabi game.

Next, the "real world" responds. It does not act exactly as expected (additional random deviations). Plus, on occasions, there are plagues that wipe out half the population and rat infestations that reduce the crop harvest and/or the amount of bushels left in storage. People also can starve if there is not enough food per capita, and they can migrate in and out of Sumeria depending on how well the economy (represented by the price of land, in bushels per acre) is doing.

Census takers survey the results, but they have to use samples, which may not represent the real world accurately (more random variation). They then give their tallies to Hammurabi's advisors, who may make certain political "adjustments" (more random variations) before presenting the results to him. Hammurabi knows this process is going on, but not the exact extent. So he has to make his own private estimates (more decisions) of, say, the population level in order to proceed with the allocation of bushels.

As now can be appreciated, Equation 14.1 reflects almost none of these factors and interrelationships directly. For example, there is nothing about starvation or migration, much less plagues or rat infestations. The regression equation thus is just a fairly crude kind of overview of a complicated situation.

The Hammurabi game demonstrates that regression may not represent the actual phenomena under observation. But a *combination* of systems dynamics and regression may help considerably in overcoming this problem.

One approach to employing these together can be exemplified with the aid of the flow chart in Figure 14.1. Assuming this schematic represents the sequence of events in Sumeria's "real world" and that this chain is *known* to Hammurabi's analysts (which it should be), then an equation should be developed for each stage in the chain.

For population forecasts, for instance, the first stage ("Administrators implement decisions") would be represented by:

$$POPAID(t) = POPEST(t) + RNDAID(t) \tag{14.2}$$

where:

> $POPAID(t)$ = Population at time (year) t after "Administrators implement decisions."
>
> $POPEST(t)$ = Hammurabi's estimate of population at time t.
>
> $RNDAID(t)$ = Random deviation (+ or −) from "Administrators implement decisions."

followed by the "real world" (RW) actions where population changes owing to births, deaths, and in and out migration:

$$POPRW(t) = POPRW(t\text{-}1) + BIRTHS(t\text{-}1) + DEATHS(t\text{-}1) +$$
$$MIGRATE(t\text{-}1) \tag{14.3}$$

where:

> $POPRW(t)$ = Actual population at time t.
>
> $BIRTHS(t)$ = Births during the period from t to t + 1.
>
> $DEATHS(t)$ = Deaths during the period from t to t + 1.
>
> $MIGRATE(t)$ = Migration (+ or −) during the period from t to t + 1.

Relationships now can be developed for each of the latter three variables. By way of illustration, the number of deaths might depend on the number of bushels used to feed the population (BUSHPOP(t)) and on any external "shocks" (like a plague; SHOCK(t)) during a time period:

$$DEATHS(t) = f(BUSHPOP(t\text{-}1), SHOCK(t\text{-}1)) \qquad (14.4)$$

This equation would be established via regression.

Similar thinking would hold for development of relationships for the actions of census takers and advisors. Eventually the loop would get back to Hammurabi, who would have to estimate the population for the *next* time period (POPEST(t+1)). This would feed back into Equation 14.2 and to a new round through the preceding equations.

The net impact of all this effort is a dynamic simulation of events that is much closer to the way the "real world" works than any single regression equation.

15

The Public Administration Genome Project (PAGP)

So far we have barely mentioned the PAGP, yet we made proportionally more of it in the first three (introductory) chapters. Basically, we did not want to muddle the picture of QCQ, which can be complicated enough. But now we will bring in the PAGP, with the immediate statement that it can be used beneficially in just about any of the seven QCQ steps (see Figure 15.1).

15.1   Introduction

Perhaps the easiest way to open a window into the Public Administration Genome Project (PAGP) (Dickey, 2009) is simply to list the most basic questions:

Supernumerary Intelligence, pages 229–241
Copyright © 2015 by Information Age Publishing
All rights of reproduction in any form reserved.

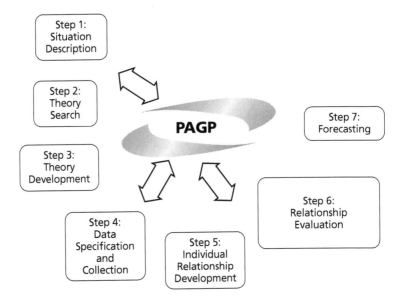

Figure 15.1 The PAGP can be of assistance in any QCQ step.

15.1.1 What Exactly Is the PAGP?

It is an attempt to digitally "map" and then usefully employ the full set of topics, variables, and interrelationships that comprise all the matters that make up public administration (PA).

15.1.2 Where Did the Name Come From?

It was based on the highly regarded and useful Human Genome Project—the effort to identify and codify 35,000 or so genes in our DNA that control a significant proportion of the structure and behavior of our life, as well as our inheritance.

15.1.3 Why Do It?

Few would deny that the PA world—like the world in general—is becoming more and more complicated. Plus, no interested person could possibly know, much less remember, the many strategies, external forces, and their interconnected impacts that might apply in a particular situation. Hence there is a need for a comprehensive, logical, readily available system to help in finding and elaborating on such topics, variables, and interrelationships.

Such a system is intended to provide a more rational and scientific approach to PA and, as a result, further enhance the field's impact on public health, security, and welfare.

15.1.4   How Does It Work?

Contributors from around the world submit source cases in a partially structured, systematic format (See Table 15.1). The cases are placed into a web database known as COMPASS (COMprehensive PA Support System). This can be modified in a collaborative way. Users subsequently can do searches for topics, variables, and relationships relevant to their situation.

15.1.5   Where Do Things Stand Now?

There currently are about 82 cases, 66 of which are on the web. These include one on planning of a new "cyber city" in Malaysia and another one on the possibility of implementing an urban congestion pricing scheme in Korea. The three large cases in the succeeding three chapters also are included. The full set of cases presently envelops about 14,000 variables and 15,000 relationships. The former translates into about 5,000 unique one-word PA topics.

TABLE 15.1   A Sample of Other PAGP Cases

Abandonment Theory
   (9 variables, 11 relations, 239 categories)
Agency Planning/Implementation Process
   (47 variables, 53 relations, 239 categories)
Bus System Reform
   (333 variables, 387 relations, 148 categories)
Carrier Conceptual Knowledge
   (30 variables, 81 relations, 239 categories)
Child Day Care Subsidy
   (354 variables, 898 relations, 23 categories)
Information Technology Implementation
   (914 variables, 342 relations, 82 categories)
Institutional Analysis/Development Theory
   (272 variables, 254 relations, 19 categories)
Korean Constitution
   (282 variables, 0 relations, 61 categories)
Impacts in the Aftermath of Hurricanes Katrina, Rita, and Wilma
   (1,903 variables, 2,039 relations, 36 categories)

15.1.6   How Is It Being Used Now?

While historic cases continue to come in, the emphasis has changed somewhat to using them to help build policies, strategies, and research theories. Another frequent use is for general ideation for management decisions. Note that many people (including ourselves) thought that, for these kind of activities to be successful, it would take a much larger data set. But that does not seem to be the situation so far.

15.1.7   Who Would Be Interested?

Public administrators, of course. But also consultants, researchers, teachers, students, and interested citizens.

15.1.8   More Information? [INT-14 PAGP Front Page]

A fuller but still brief explanation can be seen at http://pagenome-compass.pbworks.com. A partial list of cases is presented in [INT-13 Case List]. One of those on that list is a particularly intriguing illustration of government funding of some charities during Hurricane Katrina in 2005 [INT-15 Hurricane Katrina case] where management of governmental donations is important.

15.2   Building and Contributing to a Case

A "case" is essentially the same as a product of the seven-step QCQ process, whose inputs and outputs have been described in the preceding chapters. Most cases are too big and broad to have a significant quantitative side to them. But they still can have causal aspects (see Appendix D), which can be saved and utilized beneficially in an organized fashion. The format should be something similar to the output displayed in Table 9.1 and redisplayed with additions below.

Equations can be listed below, while introductions, cause and effect diagrams, a glossary, references, URL's, and other material (definitions, histories, and the like) usually are put on top.

Needless to say, things can become mighty complex when, as in the "Hurricanes" case listed in Table 15.1, there are close to 2,000 variables and above that number of bivariate relations. It takes about 96 single-spaced pages just to print out the associated model in a form like Table 15.2.

While not quite on that scale, but still large is the case on "Institutional Analysis and Development Theory" (IAD). This Nobel Prize winning theory

TABLE 15.2 Example Main Inputs and Outputs for a PAGP Case

VARIABLES ALONG WITH INFLUENCES
===

CASE: Airpolly — Update 2010-2020 vs. Time Ver2 Corrected

DATE: 03-09-2013 TIME: 23:21:23
===

ID CODE and DESCRIPTION (Subject and Action/Status)
===

UNSPECIFIED VARIABLES

(None)

,,,

CLIENT STRATEGY VARIABLES
----

* 1* APE Add'l Fed Pollution Control Expenditures

,,,

TIME CLOCK VARIABLE
----

* 3* YEAR Time (Since 1975)

,,,

INTERMEDIATE VARIABLES
----

* 1* COE Carbon Monoxide Emissions per Year
    {–}[t](0) GDPPC Gross Domestic Product Per Capita
* 1* FPE Con't Fed Pollution Control Expenditures
    {+}[t](0) GDPPC Gross Domestic Product Per Capita
* 1* PE Tot Fed Pollution Control Expenditures
    {+}[t–2](0) APE Add'l Fed Pollution Control Expenditures
    {+}[t](0) FPE Con't Fed Pollution Control Expenditures
* 1* VMT Vehicle Miles of Travel
    {+}[t](0) GDPPC Gross Domestic Product Per Capita
    {+}[t](0) POP Population

,,,

GOAL VARIABLES
----

* 0* COC Carbon Monoxide Concentration
    {+}[t](0) COE Carbon Monoxide Emissions Per Year
    {–}[t–2](0) PE Tot Fed Pollution Control Expenditures
    <C> FBPS Federal Budgetary Process Speedup
    {–}[t]] (0) VMT Vehicle Miles of Travel

,,,

RE/PRE ACTION TIME VARIABLES
----

* 0* FBPS Federal Budgetary Process Speedup
    {–}[t](0) YEAR Time (Since 1975)

,,,

(continued)

TABLE 15.2   Example Main Inputs and Outputs for a PAGP Case (cont.)

EXTERNAL [f(Time)] VARIABLES

----

* 3* GDPPC Gross Domestic Product Per Capita

    {+}[t](0) YEAR Time (Since 1975)

* 1* POP Population

    {+}[t](0) YEAR Time (Since 1975)

,,,

EXTERNAL [Data] VARIABLES

Note: Legend:

    xx Number of Other Variables Directly Influenced by that Variable

    {xx} Type of Relationship (e.g., {+ } is Monotonically Increasing)

    [xx] Time Relationship (e.g., [t–2] is a Delay of 2 Time Periods)

    (xx) Number of Cause-Effect Questions Answered Positively (Out of 6)

    <C> Catalyst (Affects the Reaction Time of the Relationship)

contained, at least by our determination, 272 variables and 254 bivariate relations. These kind of numbers make the theory even richer than might have been expected, a finding that creates a real puzzle over how well any theory "fits" a particular situation. Does it "fit," for instance, if only, say, 50% of the variables seem to be present in the particular situation? Maybe the missing 50% are quite contrary. In particular, the nature of the external forces in play may be quite relevant here because they would seem to represent the most potent reality of most scenarios.

15.3   Views of a Case

In the PAGP there actually are at least four ways of viewing a case:

1. Causal diagram,
2. List of variables,
3. Groups of variables, and
4. List of variables with associated relations.

The first has been mentioned previously in this book, but also is demonstrated in Figure 15.2. This comes from a case dealing with a high level observation and description of public ethics as documented by Reginald Shareef (2010). The oblong variables at the top are strategies (e.g., Leader Determination: Agency Outcomes); the rectangular, black boxes are external factors (e.g., Turbulent Environments); the black and white rectangular boxes are intermediate variables (e.g., Participative Work Culture); and finally the beveled-cornered boxes are goal variables (e.g., Unethical Public Management). So, as one example, if the public manager strives for an

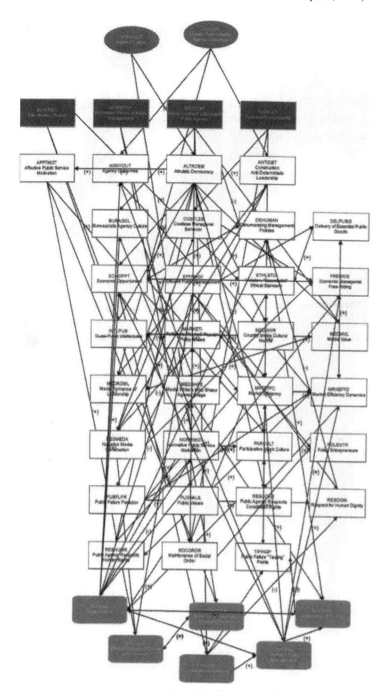

Figure 15.2 High level dynamics of public ethics.

ethical set of outcomes from those in his line of responsibility, one type of action would be to set up a participative work environment.

A "list of variables" view usually is associated with situations in which such a listing is the most that reasonably can be extracted from the case at hand. Usually these come when there is an exhausting amount of work involved just in seeking out all the relevant variables. One example would be in summarizing a long book or article. As may be seen, we work on the principle that something worthwhile can arise even from, say, a book index.

The third way to fashion a case, or a section therefrom, is to break the variables into categories. In other words, create a classification system (ontology) and assign the variables accordingly. The PAGP has its own ontology [INT-16 PAGP Ontology], and contributors are encouraged to use that one for consistency purposes. Or they can make up their own and probably be more specific. In either situation the users, say DCCS, can leaf through or do a formal search on the selected case database and pick out the relevant variables.

To illustrate, a clipping of categories and associated entries out of the "Agency Planning and Implementation Process" case (undertaken by senior representatives of social work departments in four California counties) would look something like that in Table 15.3. Most of the variables captured in this chart probably would be good to acquire for the new case being developed.

The last way to search the PAGP (that is, COMPASS) is through the "Variables in Relations" database. This is like finding a particular matching variable of interest, then following it "down" the cause and effect tree

---

TABLE 15.3 Two Groups of Variables in Categories from a Matching Case

Analysis/Research:

BCANALY Do Benefit/Cost Analysis
DISSECT Dissect the Planning (BPR) Document
PREVIEW In-Depth Preview: Planning (BPR) Document
SUCSTRY Research "Success Stories"; Get Examples
SURVEY Do Survey to Determine Potential Usage
,,,

...

Communication:

CONNECT Connect with other Agencies/CBOs/Clients
MONGER Find a Good Facilitator/Power Monger
PRESHCK Develop "Pre-Shock" Communication
SIGNOFF Get Signoffs

to see what some of the "affecting" variables might be. This activity can be followed by a sojourn "up" the tree to see what some of the "affected" variables might be. In this manner the user of the PAGP may be able see new paths, with more leads to desired goals and/or ends.

Now take, for instance, the above ethics story in which Shareef's manager is trying to set up an agency that produces ethically responsible outcomes in its endeavors (see the goal UNETHIC, and think in opposite terms). She notices that UNETHIC is tied to FRERIDE (upper right of diagram)—where managers are getting a lot of free or low cost labor and products from suppliers in exchange for contributions to various campaign funds. While this may be legal, it is bordering on the unethical, and might be so if these suppliers "call in" their favors for, say, getting undercover favors in obtaining future contracts.

15.4   Using the PAGP

It might have noticed that while we were describing QCQ and PAGP capabilities, we (DCCS) also were starting to put together a basic strategic plan of sorts for the Agency Head, employees, and DCCS. This plan will be focused mainly on one aspect of ethics: getting appropriate, desirable outcomes from the agency's activities. To this point, then, and to simplify greatly, we see the plan being created by DCCS as having a broad goal of "having suppliers refrain from calling in favors (e.g., in future road paving contracts), which surely would be a major influence on "Appropriate Agency Activity Outcomes."

But how to influence suppliers *not* to call in favors? A search through the PAGP's cases for ideas now is undertaken. In addition, the PAGP is called upon to make available its basic strategic planning process to help create a first-cut plan.

The PAGP planning Assistant has five steps, starting with "identifying the main issue" and ending with "combining selected variables and relationships to make the plan." Emphasis is given to the man/machine interaction in generating useful ideas.

Step 1. Identify client and summarize the main issue/problem/opportunity (IPO).
  – (See Chapter 4)
  – Client: Agency head
  – IPO (Opportunity): Have Suppliers *Not* Call in Favors
Step 2. Provide background and detail by dimensions.
  – (See Chapters 4, 5)

- DCCS recorded agency's background: Governmental supply agency.

Step 3. Identify single key words that describe the IPO.
- Go to PAGP Ontology (Classification) and pick two to three words.
- DCCS went to Sidebar (lower right of screen), clicked "Ontology."
- DCCS picked: corruption, equity, and bargain.

Step 4. Do a search of ComPASS for matching variables (ideas) and associated relations.
- Return to main PAGP page and select View.
- DCCS returned to main PAGP page, selected "Variables in Relationships" view.
- Put a word (or better, a word stem) in the upper right search box and press enter.
- DCCS selected "Corrupt"—got matches in four different cases.
- Select a case with a match and hit "Enter" to go to first page.
- DCCS selected the "...Katrina..." case, hit "Enter," and was taken to the top of the case.
- Press Ctrl-f and Enter search word (again) to find the matches *within* the case.

Step 5. Combine relevant variables (as ideas) and relations to form a first-cut strategic plan.
- DCCS now lists (Table 15.4, in search dialog result form) a few possibly relevant variables and some of their matches from the search in the "Katrina" case associated with the word "corrupt" (10 matches found). These matches can find "corrupt" in up to three conditions:
  1. In its own isolated variable (e.g., in CORRUPT Corrupt Government);
  2. As part of a variable that *is affected by* another (e.g., HISTCOR by FRAUDCT);
  3. As part of a variable that *affects* another (e.g., $GRAB by PLCORRT).

With this kind of connectivity, the spread of factors having an influence on the aim can become quite large—and quite a rich playground for ideas.

The story continues on, with the DCCS and agency players brainstorming over any or all of the ways they can use these "chunks" of knowledge toward improving on the aim. Most ideas are accepted initially, then many are eliminated as it becomes obvious they may not be all that helpful.

TABLE 15.4   Possibly Relevant Search Hits

* 2* HISTCOR History of *Corruption*: State/Local Govern
  FRAUDCT Fraud is in Culture of State/Locality

* 2* PLCORRT Locality National Politician Found *Corrupt*
  UNDERIN Politician under Investigation for Bribery

* 1* $GRAB Bid to Grab as Much Possible Federal Funds
  $NGOLFT Relief Donation Funds Left for Recovery
  PLANUSE Governor Outlines Plans for Disaster Funds
  PLCORRT Locality National Politician Found *Corrupt*
  SHORTCG State Feels Short Changed: Federal Funding
  TAXFUND Taxpayer Funds Involved in Finance Scheme

1 ATTNDIV Attention of Federal Government Diverted
  PLCORRT Locality National Politician Found *Corrupt*

* 1* CORRUPT *Corrupt* Government

* 2* PLCORRT Locality National Politician Found *Corrupt*

* 1* SCHCTRL Schools Under State Control (Not Locality)
  CORRUPT *Corrupt* Government
  GOVWSTE Government Waste

* 1* FRAUDCT *Fraud* is in Culture of State/Locality

Note: The number between asterisks before a variable is how many other variables it affects.

Suppose, for instance, that the variable "UNDERIN Politician under Investigation for Bribery" clicks as a basis for an idea like "INVESTP Form an Investigative Panel," with a second idea relating to the area under investigation: "CORRESI Investigate Intra-Agency Correspondence." Such an investigation, even if nothing of worth arose, most likely would put everyone on guard and make it very difficult for "Suppliers to Call in Favors." Also, it might be prudent to "(MONGER) Find a Good Facilitator/Power Monger," because the politics could get nasty.

All of the preceding considerations, plus a few more, have been captured in Table 15.5. This forms an outline for a basic strategic plan.

15.5   Recapitulation

As maybe the reader can tell, the above example could be expanded quite a bit more and become fairly complex. For starters, no connections have been made yet to the rather complicated but still very generic Figure 15.1. The output of an exercise using the PAGP thus can be very lengthy. But it also can be very concise and to the point, as demonstrated in Chapter 6. Under these conditions it is possible, and perhaps useful, to bring the PAGP

TABLE 15.5   Some Illustrative Inputs and Outputs for a Hypothetical Ethics Case

VARIABLES ALONG WITH INFLUENCES

===

CASE: Ethical Activities

DATE: 08-17-2013 TIME: 7:21:23

===

ID C and DESCRIPTION (Subject and Action/Status)

===

,,,

CLIENT STRATEGY VARIABLES

   INVESTP Form an Investigative Panel

   MONGER Find a Good Facilitator/Power Monger

   CORRESI Investigate Interagency Correspondence

,,,

TIME CLOCK VARIABLE

   YEAR Time (Since 2000)

,,,

INTERMEDIATE VARIABLES

   SHORTCG State Feels Short Changed: Federal Funding

      INVESTP Form an Investigative Panel

      MONGER Find a Good Facilitator/Power Monger

      SUPPLRS Suppliers Do Not Call in Favors

      GAAAO Get Appropriate Agency Activity Outcomes

,,,

GOAL VARIABLES

===

   SUPPLRS Suppliers Do Not Call in Favors

      INVESTP Form an Investigative Panel

      MONGER Find a Good Facilitator/Power Monger

   $NGOLFT Relief Donation Funds Left for Recovery

      HISTCOR History of Corruption: State/Local Govern

      PLANUSE Governor Outlines Plans for Disaster Funds

      PLCORRT Locality National Politician Found Corrupt

      SHORTCG State Feels Short Changed: Federal Funding

      TAXFUND Taxpayer Funds Involved in Finance Scheme

   GAAAO Get Appropriate Agency Activity Outcomes

      INVESTP Form an Investigative Panel

      MONGER Find a Good Facilitator/Power Monger

      SUPPLRS Suppliers Do Not Call in Favors

,,,

(continued)

TABLE 15.5   Some Illustrative Inputs and Outputs for a Hypothetical Ethics Case (continued)

EXTERNAL VARIABLES

HISTCOR History of Corruption: State/Local Govern
PLANUSE Governor Outlines Plans for Disaster Funds
PLCORRT Locality National Politician Found Corrupt
SHORTCG State Feels Short Changed: Federal Funding
TAXFUND Taxpayer Funds Involved in Finance Scheme

into action in several places in the QCQ process. The two entities thus can be seriously intertwined. Furthermore, the cases using QCQ alone or in conjunction with the PAGP make good candidates for cases to be put back into the PAGP.

16

Major Case

Preparing Tomorrow's Teachers for Technology

So far we have dealt mainly with small cases, particularly those that were amenable to quantification. Now, in this chapter we will dig into larger cases where quantification is limited if not impossible, primarily because of the effort involved, lack of data, and inability to define precisely what is meant by some identified variables and relationships.

16.1   U.S. Department of Education: Preparing Tomorrow's Teachers for Technology (PT3) Program

The first large case has to do with a program of the U.S. Department of Education [INT-22 PT-3 Program] known as PT3 (Preparing Tomorrow's Teachers for Technology) (2006). The purpose of this nationwide endeavor was to provide funding to a wide variety and large number of colleges and universities to help them bring more computer technology into their teacher education programs. One of the larger recipients was the University of West Georgia, which proposed and carried out an effort called "Project InSight." This involved 10

Supernumerary Intelligence, pages 243–253
Copyright © 2015 by Information Age Publishing
All rights of reproduction in any form reserved.

major tasks (that is, "strategies") such as, for examples, faculty technology training, expositions on new technologies, development of a software support center, and adaptation of technologies for "special needs" students.

In an effort to capture as much as possible of the dynamics of the implementation of Project InSight we created nine different types of QCQ conceptual models, which can be divided into three distinct categories:

1. Project InSight itself,
2. Barriers (mostly management-related) to technology infusion, and
3. Learning.

The basic underlying premise that connected these (i.e., the "strategies") was that Project InSight was intended to lead to technology infusion in the pre-service teacher education curriculum, which in turn would lead to improved learning by the pre-service students. Yet certain unanticipated barriers might arise that could stymie Project InSight unless appropriate strategies could be found that would reduce the barriers and add to the likelihood of productive implementation

16.2   Project InSight

The first set of models, as mentioned, was for the project itself. These models were based on the proposal to DoE, except that there were more variables than relationships, so we took the liberty to add more linkages, based on our own experience.

It was intriguing as a result to find 92 variables and 387 relationships. We doubt that many people would have guessed such large numbers. The breakdown by QCQ role looked like:

- Goal Variables: 18
- Client Strategy Variables: 12
- External Variables: 19
- Intermediate Variables: 42
- Time Passage Variable: 1

The 12 strategies included the 10 tasks mentioned above plus "Experimentation: Different Projects/Activities" and "Technology Infusion Strategic Planning." The 18 goals included the obvious ones like "Expanded Technology-Infused Curriculum" and "Meet Formal Tech Standards for Teachers" but also broader ones like "Meet Challenges New Era in Education/Society" and "Quality of Education in Georgia's Rural Schools."

A second model for Project InSight was created mostly as an independent exercise to examine how two people interpreted the same written material—namely the proposal. A comparison showed that the second case had more variables (118 vs. 92) and specifically more strategies (17 vs. 12) and more goals (20 vs. 18). Interestingly, it had fewer than half of the external factors (9 vs. 19). There was, moreover, little overlap between some groups of variables. For example, only six of the 12 strategies in the first case were present in the second. Obviously there can be somewhat different perspectives on a common piece of literature.

16.3   Barriers to Infusion

The DoE asked all grant recipients on its ListServ to identify barriers (which we took to mean constraining variables) they were facing to technology infusion. Dickey extracted about 238 in the public e-mails that went to DoE, and Larkin then identified an astounding 3,958 possible relationships.

Among the 238 variables were 21 goals, 89 client strategies, and 30 external factors. The goals are listed in Table 16.1, and samples from the other two role categories can be found in Tables 16.2 and 16.3, respectively. The goals are broader and more management oriented than those for Project InSight itself. They deal with cost efficiency, effectiveness (e.g., in knowledge acquisition), and equity much more than specific project task accomplishments.

A sample of the strategies, in Table 16.2, gives a good feeling for the variety of possible ideas being implemented around the country. One strategy that stands out is "Training of Students to Teach Teachers Technology." This role reversal obviously is unusual. And of equal obviousness, some teachers will have to swallow hard and grit their teeth to overcome their self-pride. But, according to informal feedback so far, the results have been positive. Maybe it is because this idea may have been combined with "FOOD Provision of Food at 'Persuasion' Events."

The sample from the 30 external variables lends credence to the fact that project managers often are faced with a plethora of factors beyond their control. Some may be immediate and nearby (e.g., "Existence of a 'Natural' Technology Champion"), while others may be far off, both in time and space (e.g., "Extent: Other Countries Leapfrogging USA"). They also may be difficult to predict, as in technology change itself (UNPREDL).

Some results associated with the vast number of bivariate relations are interesting. First, seven influenceable variables had over 100 direct connections affecting them:

TABLE 16.1   Goal-Related Variables in the "PT3 Barriers" Case

ID Name	Description
ACCOUNT	Accountability for Infusion
ACHIEVE	Achievement in the Core Subjects
ADOPT	Adoption of Technology-Infused Learning
BALNCET	Time Balance: in Our Activities and Lives
BARRIER	Extent of Barriers to Change from PT3 Program
BENCOST	Benefit/Cost of Technology Infusion
COMPLY	Compliance with Various Standards
DIGIDIV	Extent of "Digital Divide"
DISTRLN	Amount of Distributed PS Learning
EXCITE	Faculty Excited About Technology
FACKNTI	Faculty Knowledge: Tech Infusion & Learn
INSTTEC	Use of Tech in Mainstream School Instruct
KNOWNEW	Students Create New Knowledge/Approaches
PRODUCT	Teacher as Productive User/Learner of Technology
PSTIISC	Student Knowledge of Technology Infusion Process
RELEVST	Relevance: PS Students to Real World
SKILLSS	Technology Skills Possessed by Students
STUCAP	PS Student Technical Capability
SUSTAIN	Sustaining of Technology Infusion over a Long Time
TECHED	Extent of Technology in Education Programs
TIMETEC	Time Required to Make Tech Change

Note: PS = Pre-Service students

TABLE 16.2   A Sample of Strategy Variables in the "PT3 Barriers" Case

ID Name	Description
* 08* ADAPTAS	Video on Adaptive/Assistive Technologies
* 33* ADVOCTE	Teachers Advocate for Use of Technology
* 19* AGREEMG	Agreement on Mini-Grant Task Completion
* 27* ALIGNST	Alignment: US/State/Prof Org Standards
* 01* ANOMIE	Degree of "Normlessness" in PT3 Transition
* 23* ASESTEC	Use of Technology in Assessment in Schools
* 33* ASSUME	Assume Tech Improvements Self-Evident
* 30* CELEBRT	Celebration of Faculty Tech Successes
* 33* CHAMP	Existence of a "Natural" Tech Champion
* 28* EVALSYS	Evaluation Sys: Detect if Program is Working
* 12* GENWWWY	Training of Students to Teach Teachers Tech

Note: *nn* = Number of variables this variable (strategy) directly affects

TABLE 16.3   Sample of External Variables in the "PT3 Barriers" Case

ID Name	Description
ALIGNST	Alignment: US/State/Professional Organization Standards
AMBIVLE	Ambivalence of Stakeholders toward Technology
ANOMIE	Degree of "Normlessness" in PT3 Transition
ATTITTS	Attitude: Teachers to Learning from Students
BELIEF$	Believed (Perceived) Price of Technology
CENTRAL	Central Administration Provides Infrastructure
ADVOCTE	Teachers Advocate for Use of Technology
CHAMP	Existence of a "Natural" Technology Champion
COMPETE	Strength of Competing Requirements/Tasks
COMPETS	Competition for Students among Educational Entities

- Issues Not Recognized (161)
- Unpredictability of Technological Change (121)
- General Speed of Change in Higher Education (111)
- General Technological Change (111)
- Ambivalence of Stakeholders toward Tech (114)
- Unpredictability of Response to Initiatives (109)
- Faculty—Level of Interpersonal Conflicts (103)

while, in contrast, three had fewer than five:

- Demand for IT Resources (3)
- Demand for Technology-Proficient Teachers (3)
- Extent of Digital Divide (4)

The first one of the first set of seven is particularly interesting. It provides evidence for the need for something like the PAGP. With 238 variables, our case would seem to have covered most of the "waterfront" of issues as compared to the localized situations from which such a variable evolved.

A comparison now can be made. The most exhaustive possible set of relationships would occur if "everything affected everything else." This would have to be adjusted in QCQ since, by definition, a client strategy (variable) is the result of an independent choice and thus is not viewed as being influenced by any other factors. In addition, an external variable, also by definition, is beyond the client's control and therefore is viewed as influencing but not influenceable. These considerations allow us to estimate that there can be about 27,000 possible connections. As a result, the 3,958 identified relations, while quite numerous, represent only about 15% of the maximum number.

16.4 Learning

The third case—dealing with "learning"—was developed from a variety of sources. We started with an elaboration of a textbook by Roblyer and Edwards (2000). This provided 136 variables and 691 relations. A further extension raised these numbers to 209 and 1,038, respectively, based on factors identified from PT3 national conferences talks. We will not go into as much detail on this case as we did for the barriers but will focus on the goals, as shown in Table 16.4.

The first point that is instructive is that there are as many as 24 goals for learning. Most teachers, we suspect, would be surprised that there could be so abundant and diverse objectives, many of which they had been building into their courses without even knowing it (this certainly was our own situation).

TABLE 16.4   Goal-Related Variables in the "Learning" Case

ID Name	Description
COMPLEX	Complexity of Levels of Thought
CONTLRN	Type of Content Learned
CREATIV	Individual Creativity (Creative Potential)
CRITICL	Student Ability: Think Critically About Information
EFFICNC	Efficiency of Learning
GRPWORK	Student Works Well Together in Groups
INFOFND	Student Ability to Find Information
JOBEXPR	Experience for Jobs
JOBPREP	Preparation for Currently Non-Existent Jobs
KNOWQS	Knowing Questions to Ask and How to Ask
LEARNLN	Learning to Learn
METACOG	Student Self-Analysis and Meta-Cognition
OUTSIDE	Creation of "Inert" Knowledge
PACELRN	Pace of Learning
PERSONY	Development of Student's Personality
PROBSLV	Student Ability to Solve Problems
RECALL	Speed of Recall of Skill or Method
SELFEST	Student Self-Esteem and Respect
SHARE	Student Sharing of Responsibility
SPEED	Speed of Learning
STAGESP	Speed in Going through Stages of Development
TEAMWRK	Students Work Together towards Common Goals
TECHPNE	Preparation for Currently Nonexistent Technology
VALUES	Mastery of Inner Values

As an example, one of the goals that attracts attention is "Preparation for Currently Non-Existent Jobs" (JOBPREP). This might lead us to talk about, say, possible new jobs in the animated 3-D graphics industry and how teachers will need to relate to this world via, say, analytic geometry. This possibility not only gives the faculty a better understanding of the needs but also some "hot" Star Wars-like topics for their classes.

16.5   Lessons Learned

The last step was to complete a synopsis of the lessons learned. Many of the lessons learned were theoretical, dealing with such matters as the limitations of the literature in presenting variables and relationships. Still others were fairly practical, dealing with topics like the tradeoff between practitioner depth and academic depth of analysis. The following pages offer a brief summary of the lessons learned.

16.5.1   Lesson 1: Breadth over Depth

Researchers have the luxury of limiting the scope of inquiry and performing in-depth analysis on a topic of interest. The limited nature of the topic being studied also allows the researcher to control or eliminate troublesome variables. Managers, on the other hand, must deal with all the messiness and complexity of real world situations and try to determine the potential impact of a wide range of variables on a desired outcome.

16.5.2   Lesson 2: Variables

A corollary to the breadth over depth paradox is the imprecise nature of certain variables. Many variables in our QCQ model were ill-defined and almost impossible to measure. Users of the model, like managers in the real world, find themselves in the unenviable position of using commonly agreed-upon definitions and metrics as opposed to more precise methods for developing meaning and measurability.

16.5.3   Lesson 3: Sparcity

Explicit connections between variables are sparse if they exist at all. Causal paths, both linear and complex, are difficult to determine. Connections between variables often are subjective determinations made by the analyst. Thus, it is very difficult to estimate the validity of the number, meaning, and usefulness of connections in any given model. Those with few connections may ignore the complexity of a given situation. Models with many connections may provide a fairly accurate representation but exceed the manager's ability to comprehend.

16.5.4   Lesson 4: Extracting

Variables and connections are in the eye of the beholder. Texts often are used to identify variables and connections surrounding a given situation. The number of variables and connections has a strong relationship to the reading strategy the analyst uses to review the work. Slow and detailed readings will identify more variables and connections than faster, cursory passes through the pages.

16.5.5   Lesson 5: Accumulation and Forgetting

The more we delve into a situation, the more likely we are to identify additional variables and connections. Unfortunately, humans have a limited capacity for quickly storing and recalling variables and connections. Categorizations helps; however, it is not a panacea. QCQ is a valuable aid because it provides the analyst and manager with a searchable database of variables, connections, and categories.

16.5.6   Lesson 6: Generality

Large collections of variables, connections, and classifications often lead the analyst to aggregate and generalize about them. In many cases the devil truly is in the detail. Fairly clean individual variables and relationships are often turned into fuzzy generalizations through aggregation.

16.5.7   Lesson 7: Paths

We usually receive more than one possible route when we ask a computerized mapping system to chart a course from point A to point B. The routes may vary slightly in distance between the points and the time required to make the trip; however, they all provide a workable solution to our navigation problem. The same is true when we are seeking out causal relationships between variables in QCQ. There are many possible causal chains between a pair of variables and many ways to make rational connections between them.

16.5.8 Lesson 8: Strength

Not all connections and paths are equal. To illustrate, let us consider two possible logical paths between variable A and E. The first path would be A to B to C to E while the second path would be A to B to D to E. Since we do not know the strength of the connections between A to B, B to C, C to E, B to D, or D to E, we cannot be certain which path represents the most logical connection between A and E.

16.5.9 Lesson 9: Verification

Many of our daily activities are influenced by the confidence *we* have in the strength of a relationship between two variables. We are very confident about the validity of some relationship and less confident about others. For example, we know with a great deal of certainty that touching a hot stove will result in pain and possibly injury. We are much less certain about the connection between a golf lesson and a better performance on the course during our next round. QCQ models provide the analyst with a tool to examine relationships between variables in a much more complex situation than the example of stoves and golf. Various types of information, both qualitative and quantitative, can be used to examine the history of a connection and attach confidence levels to a relationship. Therefore, QCQ is especially helpful in meta-analysis.

16.5.10 Lesson 10: Mind Models

Lesson 9 raises many questions about mind models. Lesson 10 is more a series of questions than a definitive statement. How many mind models do we carry around in our heads? How did we develop these mind models in the first place? How do people fill in information gaps after reading a book, implementing a project, conducting an experiment? How close do the mind models of different individuals have to be to be considered basically the same?

16.5.11 Lesson 11: Connecting Chunks

The term "chunks" is a favorite expression of artificial intelligence (AI) researchers. The AI community uses "chunks" to refer to separate pieces of knowledge. "Domain" is a more formal way of referring to a larger scale version of a chunk. Most real work problems fall into several knowledge domains and provide a daunting challenge regarding information gathering, integration, and connections that lead to a decision or action.

16.5.12 How?

Real work managers face problems that fall into several knowledge domains simultaneously on a daily basis. They are confronted with the task of gathering information from the different domains, integrating the information, making connections, and producing decisions or actions. The manager performs all the aforementioned tasks within the confines of the human mind. How do they accomplish their tasks? More fundamentally, how do we as humans learn and use the knowledge to guide our actions? What role can technology play in the learning process? Can we ever get to know the answers to these questions?

There is an old adage about someone whose original intent was to drain the swamp and suddenly forgot about the initial task once he found himself surrounded by alligators. The original intent of this chapter was to review the use of QCQ as a tool to assist in project evaluation. The introduction of QCQ into the project evaluation process did not cause the evaluators to forget their original task of evaluating the University of West Georgia's PT3 grant performance. Instead, QCQ allowed the evaluators to use the initial task as a springboard to explore larger questions surrounding the use of educational technology and address the ultimate question facing all educators. How do we learn?

The first three assessments were mainly formative, and the fourth assessment was summative. The latter involved a series of "before" tests to establish baseline data to compare to "after" test results. Because of the three-year time frame of this grant, the completion of thorough and accurate impact assessments for each of the ten tasks was impossible. To gain an accurate assessment of each task's "after" impact, the test would have had to be administered for several years.

The overall conclusion of the traditional project evaluation was that Project InSight was a success. Since the time that the PT3 grant was first funded, the use of technology to train teachers has evolved from an afterthought to an integral part of the educational philosophy and organizational culture of the University of West Georgia. It would be unreasonable to assume that Project InSight was the sole cause of the change in attitudes about technology; however, it is perfectly reasonable to assume it was a leading catalyst in bringing about such change.

16.6 Evaluation with Quantitative Cyberquest

The final evaluation of Project InSight involved the use of QCQ to create three categories of conceptual models focusing on the overall impact of technology infusion efforts on implementation and learning. Evaluations of the type outlined below represent a unique new approach to evaluation research. The innovative nature of the work resulted in the evaluators spelling out various aspects of the QCQ evaluation process as part of conferences (see, for example, Dickey and Larkin (2002).

16.7 Recapitulation

This chapter has focused on presenting a major case study that has been developed by taking advantage of QCQ and the Public Administration Genome Project. This first case dealt with technology training for future school teachers. Nine different models were developed, but of particular interest was the one based on the actual implementation problems faced by over 400 colleges nationwide and some of the strategies undertaken to overcome those problems.

17

Major Case

Reorganization of the Seoul Bus System

The second major case to be described is that involved with the substantial reorganization of the Seoul (South Korea) bus system (Kim, Kim, & Dickey, 2007). Let it be known that most of the activities described here are hypothetical and were done about two years after the reorganization as illustrations of the potential uses of QCQ and the PAGP.

17.1 Background

Described here is a new and extraordinary source case and how it has been added to the PAGP. The case has to do with a rare monumental bus system reform effort, as implemented by the Seoul Metropolitan Government (SMG), covering a population of about 20 million people. The reform focused on an integrated approach combining organizational measures (e.g., use of a citizen committee), innovative technology (e.g., new natural gas buses), infrastructure development (e.g., exclusive median lane busways), and substantial changes in transport operations (e.g., new feeder lines).

Supernumerary Intelligence, pages 255–268
Copyright © 2015 by Information Age Publishing
All rights of reproduction in any form reserved.

Kim and Kim were intimately involved with the case and have helped to identify and classify the numerous variables that contributed to (or helped to hinder) the successful implementation of the bus system reform. In addition, they have noted the presumed causal relationships between and among most of these variables. With the help of Dickey they then input this information into the PAGP database.

Note that there currently are 333 variables and even more (387) bivariate relationships in the bus reform case. These, of course, are much too numerous to present here, Hence use will be made at times of a summary of the case, containing 23 variables and 38 relations, to illustrate certain principles.

17.2 Introduction

The summary example mentioned above has been derived from the next four paragraphs, which have been quoted word for word from a report by the Seoul Development Institute (SDI, 2005, pp. 7–8). This has been done here so that the reader can see the exact context for the development of the model.

> Throughout the 1990s, Seoul faced demographic changes that created new transportation demands that Seoul could no longer respond to. These changes in transportation patterns increased private car use, unorganized bus transportation routes and travel. Buses were one the most widely used mode of transportation, but demographic changes devastated the service. The transportation system was in chaos and urged for reform.
>
> The traditional method of piecemeal approaches for the bus system reform no longer worked, as evident in the mid-1990s in Korea. Innovative and intensive reorganization strategies were necessary rather than fragmented approaches. The Public Transportation Reform is a major step toward sustainable mobility. The key of its success lies in an integrated approach combining organizational measures, innovative technology, infrastructure development, and transport operation.
>
> Seoul is one of the rare cities to have implemented such a comprehensive reform in such a short period of time and simultaneously at different levels: construction of median exclusive bus lanes, reorganization of the bus network (categorization of the bus lines into: express lines, trunk lines, feeder lines, and local lines), reform of the institutional framework (contract provision of bus operators and semi-public operation system), integrated multimodal electronic fare system (T-Money), integrated transport operation and information service (TOPIS), compressed natural gas (CNG) buses, car traffic management and enforcement of illegal parking, etc.
>
> The reform has generated many benefits: better efficiency of operation by improved coordination between transport capacities and demand, growing number of passengers leading to increased revenues collected by transport

operators following the launch of the integrated fare system and therefore a decrease of overall transport deficiency and government subsidy, improved traffic conditions for buses, better decision-making process and greater transparency as far as the relationships between operators and the Seoul Metropolitan Government are concerned.

Not mentioned in these paragraphs but important to the description are three items. First, a Bus System Reform Citizen Committee (BSRCC) was created to help make decisions that would lead the reform (Kim & Dickey, 2006). Second, there were significant positive environmental impacts from the transit changes (SDI, 2005). Third, and perhaps most significant, the reform had substantial political backing from the mayor at the time, which was not the case either before or after his tenure in office.

The before and after statistics seem to bear out the positive impacts of the reform. A cross-section can be found in Table 17.1. One negative impact was the quantity of complaints, especially about the transport card and fare system. These numbered 59,871 toward the beginning of implementation (April, 2004) but dropped to just 640 a little over a year later (May, 2005).

17.3   A Case Description

Social science research texts (e.g., Babbie, 2012) present several ways in which case studies can be undertaken and analyzed. As examples, a researcher may decide to question one individual in depth or ask many individuals fewer questions on the same topic. The PAGP accepts both these and other types of cases. It also can accept variables measured in strictly qualitative terms or strictly quantitative or a combination of both (as befits most real situations). References also can be made to graphics, music, URL's, and the like.

The main question for QCQ and the PAGP is how to represent the variables and relationships. The answer takes the form of simple cause and

TABLE 17.1   A Selection of Bus Reform Statistics

Variable	2003 (Before)	2004 (After)
Daily bus passengers (1,000)	4,869	5,350
Daily transit passengers (1,000)	9,307	9,888
Bus related traffic accidents	654	478
Car speed: Road A (km/hr)	18.5	19.9
CO air pollutant emissions (tons)	1798.8	1526.4

Source: (Seoul Development Institute, 2005, various pages).

ID Code	Name	Role	Def	Measure	Infl Vars	Data
#BUSCOM	Number of Bus Companies	Int	Yes	No	2	No
$BUSDIS	Disparity in Bus Company Profits	Int	Yes	No	1	No
$CC%GDP	Congestion Cost: % Gross National Product	Goal	Yes	No	1	No
$CMPLSS	Bus Companies Running at a Loss	Int	Yes	No	1	No
$CONCST	Congestion Costs	Goal	No	No	2	No
$HOUSPR	Housing Prices	Int	Yes	No	1	No
$RTELSS	Bus Companies with Non-Profitable Routes	Int	Yes	No	2	No
$TRNFER	Cost of a Transfer	Strat	Yes	No	N/A	No
%CAROWN	Percent Population Owning Cars	Int	Yes	No	2	No
%OP$COV	% Operating Cost Covered by Fares	Int	Yes	No	1	No
%SWDMGD	% Subway Debt of Metro Government Debt	Goal	Yes	No	2	No
%SWPFOC	% Subway Passenger Fares of Operating Costs	Strat	Yes	No	N/A	No
ABRTACC	Abrupt Bus Acceleration	Int	Yes	No	1	No
ABRTSTP	Abrupt Bus Stopping	Undef	Yes	No	1	No
ACCESS	Accessibility	Goal	Yes	No	3	No
ADOPTGS	Adoption of Global Card Standards	Strat	Yes	No	N/A	No
ADOPTIT	Adoption of Innovative Technologies	Int	Yes	No	1	No
ADOPTSO	Operators Adopt Service Oriented Approach	Int	Yes	No	2	No
AGENCYC	Creation of Oversight/Regulatory Agency	Goal	Yes	No	3	No
AGRESBD	Aggressive Bus Driving	Int	Yes	No	1	No
AIRPOLN	Air Pollution	Goal	Yes	No	3	No
ALIGNIE	Alignment: Investments, Environment Concern	Goal	Yes	No	<none>	No
ANTQBUS	Antiquated Buses	Int	Yes	No	1	No
ASSESSP	Assessment of Bus Position	Int	Yes	No	1	No
ASSIGNC	Coordination: Bus Route Assignment	Int	Yes	No	3	No
AUTOTOT	Total Automobiles Registered	Undef	Yes	No	2	No
AWARDS	Awards Recognizing Successful Reform	Undef	Yes	No	1	No

Pick the Variable to Change (Including Links)
Back Forward Search Display a Variable Help
Please select a variable, then select a menu option

Figure 17.1 Sample of (elaborated) case variables (first 27).

effect listing and diagramming concepts developed and used by Friend and Jessop (1969), Checkland (1981), Ishikawa (1982), and Eden, Jones, and Sims (1983).

In the case at hand, searches of the literature plus conversations with those in or close to the project turned up 333 variables and 387 bivariate relations for the main model. These figures translate into about a 25-page report and an extremely big causal diagram. Figure 17.1 shows a list of the first set (alphabetically) of (27) variables.

Perhaps what stands out in this list is the obvious wide variety of variables and their potential usefulness. Take, for instance, "Assessment of Bus Position" and "Antiquated Buses." The former may fall under the domain of the (hypothetical) geographic information systems (GIS) group, while the latter under the (hypothetical) sales group. Now that the groups know more about each other, they may see an opportunity to get together to find ways to, say, sell GIS-enhanced old but updated buses to medium income countries.

A sample of other kinds of possible QCQ and PAGP applications:

▪ Identifying possibly important topics that may be underrepresented in organizational thinking.

- Help project managers anticipate external factors that might affect the success of their projects,
- More generally, use by management not only to keep up with developments within their organization but in the topical areas generally.

17.4   A Simpler Example

For demonstration purposes we also have created a much smaller, but hopefully still fairly representative model of the situation at hand with 23 variables and 38 relations. Also for simplicity, we have limited the roles a variable could play to "Goal" or "Unspecified."

Figure 17.2 shows the graphic results (causal diagram) for the simplified Bus Reform case. The brackets on the links in the figure are reserved to show direct (+) or inverse (–) relationships between the variables as well as time affinities (e.g., a "t–2" would show a time delay of two time periods—years in this case—in the relationship) if such delays have been specified (which they have not been so far).

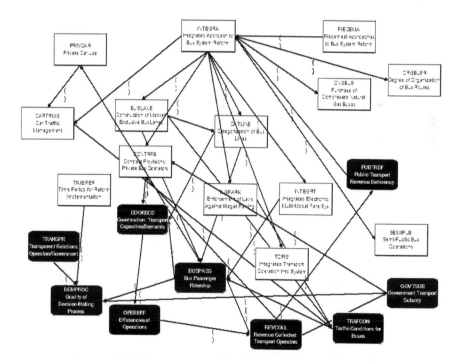

Figure 17.2   Causal diagram of simplified bus reform model.

There were many issues to be faced in the process of creating such a diagram. An obvious one, for example, is in identifying and handling apparent redundancies with variables and links already in the case. This, in turn, depends on devising some measure of "redundancy" (i.e., "similarity"). A fuller discussion of this and other issues can be found in Section 16.4.

It should be noted that the causal diagram already looks a bit complicated, and with only 23 variables and 38 relationships. So trying to display a much bigger diagram could prove to be very cumbersome. A *listing* then generally is preferable for larger cases (and it is almost required in the PAGP anyway).

A listing for the small model is presented in Table 17.2. There are nine "goal" and 14 "unspecified" variables. Probably the most important goal is "Bus Passenger Ridership" (BUSPASS). That is shown as being influenced by five other variables and influencing four. Perhaps the most important "Unspecified" variable is "Integrated Approach To Bus System Reform" (INTEGRA). That is located at the top middle of Figure 17.2, while BUSPASS can be found in the lower middle area. According to the (hypothetical) developers of this model, there is no "direct" connection between the two, but several indirect ones (e.g., through "enforcement of laws against illegal parking" [ILGPARK]).

Such findings may be good examples of the value of looking for the connections between certain variables so that, say, they can be made to be as visible to the public as possible.

17.5   Categories and Ontologies

Perhaps the second step in the development and use of the Bus Reform QCQ/PAGP case is to look toward categorization. Most people cannot deal with 333 separate items (variables), much less another 387 (relations). So they try to put those items (variables) into a set of categories and do it so the items in each category are as similar to each other as possible. In science the result usually is called an "ontology," which can be defined as:

> ...the study of being or existence. It seeks to describe or posit the basic categories and relationships of being or existence to define entities and types of entities in its framework. (http://en.wikipedia.org/wiki/Ontology)

17.5.1   *The PAGP Ontology*

There are several ways of making and using ontologies, but we will concentrate on an alterable one that is the basic standard in the Public Administration Genome Project (PAGP).

TABLE 17.2   Listing: Simplified Model of Bus System Reform

CASE: Seoul Bus Reform

DATE: 09-22-2013 TIME: 12:34:34

==

ID CODE and DESCRIPTION (Subject and Action/Status)

==

UNSPECIFIED VARIABLES

----

* 3* BUSLANE Construction of Median Exclusive Bus Lanes
   { }[t](0) INTEGRA Integrated Approach to Bus System Reform
* 1* CARTRMG Car Traffic Management
   { }[t](0) INTEGRA Integrated Approach to Bus System Reform
   { }[t](0) PRIVCAR Private Car Use
* 2* CATLINE Categorization of Bus Lines
   { }[t](0) BUSLANE Construction of Median Exclusive Bus Lanes
   { }[t](0) INTEGRA Integrated Approach to Bus System Reform
* 0* CNGBUS Purchase of Compressed Natural Gas Buses
   { }[t](0) INTEGRA Integrated Approach to Bus System Reform
* 1* CONTRPB Contract Provisions: Private Bus Operators
   { }[t](0) GOVTSUB Government Transport Subsidy
   { }[t](0) INTEGRA Integrated Approach to Bus System Reform
   { }[t](0) REVCOLL Revenue Collected: Transport Operators
* 1* ILGPARK Enforcement of Laws Against Illegal Parking
   { }[t](0) INTEGRA Integrated Approach to Bus System Reform
* 10* INTEGRA Integrated Approach to Bus System Reform
   { }[t](0) ORGBUSR Degree of Organization of Bus Routes
   { }[t](0) PIECEMA Piecemeal Approaches to Bus System Reform
   { }[t](0) PUBTRDF Public Transport Revenue Deficiency
* 1* INTEGRT Integrated Electronic Multi-Modal Fare Sys
   { }[t](0) INTEGRA Integrated Approach to Bus System Reform
* 1* ORGBUSR Degree of Organization of Bus Routes
   { }[t](0) INTEGRA Integrated Approach to Bus System Reform
* 1* PIECEMA Piecemeal Approaches to Bus System Reform
* 2* PRIVCAR Private Car Use
   { }[t](0) BUSPASS Bus Passenger Ridership
* 0* SEMIPUB Semi-Public Bus Operations
   { }[t](0) INTEGRA Integrated Approach to Bus System Reform
* 1* TIMEPER Time Period for Reform Implementation
* 0* TOPIS Integrated Transport Operation/Info System
   { }[t](0) INTEGRA Integrated Approach to Bus System Reform

,,,

GOAL VARIABLES

----

* 4* BUSPASS Bus Passenger Ridership
   { }[t](0) BUSLANE Construction of Median Exclusive Bus Lanes
   { }[t](0) CATLINE Categorization of Bus Lines

(continued)

TABLE 17.2   Listing: Simplified Model of Bus System Reform (cont.)

{ }[t](0) INTEGRT Integrated Electronic Multi-Modal Fare Sys
{ }[t](0) PRIVCAR Private Car Use
{ }[t](0) TRAFCON Traffic Conditions for Buses
* 1* COORDCD Coordination: Transport Capacities/Demands
{ }[t](0) BUSPASS Bus Passenger Ridership
{ }[t](0) CATLINE Categorization of Bus Lines
{ }[t](0) CONTRPB Contract Provisions: Private Bus Operators
* 0* DEMPROC Quality of Decision-Making Process
{ }[t](0) BUSPASS Bus Passenger Ridership
{ }[t](0) GOVTSUB Government Transport Subsidy
{ }[t](0) TIMEPER Time Period for Reform Implementation
{ }[t](0) TRANSPR Transparent Relations: Operators/Government
* 2* GOVT+SUB Government Transport Subsidy
{ }[t](0) REVCOLL Revenue Collected: Transport Operators
* 1* OPEREFF Efficiencies of Operations
{ }[t](0) COORDCD Coordination: Transport Capacities/Demands
* 1* PUBTRDF Public Transport Revenue Deficiency
{ }[t](0) REVCOLL Revenue Collected: Transport Operators
* 3* REVCOLL Revenue Collected: Transport Operators
{ }[t](0) BUSPASS Bus Passenger Ridership
{ }[t](0) OPEREFF Efficiencies of Operations
* 1* TRAFCON Traffic Conditions for Buses
{ }[t](0) BUSLANE Construction of Median Exclusive Bus Lanes
{ }[t](0) CARTRMG Car Traffic Management
{ }[t](0) ILGPARK Enforcement of Laws Against Illegal Parking
* 1* TRANSPR Transparent Relations: Operators/Government

Legend:
xx Number of Other Variables Directly Influenced by that Variable
{xx} Type of Relationship (e.g., {+ } is Monotonically Increasing)
[xx] Time Relationship (e.g., [t-2] is a Delay of 2 Time Periods)
(xx) Number of Cause-Effect Questions Answered Positively (Out of 6)
<C> Catalyst (Affects the Reaction Time of the Relationship)

To start, another name for creating categories, in genetics this time, is "genotyping." Genotypes refer, of course, to internal genes. To the authors' knowledge, no classification has been developed for the external environment (e.g., radiation) that may work with various genes to influence human behavior. Dawkins (1989) tried to alleviate this problem by referring to items in the external environment as "mimemes" (for "memories") or, for short, "memes." But these were only for abstract concepts like love, not for concrete items like buildings or trees or various groups of people.

As a result there was a need to develop a new ontology for what has been called the "exo-genome." And, because it is difficult to distinguish

TABLE 17.3 Example PA Exo-Genome Topical (Cistron) Classification

GLOBAL (ALL CISTRONS)

    SOCIOTRONS (INDIVIDUALS AND GROUPS OF PEOPLE) [23]

        Business   Family   Government   Religious Group

    PHYSIOTRONS (BODILY FUNCTIONS) [15]

        Gene   Reproduction   Speech   Thought

    ENVIRONTRONS (NATURAL ENVIRONMENT) [12]

        Animal–Vertebrate   Climate   Energy   Marine System

    TECHTRONS (MANMADE ENVIRONMENT/ARTIFACTS) [20]

        Chemical Compound   Information Technology

        Production Facility   Transportation System

    MEMETRONS (ABSTRACT CONCEPTS) [102]

        Attitude   Behavior   Experience

        Knowledge   Love   Management

public administration (PA) topics from those that are not PA, the same ontology will be utilized to cover both PA and external-to-PA elements.

As mentioned in Chapter 15, "genes" in the PAGP are known as "topics" or, more formally, "cistrons" (an older name for "genes"). The main categories in the PAGP thus have been created using the "tron" suffix. A subset is shown and illustrated in Table 17.3. The number of genotypes in each major category is shown in brackets next to its title. The total is 174 + 5 major categories, + 1 global category = 180. Some categories are completely irrelevant to a particular case and thus can be dropped off (thus the 148 for the Bus Reform case).

The current version of the ontology can be seen by going to the PAGP (at http://pagenome-compass.pbworks.com) and then going to the sidebar and selecting to go to the ontology.

Users of the ontology are free to add their own subcategories in a particular case situation (e.g., "Bus Transit," "Subway," and "Auto/Highway" have been added under "Transportation System" for the Bus Reform case).

17.5.2   Use of the Ontology: Case Example

An example deployment of the ontology has been derived from the full model of the Seoul Bus Reform case (see Figure 17.3). It may be remembered that there are 333 variables in the case. These are listed alphabetically (by variable ID Code) on the upper right side of Figure 17.3, which is a screen capture from the QCQ classification procedure.

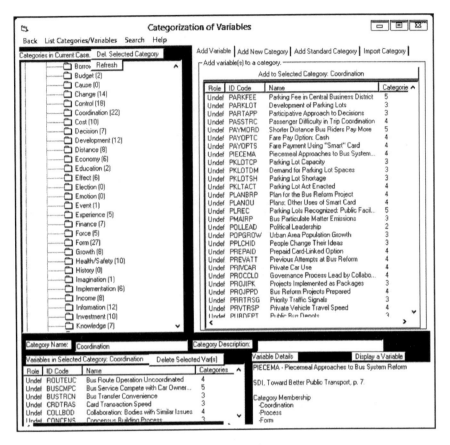

Figure 17.3 Classifying the PIECEMA variable into the "coordination."

A review of the counts of matches of case variables with the ontology categories (see, for example, the upper left box in Figure 17.3) leads to the discovery of 13 categories with 20+ counterparts (excluding "Transportation System" entities themselves). These are, in decreasing numeric order:

- Quantity (45)
- System (35)
- Business (28)
- User (27)
- Form (27)
- Operation (25)
- Time (25)
- Government (25)

- Opposition (21)
- Coordination (22)
- Information Technology (21)
- Service (20)
- Rules/Regulations (20)

These give a picture of the nature of the emphases in the case as a whole, as well as the individual focuses. These findings then can be employed to help "fill in," say, missing sections of strategic plans (see Chapter 15) where there already are partial similarities.

Note that a click on any variable on the top right hand list box will show the properties of that variable, including category membership (seen in the lower right text box). This is exemplified in Figure 17.3 where it can be seen that (PIECEMA) "Piecemeal Approaches to Bus System Reform" has been placed in four categories: "Coordination," "Process," "Form," and (not visible but scrollable) "Bus Transit."

Similarly, any category can be clicked to give a listing (lower left box) of all variables contained therein. The "Coordination" category, for example, includes 22 variables (a fact that also is displayed in parentheses next to the category name in the upper left box). Six of these variables are displayed in the scrollable lower left box.

Two cases now can be compared in terms of the relative percentage of variables falling within the standard ontology classes. This has yet to be done, but it eventually should help in using one case as an analogy to help in strategizing for another.

17.6 Connections

A subsequent real benefit of having data on a network of interconnections is to be able to trace the logical relations from one variable to another (see Chapter 9 for details). In the case at hand, and using the full (333 variables) database, we can look for strings of connections from one variable of interest to another.

Suppose, for instance, to help avoid possible mismanagement problems we wanted to trace down some possible impacts (if any) from, say, "Bus Management Systems" (BMS). From the upper left listing in the chart in Figure 17.4 we locate BMS. The upper right hand listing then displays all of the other variables and the connections, if any, to BMS. Suppose that "Bus Accident Deaths" (BUSACCD) catches your attention. You select that and the chain of relations (Table 17.4) is displayed in the bottom listing.

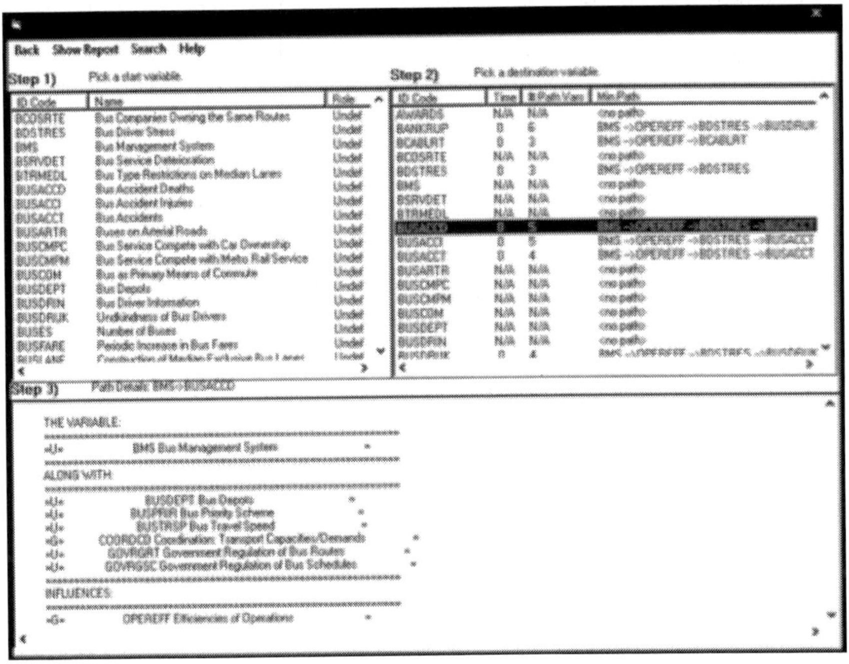

Figure 17.4 Tracing the connection from one variable to another.

TABLE 17.4   One Chain of Variables Connecting BMS to BUSACCD

THE VARIABLE:

=U=	BMS Bus Management System	=

ALONG WITH:

=U=	BUSDEPT Bus Depots	=
=U=	BUSPRIR Bus Priority Scheme	=
=U=	BUSTRSP Bus Travel Speed	=
=G=	COORDCD Coordination: Transport Capacities/Demands	=
=U=	GOVRGRT Government Regulation of Bus Routes	=
=U=	GOVRGSC Government Regulation of Bus Schedules	=

INFLUENCES:

=G=	OPEREFF Efficiencies of Operations	=

WHICH ALONG WITH:

=G=	TRAFCON Traffic Conditions for Buses	=

(continued)

TABLE 17.4   One Chain of Variables Connecting BMS to BUSACCD (continued)

INFLUENCES:

=U=	BDSTRES Bus Driver Stress	=

WHICH ALONG WITH:

=U=	COMPEDP Competitive Education Program	=
=U=	DRQLCER Mandatory Bus Driver Quality Certification	=

INFLUENCES:

=U=	BUSACCT Bus Accidents	=

WHICH INFLUENCES:

=U=	BUSACCD Bus Accident Deaths	=

17.7   Description of a Variable

A related valuable use for a data base like that described here is to give a detailed look at a particular variable. An example can be seen in Table 17.5, with the variable being "Piecemeal Approaches to Bus System Reform" (PIECEMA). In this situation the variable happens not to be affected by any other and only affects one other (INTEGRA). But, as it turns out (using the full model and the minimum path algorithm from the preceding section), this single connection is sufficient to give further connections to eight of the nine goal variables in the case. This finding is recorded in the last lines in the table. More on this process can be found in Chapter 9.

17.8   Recapitulation

This second major case had to do with a very large undertaking of bus reform in Seoul, Korea. The emphasis in our endeavor, which occurred after the reform project was finished, was to (1) document the variables and relationships involved (of which there were 333 of the former and 387 of the second), and (2) provide examples of how the knowledge so gained could be used productively. In response to the latter we developed and illustrated some of the processes and product of dealing with relatively large data sets, showed how to use QCQ's capabilities in finding pathways between pairs of variables, and demonstrated the process for building classification systems (ontologies) and using them to characterize the nature of the case entity under study.

TABLE 17.5   Description of a Variable (PIECEMA)

ID CODE: PIECEMA
DESCRIPTION: Piecemeal Approaches to Bus System Reform
ROLE: UNSPECIFIED
===
DEFINITION: SDI, Toward Better Public Transport, p. 7.
SHORT MEASURE: (Not Entered Yet)   FULL MEASURE: (Not Entered Yet)
===
CATEGORY (Ontology) MEMBERSHIP
    Coordination   Process   Form   Bus Transit
===
DIRECTLY INFLUENCING VARIABLES/CATALYSTS
===
<Not Applicable>
===
VARIABLES/CATALYSTS DIRECTLY INFLUENCED BY THIS ONE
===
{ }[t 0](0) INTEGRA Integrated Approach to Bus System Reform
===
    LEGEND FOR INFLUENCING/INFLUENCED VARIABLES:
    {xx} Relation Type (e.g., {+ } is Monotonically Increasing)
    [xx] Time Relation (e.g., [t-2] is Delay of 2 Time Periods)
    (xx) # of Cause-Effect Questions Answered Positively (max=6)
    <T> The Pre/Reaction Time Variable in the Relationship
===
VARIABLE PERVASIVENESS MEASURES:
===
8 Goal Variables Are Influenced Out of a Total of 9 (88%)
8 Relatable (Dependent) Variables Are Influenced Out of a Total of 9 (88%)
36 Relationships Are Influenced Out of a Total of 38 (94%)

Note: More on this process can be found in Chapter 9.

18

Major Case

U.S. Department of Defense
Joint Total Asset Visibility (JTAV) Project

The first part of this chapter has to do with a case study of logistics in the military. This is followed by an effort by Colonel Birdsall (2004), the author of that case, to keep experiences within the case, as well as across this book, in a realistic vein by elaborating on a series of interesting "behind the scenes" vignettes that might bear on the case's success.

18.1 Introduction to the JTAV Case

Joint Total Asset Visibility (JTAV) is the Department of Defense (DoD) capability that provides United States military Combatant Commanders, the military services, and the service components with timely and accurate information about the location, movement, identity, and status of units, personnel, equipment, and supplies [INT-21 Total Asset Visibility; INT-6 Visible Assets]. This capability is achieved by fusing data retrieved from the myriad logistics systems throughout DoD that support the logistics functional processes such as supply, transportation, and maintenance. The JTAV

Supernumerary Intelligence, pages 269–283
Copyright © 2015 by Information Age Publishing
All rights of reproduction in any form reserved.

goal is to provide a capability that facilitates improvements in the performance of those logistics functional processes. JTAV's genesis is found in the experiences of Operations Desert Shield and Desert Storm and the DoD Inventory Reduction Plan (IRP). Desert Shield and Desert Storm reaffirmed suspected deficiencies in both asset management and order status experienced in previous conflicts. The inability to "see" assets in the pipeline and the status of orders was responsible for duplicate orders, resulting in unnecessary material shipped into theater, creating backlogs at aerial and water ports, and difficulty in prioritizing these cargo backlogs. The IRP was a major initiative to downsize material inventories while maintaining peacetime readiness and combat sustainability.

The purpose of this case study was to explore forces acting on the implementation of strategy in the public sector. We accomplished the task by studying the implementation of a logistics automated information system in the DoD—the Joint Total Asset Visibility (JTAV) Project. Many forces are extant in the public arena, and some affect the implementation of strategy. Some forces aid the implementation of strategy and are seen as positive forces; other forces act to hinder the implementation of strategy and are seen as negative.

18.2 Concept of Forces

The forces we identified are those that impact the success or failure of strategic choices. This means that at times those forces may be pushing (or pulling) the strategy toward success and sometimes the forces may be pushing (or pulling) the strategy away from success. A useful construct for analysis of these forces is Kurt Lewin's (1943) force field theory (FFT). Primarily a psychologist, he was one of the founding fathers of both social and organizational psychology. FFT grew out of his psychological studies of how humans change attitudes. FFT emphasizes the fact that any event is the result of a multitude of factors and the forces acting upon them. Force field analysis (FFA) is the associated problem solving technique based on the concept that a change in any of the forces might alter the result or influence the change. Lewin originated the idea as a strategy for changing behavior.

Lewin's change model is based on the observation that the stability of human behavior rests on the quasi-equilibrium of a large force field of driving and restraining forces. For change to occur, this force field has to be fundamentally altered because merely adding a driving force often produces an immediate counter-force to maintain the equilibrium. This observation led to Lewin's important insight that the equilibrium could more easily be altered by removing or weakening restraining forces because simply pushing harder against the restraint is likely to increase the strength of the resistance. Lewin's change model (FFA) has been applied in many other fields such as information systems development, organization management, and medicine.

We borrowed the general concept of forces as outlined in the FFT and applied it to the implementation of public strategies for an information technology project. We also adopted Lewin's terminology and refer to the forces as driving and restraining forces.

FFA was introduced in the early 1950s and has been used in organizational development as a technique for implementing changes in structure, technology, and people. FFA has also been included in organizational behavior texts as a technique for evaluating forces affecting change (Steers, 1981). The generic FFA framework from is displayed at Figure 18.1. The current state of the organization is depicted at "A," and the desired state, or vision, is depicted at "B." A number of forces operate within the organization and the environment. The forces are represented by the arrows or vectors. Some of these forces favor the proposed change to the vision, and some of the forces oppose the change, favoring the status quo. An equilibrium point is achieved when the sum of each set of forces is equal. Movement from "A" to "B" requires that forces driving the change exceed forces resisting the change. Movement can be achieved by either increasing the forces for change or decreasing the forces resisting change; however, Lewin suggests that movement is better achieved by reducing resistance rather than increasing the driving force.

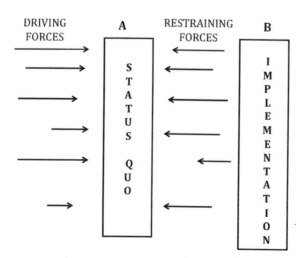

Figure 18.1 Lewin's force field theory applied to strategy implementation.

18.3   Procedure

18.3.1   Methodology

We conducted interviews with 25 people who played an intimate role in the development of the JTAV Program. These included, in one categorization: military officers, civilian DoD employees, and various contractors; and in another categorization: managers, programmers, and congressional contact people. We employed a regimen of data reduction to analyze the data and data synthesis to reconstruct the data into categories. We reduced the interviews to data protocols, reduced the data protocols to key words and concepts, and further reduced the key words and concepts to data codes, completing the data analysis. We then interpreted and synthesized those data codes into higher level categories that revealed the high level forces at work in the implementation of the strategies for JTAV.

18.3.2   Developing Initial Data Codes

We first developed an initial list of data codes (the bulk of the codes will emerge from the study). As stated above, we created a start list of codes and used the research questions as the starting point. Rules governing the coding of data are relatively flexible; however, the codes are the basis for establishing categories, which are the foundation of the case. Our coding schema was based upon the coding format in Quantitative Cyberquest. This data code consists of seven digits. The first two digits correspond to the codes relating to the essential elements of information as determined by the data protocol. The last four digits correspond to the initial data codes developed in the TextAnalyst2 analysis (explained in the following paragraph). The third digit is a constant colon for ease of reading and separation of the two subordinate codes. Thus, the code "DF:GRID" would indicate that one of the driving forces identified in an interview was that JTAV was a "*great idea.*"

18.3.3   Data Analysis

The analysis process for the interview material is too intricate to be discussed in detail here. The interested reader is referred to a summary in Dickey and Birdsall (2006) and the full version in Birdsall (2004). Briefly, we developed an initial list of forces identified in the interviews. This initial list served as the foundational, or lowest, level of forces in the study. Initially, 2,839 such variables were extracted from the interviews. That task was accomplished by using TextAnalyst2 (TA2) to analyze the interviews. One of the products provided by TA2 is a semantic network, in tabular form, showing the concept frequency and semantic weight. Frequency merely means the number of times that word appears in the analyzed text. The semantic weight is the measure of the probability that this concept is important in the studied text. In order to more readily determine the concepts with the strongest relationships, the results were sorted based upon highest frequency and largest semantic weight. The 15 concepts with the highest frequency and any other concept with a semantic weight above 50 were selected. This provided a list of 260 variables. We reviewed and adjusted that list to eliminate obvious redundancies or words that were inconsequential (e.g., many, year, etc.). We then coded each of the remaining concepts as we had coded the research questions that provided the initial data code list. The codes only correspond to the last four digits of the coding schema because the first two digits were determined within context of the interview.

At the next level up, the variables were aggregated into a total of 95 more abstract factors and then reconstructed into driving and restraining forces. The result of this generalization process was a list of 21 different driving forces and 31 restraining forces. The most popular one of the former was simply that JTAV was "a great idea." The second most popular was "quality of contractor support," indicating that a great degree of advocacy was a necessary component of a successful program.

On the other side of the ledger, the most mentioned restraining force was "parochialism," particularity among the services (Army, Navy, and Air Force), each of whom wanted a JTAV-like program but wanted to do it in their own particular way.

Thus, the variables identified in the interviews were presented at four different levels of generality. In addition, the interviewees were asked to review the results at one midlevel stage and give some indication of the impact—from very weak to very strong—of each variable on JTAV implementation. It should be noted that the variables at the top three levels also were divided into two major classes: driving forces and restraining forces. This was done to highlight the fact that some variables (also called "forces") helped to enhance implementation while others acted to hold it back. Moreover, some variables could do both.

18.3.4 Data Synthesis

Michael Porter (2002) says that a framework captures the full richness of phenomenon with the most limited number of dimensions (Argyres & McGahan, 2002). He goes on to say that if those dimensions are presented to the practitioner, they must make sense in the context of his or her industry. In order to make sense of specific details or discrete events, we intuitively put them into broad categories that are more easily related to each other. Arranging the categories, naming them, and determining their relationships are the essence of a conceptual framework, and this is also where the categorization function in QCQ helps this project the most.

In determining broader levels of categories of forces, we needed to recognize two issues. One, that forces were identified at various levels of hierarchy in the strategy implementation environment. In other words, some forces were seen as very specific and detail oriented and others as more broad. Second, forces were identified with various magnitudes or strengths. One of the purposes of the higher level categories was to provide a context in which the forces could be related to each other in terms of hierarchy and magnitude. Consequently, to gather data concerning hierarchy and magnitude, as well as to satisfy Porter that our list of forces makes sense to the practitioners, our next step was to return to the interviewees. To gather data concerning magnitude, we asked them to rate each force in terms of impact on the strategies on a five-point Likert scale, from 1 (very weak impact) to 5 (very strong impact). They also were requested to conceptualize some "overarching" concepts that would adequately represent most of the previously identified forces. These concepts turned out to be about the same as the most popular forces found in the previous analysis.

18.3.5 *Likert Scale Rating of Driving Forces*

The only driving force selected by every respondent as having a .very strong impact on the implementation of JTAV strategies was the "great idea." Support from the warfighter was also seen as key for successful strategy implementation. This is an interesting observation, because the warfighters were the actual customer (JTAV was being developed for their use, and it would be to their primary benefit); however, they provided no financial support to JTAV. Although the warfighters were strong JTAV advocates to the Office of the Secretary of Defense (OSD) and the services (who provided most of the money), none of the warfighter support was financial in terms of development, software, and so on. The warfighters did help in identifying requirements, and they served as test beds, so they did expend some resources, but not the "hard cash" used to contract out for technical support such as writing code, or for any of the support of the JTAV Program Management Office.

18.3.6   Likert Scale Rating of Restraining Forces

The survey results concerning the restraining forces were more diffused. There was not one restraining force that was selected on every survey as having a .very strong impact. Two of the driving forces ("great idea" and "warfighter support") were seen as having a stronger impact than the highest rated restraining force ("parochialism"). Other restraining forces seen as having an impact ranging from strong to very strong were "politics," "change," "personalities," and "lack of loyalty to the project." It may be notable that politics is the only force that appeared in the strong to very strong category of both driving and restraining forces.

18.3.7   Determination of Higher Order Forces

In order to develop a list of higher order forces, it is necessary to place the data in a hierarchy; otherwise there can be no higher order. Up to this point, three levels of forces have been identified. At the lowest level of analysis, we have the individual forces as identified by the TA2 analysis and our manual review of the interviews. At the next higher level of analysis are the driving and restraining forces identified by the interviewees in response to the direct question concerning driving and restraining forces. At the highest level of current analysis are the overarching forces identified by the interviewees at the time they were rating the strength of the forces. Our goal was to use QCQ to develop a fourth level of analysis, the highest order of forces present, through a continuous process of comparing the lower forces with the next higher level by using the higher level topics as categories in which to place the lower level forces.

For example, we used the Level 3 driving and restraining forces as categories in QCQ and mapped each of the Level 4 forces identified by TA2 in one of those categories. We considered eliminating Level 3 categories if they failed to map to Level 4 TA2 forces. Conversely, we added Level 3 categories if we found Level 4 forces that did not map into a currently identified Level 3 force. We then performed the same mapping procedure between Level 3 and Level 2. We used the Level 2 overarching forces as categories and associated Level 3 categories to them.

18.4   Determining Level 1 Forces

In determining the Level 1 forces, we adhered to Porter's admonition (Argyres & McGahan, 2002) that a framework must capture the full richness of the phenomenon with the *most limited number of dimensions*. The operative question remains, "What is that limited number of dimensions?" Vinzant and Vinzant (1996) present an interesting framework for strategy implementation analysis. They posit that successful efforts to implement strategy must address a complex mix of both internal and external factors. They note two primary external factors: organizational autonomy and stimuli. Organizational autonomy is self-directing freedom or independence, while stimuli consist of crises that can produce either threats or opportunities. They also note four primary internal factors: human and behavioral issues, structural and technical factors, prior experience, and process design. Human and behavioral issues include leadership, management style, and organizational culture. Structural and technical factors include the size, design, and infrastructure of the organization. Prior experience primarily refers to experience in planning, budgeting, and other administrative areas. Process design encompasses the issues of who, what, when, and how in the strategic management approach. We used Vinzant and Vinzant to establish a draft set of Level 1 forces. However, the forces proposed by Vinzant and Vinzant differ markedly from ours in that they do not assume a value such as a positive (driving) force or a negative (restraining) force. Consequently, we established each of their proposed factors as both driving and restraining forces for the purposes of identifying draft Level 1 forces. This allowed our data to determine whether each of Vinzant and Vinzant's forces is either a driving or restraining force. As we mapped the Level 2 forces into them, we modified them accordingly based upon our data. For example, if one of their factors did not map to any of the Level 2 forces, we considered its elimination. Conversely, if we have to add a new category to provide a Level 1 place for Level 2 forces, we did so. This process provided some initial structure for the analysis, yet did not restrict findings to arbitrarily agree with any preconceived notions. It provides a framework grounded in the literature, while also allowing patterns to emerge from the research.

The Level 2 forces mapped rather neatly into the draft categories. We did have to add two categories to the Internal and External groups: requirements and technical knowledge (a total of four added categories). We added requirements because Vinzant and Vinzant's categories provided no place for the forces associated with the problem, solution, or the technical requirements of the project. The interviewees were very adamant that one of the greatest forces in JTAV's favor was that it was a great idea and potentially solved some serious long-standing logistics problems for DoD. Second, we added technical knowledge—because Vinzant and Vinzant's categories did not provide a mapping home for the contractor support (which is primarily technical knowledge) or for the technology itself. We also deleted one of Vinzant and Vinzant's categories (prior experience) from both the internal and external groups because none of the Level 2 forces mapped to it, and the interviewees did not specifically call it out as an important force. This process left us with 14 total forces: five internal driving forces and five internal restraining forces and two external driving forces and two external restraining forces. These can be seen in Table 18.1, with some descriptive information summarized in Table 18.2.

By dropping down one level of analysis, one can see that the one on one relationship (every characteristic force is a driver and restrainer) does not necessarily hold true. However it is interesting to note that many of the same Level 2 characteristic forces do map into the opposing Level 1 forces. For example, a lack of enthusiasm helps to comprise the restraining

---

TABLE 18.1   Highest Level Forces and Their Impact Scores

Force	Driving Force Impact Score	Restraining Force Impact Score
Internal: Human behavioral	199	141
External: Stimuli	70	84
Internal: Process design	101	81
Internal: Structural	63	69
Internal: Technical knowledge	66	105
External: Organization autonomy	45	58
Internal: Requirements	76	46

Note: Based on Birdsall (2004), Dickey and Birdsall (2006)

TABLE 18.2   Description of Highest Level Force Terms

Internal: Human behavioral
    Leadership, management style, organizational culture
External: Stimuli
    Crises which can be either threats or opportunities
Internal: Process design
    Approach to strategic management
Internal: Structural
    Organizational size, design, and infrastructure
Internal: Technical knowledge
    Technology, team technical expertise, contractor support
External: Organization autonomy
    Self-directed freedom or independence
Internal: Requirements
    Problems, solutions, technical requirements

Note: Based on Vinzant and Vinzant (1996), Dickey and Birdsall (2006)

human and behavioral force, whereas the presence of enthusiasm helps to comprise the driving human and behavioral force. Also, good leadership helps to comprise the driving human and behavioral force, whereas bad leadership helps to comprise the restraining human and behavioral force.

The numbers in Table 18.1 represent the accumulation of scores from the ratings of the third level variables (forces). The computational process used to arrive at these numbers is a little too complex for reporting here but can be found in Birdsall (2004). At this point, though, we can say that the magnitude of the numbers represents the total of the scores over all the interviewees. So we can conclude from Table 18.1 that the "Internal: Human Behavioral" variable was felt by the responders to have the biggest impact driving force and, interestingly, also the largest restraining force. And it is quite significantly larger in impact than any of the other six forces. Next in size, for instance, is "Internal: Process Design," which is much smaller in magnitude then the "Internal: Human Behavioral" force.

Of particular note is the "Internal: Technical Knowledge" force, which is significantly stronger in the restraining motion than it is in the driving mode. This result should alert managers to focus more on available technology and team technical expertise, as well as the support of contractors.

18.5   Relationships

Nothing has been said so far about relationships, and these were not part of the original study by Birdsall (2004). But later on he did develop a QCQ model of the connections among the seven highest level forces. These relations are portrayed in Figure 18.2. Of course, it is important to know that any one force affects some, if not all, of the other forces and thus assumedly influences the impact scores for those other forces. For instance, ES ("External: Stimuli") is shown as affecting ITK ("Internal: Technical Knowledge"). This is very reasonable given the possibilities of rapid changes in external technology and the need to absorb knowledge about these changes internally. Without such absorption, it is entirely possible that implementation will be affected adversely (and thus one possible reason for the relatively high restraining impact score for ITK in Table 18.1).

Three features can be recognized in this diagram (Figure 18.2). First, each connection has been given a sign. That between ITK ("Internal: Technical Knowledge") and "JTAV Program Implementation" (JTAVI, the oblong-cornered box) is presented as positive, signifying that an increase in ITK should enhance the chances of "JTAV Program Implementation." While this relationship is fairly clear, some of the other ones are relatively fuzzy. How is the negative sign between IHB and JTAVI to be interpreted, for instance?

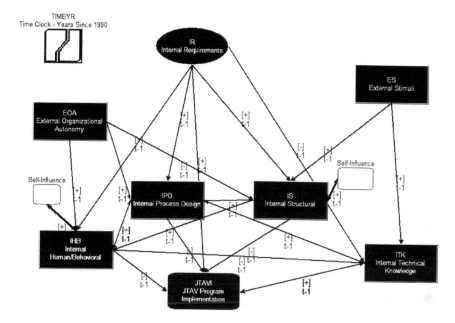

Figure 18.2 Hypothesized relations between high level JTAV implementation forces.

Most of the "fuzziness" can be attributed to the high level of aggregation of these variables.

Second, each relationship also has associated with it a time delay, in all instances taken as one time period (in this case specified to be one year). Of course, in reality time delays may differ depending on the particular relationship. But here we have decided to look only at the affected changes specifically after a one year time interval.

Third, two of the variables are seen as being self-influencing. This means that they influence themselves during the specified time interval. As an example, IHB is hypothesized to affect itself. The thought may be that good leadership (a part of IHB) will lead to further good leadership.

18.6 The Framework

In order to develop the framework, it may be informative to briefly review Lewin's force field analysis (FFA). Lewin's change model is based on the stability of human behavior resulting from a quasi-equilibrium of a large force field of driving and restraining forces. For change to occur, this force field has to be fundamentally altered to a non-equilibrium. This observation led to Lewin's insight that the equilibrium could more easily be altered by

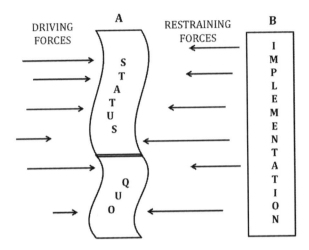

Figure 18.3 Level 1 driving and restraining forces in the JTAV environment.

removing or weakening restraining forces because simply pushing harder against the restraint is likely to increase the strength of the resistance.

Although a snapshot, Figure 18.3 attempts to depict the fluid nature of strategy implementation. The forces are not equally applied; thus the status quo is at some points closer to successful implementation than it is at others. Our experience would indicate that this depiction is closer to what an implementer actually faces. Some aspects of the project are going well, because the forces that drive it are stronger than the restraining forces. Some aspects of the project are not going as well, because the restraining forces are stronger than the driving forces.

18.7 Recapitulation

This source case presents some interesting differences from most of the others in the PAGP. The main difference concerns the initially great number and breadth of variables—being close to 3,000 and of a wide variety of natures. The response to this situation has been to aggregate the variables at various levels of abstraction, with the most general having just eight variables (including the "bottom line" of JTAV implementation).

The case also was unique in noting that those variables (a.k.a. "forces") were drivers toward a successful implementation and at the same time also served as restrainers. And this case is the only one so far where interviewees were asked to rate the forces in terms of their driving and restraining impacts, thereby giving a measure of their relative importance.

18.8 Behind the Scenes

When you are undertaking a project as large, complex, and notorious as JTAV, there is a lot that goes on behind the scenes. I have captured some of the highlights below.

18.8.1 How the Government Saves Money

When Robert McNamara was Secretary of Defense he had an enterprising young Air Force Colonel working for him. One day this young Colonel said, "Secretary McNamara, I'm very proud of myself. Today I saved 50 cents because I walked to work instead of taking the bus." Secretary McNamara smiled and said, "Very good. I'm very proud of you. But tomorrow don't take a cab and you will save $2.50."

18.8.2 How the Government Accounts for Money

When I was assigned to the Office of the Secretary of Defense in The Pentagon, one of my responsibilities was to be the packaging manager for all of DoD. You would be surprised at what a huge business packaging is. I chaired a group called the Defense Policy Packaging Group (DPPG—pronounced "dip-pig"). We had members from all the services and defense agencies. One of my tasks was to serve as the advocate for the Military Packaging School at Aberdeen Proving Ground in Maryland. The Army managed the school for all of DoD. The school wanted $400,000 to do some infrastructure work and to revise some classes. I tracked down the person in the DoD budget office responsible for the school and went to visit him to lobby for a wedge in the budget. His exact words to me were, "You only want $400,000? Tell the Army to take it out of their hide—that's round-off money to us."

18.8.3 Priorities

Throughout my Air Force career, it was emphasized to me, in clear terms, how important it is to turn your work in on time or early if possible. Then I went to work in the Pentagon. A civilian, who had been working in the building for about 15 years and was the Deputy Director of our office, gave me some advice. He said, "Whenever you are given a project, never turn it in on time. If you do, they will think one of two things—either you did not spend enough time on it and it is not complete, or you don't have enough work to do and you'll get more."

18.8.4 *Discipline inside the Beltway*

When you are in the military, you get used to following orders, sometimes called "guidance." If someone in a higher rank tells you to do something, you do it if it is not illegal or immoral. When I worked in the Pentagon, I worked in the Office of the Secretary of Defense (OSD), and we provided "guidance" to the service chiefs in the name of the Secretary of Defense. So here we are, a staff agency, telling a four star general what to do. Naturally, the four star often ignored us. I said to my boss one day, "How does anyone expect us to get anything accomplished if the services can just ignore us when they want to? They need to publicly execute (figuratively, of course) a four star, and then maybe we'll get some cooperation." My boss very calmly said, "That will never happen. Logistics is just not seen as important enough to fire a four star, and they know it."

18.8.5 *The Color of Money*

In the government, money is appropriated for large categories of uses such as research and development, operations and maintenance, personnel salaries, procurement, and so on. As the money is appropriated by Congress for those categories, it takes an act of Congress to move money between categories. They are thereafter referred to as being "different colors of money." For example, "I have money, but it is the wrong color and I can't fly any more training sorties." When I worked in the Pentagon, we had a specific "color" of money that could only, by law, be spent in West Virginia, thanks to Senator Byrd.

18.8.6 *Can I Get a Little Help?*

In The Pentagon my boss was an Assistant Deputy Under Secretary of Defense. As you might imagine, there were several Assistant Deputy Under Secretaries for something or other. My boss was not particularly well liked by some of them, so when I was trying to get something accomplished for my project, I often ran into turbulence that was a direct result of personality conflicts. I actually had another Assistant Deputy Under Secretary tell me that she did not like my boss and was not going to cooperate even though my project was recognized as a good idea.

18.8.7   The "Real" Work

When I worked for the Defense Logistics Agency, I was the Deputy Program Manager for the program to re-engineer the standard logistics data systems to conform to national standards for electronic data interchange. One day I was particularly frustrated with the guidance I received and told my boss that our problem is that we too often get the real work confused with the bull. Without missing a beat, he said, "Colonel, I'm really disappointed in you. You've been working here for two years and haven't yet realized that in this job the bull *is* the real work."

18.8.8   The "B" Team

Many of the personnel billets at the headquarters are filled by civilians because they provide the continuity needed. This is especially true at logistics bases. When I was assigned to Headquarters, Air Force Logistics Command at Wright-Patterson AFB in Ohio, I was in the minority as a uniformed member. I was trying to change the way our computer accounted for conventional bombs and ammunition but encountered resistance from a civilian. He did not want to change. Finally I told him I was just going to make the change and in order to stop me he was going to have to find someone with more horsepower than he had. He smiled and said, "Major, I'm on the 'B' Team. Have you ever heard of the 'B' Team?" I told him that I had heard of the "A" Team, but not the "B" Team. He said, "That means that I'll *be* here before you are here; I'll *be* here while you are here; and I'll *be* here when you are gone!" I got that message loud and clear—I could do whatever I wanted, and as soon as I left, it was going back to the way *he* wanted.

19

Supernumerary Intelligence in Perspective

Every day, each of us is faced with issues we must confront, problems we must overcome, and obstacles we must hurdle. This happens in both our personal as well as our professional lives. Some problems are quantitative in nature, such as: How much can I spend on a new car? How many miles do I need to walk to maintain my current weight if I continue to eat the same? How long do I have to work before I can retire at a comfortable lifestyle? On the other hand, some problems are qualitative in nature, such as: What are the qualities I look for in a new car? How does exercise affect human physiology? What characteristics represent a comfortable lifestyle? We hope you can see from our example questions that some problems (in fact, most problems) have both quantitative and qualitative elements. These types of issues are best resolved using methods that are both quantitative and "beyond the numbers"—what we call "supernumerary intelligence" (SI).

Supernumerary Intelligence, pages 285–291
Copyright © 2015 by Information Age Publishing
All rights of reproduction in any form reserved.

19.1 Putting It All Together

SI can be viewed from both a process and a content perspective. From a content view, SI consists of data—but it is more than data. If it were merely data, we could discuss it in terms of mixed-methods research. SI content consists of intelligence, and that is where SI diverges from current concepts of knowledge. SI is the integration of quantitative and qualitative data at a basic level to create a melded form of intelligence we refer to as SI. SI is data, information, knowledge, and intelligence. One repository for SI data that we have developed is in the Public Administration Genome Project (PAGP).

From a process perspective, we used an analytic discovery tool called Quantitative CyberQuest (QCQ). The QCQ seven-step process is the path we followed to develop our model. Like most goals, ours remains somewhat elusive; however, striving to achieve a goal that stretches one's boundaries inevitably leads to substantial progress.

19.2 The Public Administration Genome Project (PAGP)

The PAGP is an innovative approach to public policy analysis that we have developed to improve administrative theory, strategy, decision-making behavior, and the ultimate effectiveness of public managers in the 89,000 "governmental units" in the United States (not to mention those in other countries!). A government so large is fraught with duplicative effort, conflicting purposes and goals, oversight of oversight in some areas and no oversight in other areas, incompatible procedures and lack of supervision in funds expenditure, and so on. The old approaches do not work, and a new approach is needed.

The PAGP is a grand analogy of the Human Genome Project to public administration. The goal is to map public administration variables and relationships much as the Human Genome Project maps human genes to discover the secrets of life. All of the public administration "genes" are captured from source cases and stored in a PAGP internal information and guidance system (called "ComPASS"), designed to assist in using this knowledge in every day public strategy development.

19.3 Quantitative Cyberquest (QCQ)

Our process tool is QCQ. Process consists of how a thing works. QCQ's seven-step process provides us with a model of SI. The seven steps are:

1. Situation description,

2. Theory search,
3. Theory development,
4. Data specification and collection,
5. Individual relationship development,
6. Relationship evaluation, and
7. Forecasting.

Quantitative CyberQuest (QCQ) is a philosophy as well as an analytic tool that we use to help in exploring the supernumerary. QCQ involves a combination of statistics, systems analysis, research methodology, qualitative research, and artificial intelligence. QCQ provides a relatively easy-to-understand yet powerful set of tools to guide users in searching for supernumerary relationships.

One point needs to be made about QCQ. Despite its name, QCQ is an analytic rather than just a quantitative discovery tool. In our investigations and musings we have found that much of the development of good quantitative models starts way back in the nebulous mist of the qualitative— much as our example questions at the beginning of this chapter. Somehow the vague, intuitive, and unsubstantiated impressions about a situation under investigation are transformed into much clearer, well-integrated, and "hard" models that many times can be used for forecasting purposes. One

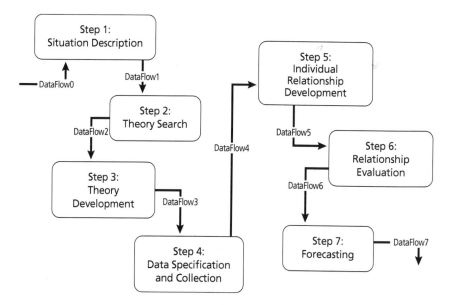

Figure 19.1 The QCQ steps and dataflow.

of' the goals for the further development of QCQ is to capture as much as possible of that transition process and thus actually incorporate a considerable number of "qualitative" elements in it.

In addition, SI not only integrates quantitative and qualitative data, but also requires the assimilation of different types of paradigmatic thinking. For example, it combines art and science, analysis and synthesis, and left brain and right brain thinking. Quantitative data requires a structured analytic approach, much as we use in mathematics. Thus it is a left brain, linear process. Qualitative data requires a creative approach that synthesizes ideas and discerns trends and patterns. Thus it is a right brain, non-linear process. SI integrates and assimilates all of those concepts.

A major premise in this quest is that people often are not aware of the wide range of factors that may come into play in the many situations they encounter. When tackling any issue or problem, we encounter the same surprises and unknowns for which we planned (the things that we know we do not know) but also the chaos and disorder that we do not yet understand (the things we do not know that we do not know).

Many people do not appreciate that if we know about the issue *in the first instance—we know* that we know or *we know* that we do not know—those ideas are in our conscious thoughts. However, if we do not know those things *in the first instance—we do not know that we know* (and *we do not know that we do not know*)—those ideas, such as tacit knowledge or unintended consequences, are not in our conscious thought, because we do not know them. If we knew them, they must go in the first two categories. Ironically, as soon as we realize that we have the tacit knowledge, it immediately moves to the *we know* categories, and, as we notice an unintended consequence, it also immediately moves to the *we know* categories. Thus we want to identify, as quickly as possible, those items that are hidden from us in the *we do not know* categories and move them into the *we know* categories so that we can deal with them. QCQ is particularly well suited to help us do that.

19.4   Contribution to Analytics

Analytics is the discovery and communication of meaningful patterns in data and is most effective in areas flush with information (big and/or wide data). "Big/wide data" consists of data sets so large and complex that they cannot be processed using current database management tools or traditional data processing applications. Analytics uses new methods that depend on the simultaneous application of statistics, computer programming, and operations research to quantify performance.

As alluded to above, analytics is an innovative approach to the numerary, but it can miss important and useful information existing in the supernumerary, including a wide variety of important factors, relationships, and perspectives. SI melds the numerary and supernumerary into one concept so that all information and knowledge can be brought to bear in an integrated manner.

The point is that no matter whether it is bigger or wider data sets, there is a great potential to sift out some very interesting relationships that may lead to significant gains in SI.

19.5   Contribution to Management

There is an old management adage that "What is important to the boss gets the attention." This maxim simply means that if the boss is interested in a specific topic, then the middle managers will also be interested and will actively manage that area to ensure that the boss remains happy. In most cases what gets management attention are graphs, statistics, and numbers because a graph, statistic, or number provides a clear understanding of measured success or failure. Topics that cannot be measured generally provide unclear feedback and are much more difficult to manage. Therefore they often are not managed, leaving management attention voids. SI can provide a solution to some of those woes.

Through the true integration of numerary and supernumerary, managers have a powerful and creative tool to analyze problems and issues. No longer restricted to the analysis of numeric measures, managers can focus the necessary time and effort on issues where success or failure is not easily determined by a single measurement. As a result, managers can fill the management voids mentioned above.

19.6   Contribution to Education

The separation of data into numerical and non-numerical has its advocates and advantages and often separates schools of thought and personalities as well as data. To make matters worse, there is a wide gulf between "qualitative" and "quantitative" dimensions, with people in the latter category sometimes, and not always affectionately, called "quants" or "quant-heads." Despite these divisions, it is important that both sides remember that the identification of any variable starts with a fuzzy notion and works its way to a clear statement.

Academic research is usually divided into qualitative or quantitative. That division is usually fairly hard, and when researchers want to bring the qualitative and quantitative together, they use a "mixed-methods approach." Mixed-methods is simply using both qualitative and quantitative methods in the same study. The methods are kept separate and usually only related through the research questions that drive the methods. SI melds the qualitative and quantitative into one philosophical and methodological approach, thus providing a more integrated solution to academic research and education.

19.7 Development of Visualization

As our analytical techniques gain increased sophistication and power, there is an associated need to be able to communicate the results in clear and powerful ways. Analytics, for example, often favors data visualization to communicate insight. Data visualization is more than merely looking at the numbers on a screen. Data visualization is translating those numbers into concepts or ideas and graphics that both display and explain the numbers. As the 1960s philosopher Marshall McLuhan said, "The medium is the message." (McLuhan & Fiore, 1967). He was simply saying that the medium used to send a message tells a lot about the message itself. That is what data visualization is all about. The graphics or figures used to display the message also help to tell the story.

A good example is the "CAVE" at Virginia Tech. The "CAVE" is a virtual 3-D immersible environment (meaning that it is a three dimensional technological model in which the user can be totally immersed). While inside the "CAVE" the user can become part of the flow and actually travel from node to node in the causal diagram (Dickey & Malhotra, 2003). See Chapter 1, Section 1.6.

Data visualization tools and techniques allow users to widen their experiences through a broader perspective, hopefully prompting these same users to make more informed designs, plans, policies, works of art, and the like. These tools are designed to increase the users' SI, where some of the insights will be beyond what numbers alone can provide, particularly where numbers already play a leading role.

19.8 Recapitulation—In Search of Supernumerary Intelligence

SI is more than merely bringing the quantitative and the qualitative together. SI is a cohesive philosophy and strategy that actually melds the two methods into one. QCQ, as noted earlier, is the analytic tool/process we used to make meaningful models of data. Developed to their fullest, such models can help researchers forecast the future (since, as it is said, that is where we will be spending the rest of our lives). These forecasts can be made for different "what if" strategy conditions and various anticipated external condition levels. Such analyses hopefully will lead to better research, analytics, and management.

As the subtitle of this book suggests, it is focused primarily on improving analytics and management effectiveness. While that may be enough, there also is a substantial interest in developing and/or revising the whole process, involving as it does all the components of SI.

Most quantitative questions are actually preceded by another, more qualitative set. For example, before we can determine how much more money or free time will help us "feel good," we need to understand those characteristics that *will* make us "feel good" and how they accomplish that. We spend much of our lives trying to find answers to such questions—both the quantitative as well as the qualitative issues that surround, precede, and accompany them. We are, then, in search of a kind of intelligence that includes but also is above and beyond numbers—"supernumerary" intelligence.

APPENDIX A

Some Basic Statistics and Mathematics

A.1 A Brief History of Regression

Regression as a technique for curve fitting goes back to the mid-1700s (1), as there is evidence that Jean le Rond D'Alembert employed a technique similar to regression for analyzing the motions of rigid bodies [INT-5 D'Alembert].

It was around the late 1700s that the notion of the squared deviation arrived. This gave birth to the process of minimizing the sum of the squared deviations. This foundational concept of regression, the method of least squares, was developed by Adrien-Marie Legendre in 1805, and by Johann Carl Friedrich Gauss in 1809 [INT-9 Gauss]. He stated that he had used the method since 1795. That claim cannot be proved, so we do not know who has the honor of discovering "least squares."

In the mid nineteenth century Francis Galton [INT-8 Galton] used the phrase "regression toward the mean" to describe how the heights of descendants of tall ancestors tend to regress down towards a normal average. Thus "regression analysis" was born (Barnes, 1998). This was soon followed by the now well-used concept of the correlation coefficient as a measure of goodness of fit (GoF).

Supernumerary Intelligence, pages 293–305
Copyright © 2015 by Information Age Publishing
All rights of reproduction in any form reserved.

Pedhazur (1982) has summarized nicely and completely many of the techniques and philosophies that have grown from these starting points. His discussion includes linear bivariate and multiple regression, "controlling," covariance analysis, nonlinear regression, time series (3.19), and development of systems of linear relationships via path analysis and linear structural relations (LISREL).

He also addresses techniques dealing with a mixture of ratio-scaled and nominal-scaled (categories) variables. As with most statistics texts, Pedhazur's book deals extensively with experimental designs as well as sampling and hypothesis testing.

A.2 A Statistical Slideshow

Seeing that so many people have difficulty understanding and hanging on to statistical concepts, we have opted for a completely different approach. We have developed a notebook (see Figure A.1) that takes the simplest possible example, creates a diagram for that, then gives a short list of the major characteristics as well as advantages and disadvantages. We start with deviations from the average (mean), followed by deviations (referred to as "errors") from a regression line (see Figure A.1), and finally measures of goodness of fit (GoF) of the data (see Figure A.2) from the model (e.g., regression line).

A.3 Variations from the Average (Mean)

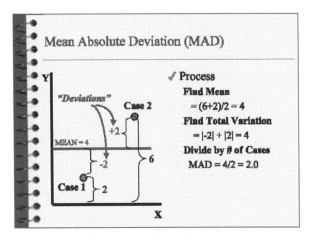

Figure A.1 Variation from the average (mean).

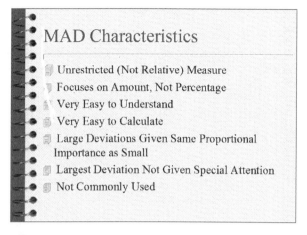

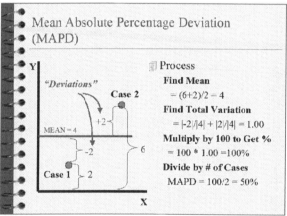

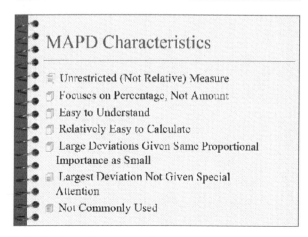

Figure A.1 Variation from the average (mean).

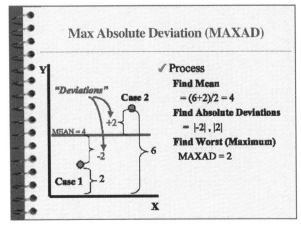

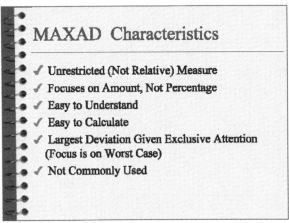

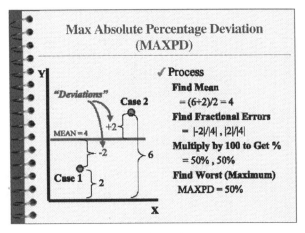

Figure A.1 Variation from the average (mean).

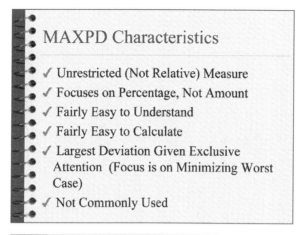

MAXPD Characteristics

✓ Unrestricted (Not Relative) Measure
✓ Focuses on Percentage, Not Amount
✓ Fairly Easy to Understand
✓ Fairly Easy to Calculate
✓ Largest Deviation Given Exclusive Attention (Focus is on Minimizing Worst Case)
✓ Not Commonly Used

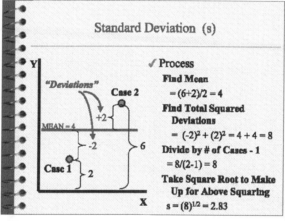

Standard Deviation (s)

✓ Process

Find Mean
$= (6+2)/2 = 4$

Find Total Squared Deviations
$= (-2)^2 + (2)^2 = 4 + 4 = 8$

Divide by # of Cases - 1
$= 8/(2-1) = 8$

Take Square Root to Make Up for Above Squaring
$s = (8)^{1/2} = 2.83$

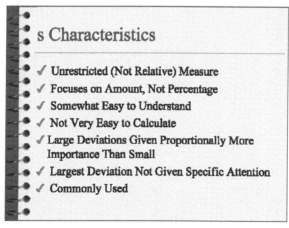

s Characteristics

✓ Unrestricted (Not Relative) Measure
✓ Focuses on Amount, Not Percentage
✓ Somewhat Easy to Understand
✓ Not Very Easy to Calculate
✓ Large Deviations Given Proportionally More Importance Than Small
✓ Largest Deviation Not Given Specific Attention
✓ Commonly Used

Figure A.1   Variation from the average (mean).

A.4 Goodness of Fit Measures

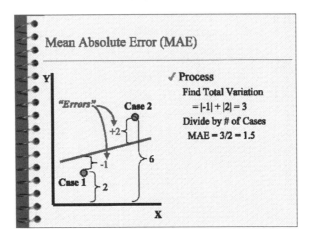

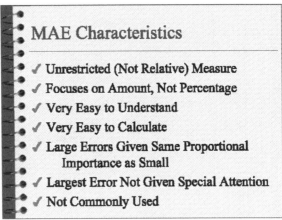

Figure A.2 Goodness of fit measures.

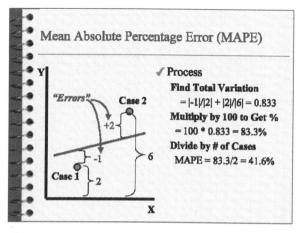

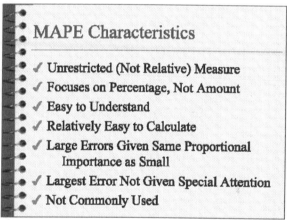

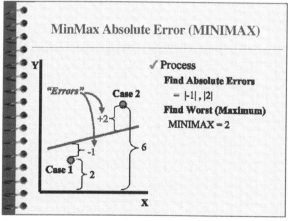

Figure A.2 Goodness of fit measures.

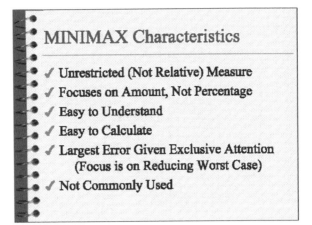

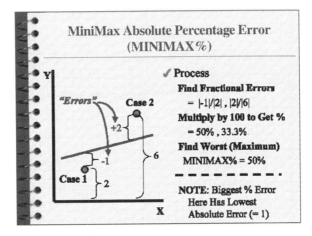

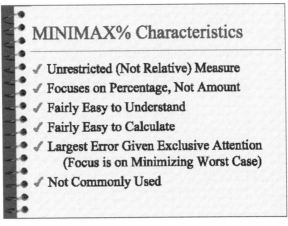

Figure A.2 Goodness of fit measures.

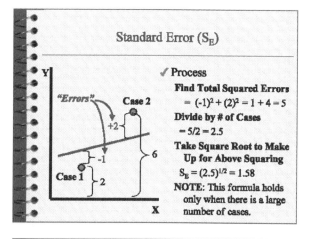

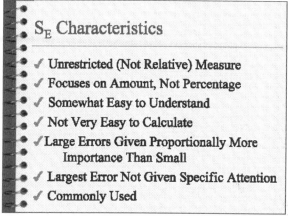

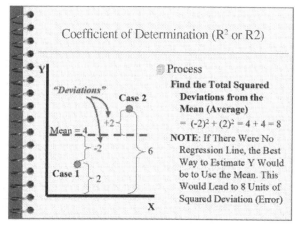

Figure A.2 Goodness of fit measures.

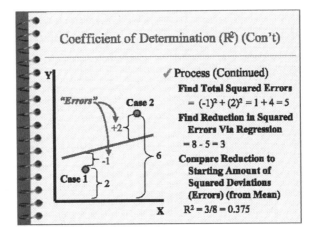

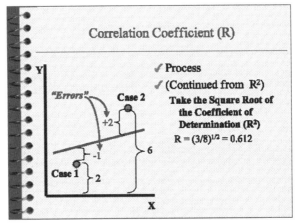

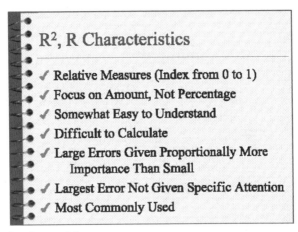

Figure A.2 Goodness of fit measures.

A.5 The Mathematics of Minimization of the MAE and MAPE

Minimization of the mean absolute error (MAE) and mean absolute percentage error (MAPE) in regression involves linear programming. A "program" here is an objective function and one or more constraints. For the MAE the former can be expressed as:

$$\min z = \text{MAE} = \Sigma\, E_i \tag{A.1}$$

where E_i is the "error" (plus or minus) of the point (X_i, Y_i) from the regression line.

There is a constraint associated with each point. Since:

$$Y_i = A + BX_i + E_i \tag{A.2}$$

where A is the (unknown) intercept and B is the (unknown) slope, then, putting the constant on the right hand side gives:

$$A + BX_i + E_i = Y_i \quad \text{(all i)} \tag{A.3}$$

A condition of linear programming is that the unknowns (A, B, and the E_i's) all must be positive or zero. Hence, let us make the transformations:

$$E_i = O_i - U_i \tag{A.4}$$

$$A = A' - A'' \tag{A.5}$$

$$B = B' - B'' \tag{A.6}$$

where:

O_i = amount by which point i is above the line (also called the "surplus");

U_i = amount by which point i is below the line (also called the "slack");

A' = A if the intercept is ≥ 0;

A'' = A if the intercept is < 0;

B' = B if the slope is ≥ 0; and

B'' = B if the slope is < 0.

All of these are restricted to be ≥ 0.

Another condition of linear programming is that the number on the right hand side (Y_i) must be ≥ 0. If Y_i is negative, then both sides of Equation A.3 simply are multiplied by -1.

The linear program (now actually referred to more specifically as a "goal program") looks like:

$$\min z = MAE = (1/n) \Sigma \ (O_i + U_i) \qquad (A.7)$$

subject to (s.t.):

$$A' - A'' + B'X_i - B''X_i - O_i + U_i = Y_i \quad \text{(all i)}$$

$$A', A'', B', B'', O_i, U_i \geq 0 \quad \text{(all i)}$$

The redeeming mathematical feature of a goal program is that both A' and A'' cannot be positive at the same time. Nor can B' and B''. Nor can O_i and U_i. At least one in each pair has to be zero.

Minimization of the mean absolute percentage error (MAPE) also involves a goal program:

$$\min z = MAPE = (100/n) \Sigma \ ((O_i + U_i) / |Y_i| \qquad (A.8)$$

subject to (s.t.):

$$A' - A'' + B'X_i - B''X_i - O_i + U_i = Y_i \quad \text{(all i)}$$

$$A', A'', B', B'', O_i, U_i \geq 0 \quad \text{(all i)}$$

Note in the objective function that the absolute value of Y_i is employed to keep negative numbers from canceling out positive ones. Note, too, that if Y_i were 0, it would make the MAPE infinite. In this situation, the observation is ignored.

An example of equations generated to maximize R^2 versus to minimize the MAPE is presented below. Both of these are power curves. The Y variable is the mean value of owner housing in five census tracts in Roanoke, VA. This is related to the mean crowding level (X, fraction of housing units with 1.01 or more people per room).

The linear regression run to maximize R^2 is:

$$Y = 9{,}125 + 19{,}084 \, X \qquad\qquad (A.9)$$

with an R^2 of 0.437, MAE of \$1,213, and MAPE of 10.8%.

On the other side, the equation to minimize the MAPE (which turns out to be the same as for minimizing the MAE) is:

$$Y = 7{,}900 + 23{,}936 \, X \qquad\qquad (A.10)$$

with an R^2 of 0.335, MAE of \$1130, and MAPE of 8.9%. So there definitely can be a difference in the results.

A curious aspect of a linear programming solution for regression is that the resulting line usually will go through two of the points. Alternately, in some cases in *multiple* linear regression, one or more of the variable coefficients (and possibly the intercept) will be set to 0, with correspondingly fewer points being right on the line. This means that the associated variable essentially is dropped from consideration.

Some Additional Case Studies

For the reader's greater learning experience we present some additional case studies.

B.1   The Rainfall Model Case

Figure B.1 shows the rainfall (in inches) in Roanoke, Virginia in the month of March in each of consecutive years. The order in the data is different from that in any of the preceding examples because it is cyclical—going up and down over time rather than increasing or decreasing monotonically. A linear or exponential regression line obviously would not be very useful in this situation.

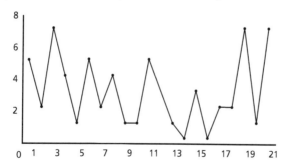

Figure B.1   Rainfall (inches) in Roanoke, VA in March in a sequence of years.

Supernumerary Intelligence, pages 307–316
307

Still, there is a vague sine–cosine pattern, with increases following decreases every second or third year in the context of a longer term cycle every nine years. The (Fourier Series) equation for the combination of three and nine year cycles is:

$$RF(t) = 4.124 + 0.985*COS(6.283*t/3) + 0.166*SIN(6.283*t/3) +$$
$$0.010*COS(6.283*t/9) + 0.857*SIN(6.283*t/9) \qquad \text{(B.1)}$$

With an R^2 of 0.243 and a MAPE of 38.7% (vs. a MAPD of 65.0%), this is not a particularly strong equation.

Perhaps rainfall is "chaotic," meaning that it has "regular irregularities" (Gleich, 1987). A graph of one such situation can be found in Figure B.2 This was generated from the logistic equation:

$$Y[t + 1] = r * Y[t] * (1 - Y[t]) \qquad \text{(B.2)}$$

with $r = 3.9$ and $Y[0]$ is set at 0.1. There appears to be a pattern (actually several patterns) in this plot, yet, frustratingly, it never really repeats itself exactly—it has "regular irregularity."

With some adjustments for height, parts of the plot in Figure B.2 might bear similarity to the pattern in Figure B.1. Still, we have been unable to find a "chaos" formula like that in Equation B.2 that fits the rainfall data well.

Perhaps, as most of us know already, the weather really is "*irregularly* irregular." In any case, for some reason it certainly is a "naturally" volatile variable (as compared, say, to that in the COC chart in Figure 11.2). This

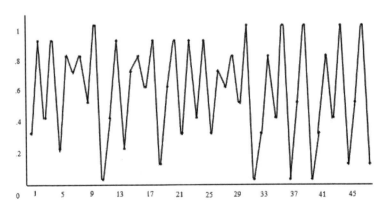

Figure B.2 Example of chaotic behavior.

situation begs the question of what to do when faced with too much scatter, even after incorporating many variables.

QCQ currently does not support either Fourier Series or "chaos" formulae as in Equation B.1 amd B.2, respectively. It does, however, let the user comment on the forecast validity or volatility of a variable such as yearly rainfall.

B.2 Auto Scrappage Case

In many transportation-related air pollution and energy consumption investigations, it is important to know the distribution of the ages of automobiles in the geographic area under study. The reason is that earlier model cars tend on average to emit more pollutants and consume more fuel per mile.

Table B.1 shows, at the national level, the cumulative percentage of autos of a given model year (1970) that were scrapped in succeeding years (i.e, at a given age) (Berkovec, 1985):

The limit on "% Scrapped" (PS) obviously is 100%. A linear regression run on these data gives:

$$PS = -23.74 + 7.350*AGE \tag{B.3}$$

with an R^2 of 0.917. The difficulty here is twofold: (a) if AGE is less than about 3, the estimated PS is less than 0 (e.g., it is –9.04% at AGE = 2); and (b) if AGE is over about 17, then PS exceeds 100% (e.g., it is 123.26% at AGE = 20).

Traditional linear regression obviously is inappropriate when there are upper as well as lower limits on the dependent variable.

An alternate approach is to employ a Gompertz or s-shaped curve (Skiadas & Skiadas, 2008).

$$\%SCRAPPED = 100 * (0.00001576 \wedge (0.7537 \wedge AGE)) \tag{B.4}$$

with an $R^2 = 0.99$. This equation stays within the limits of 0 to 100.

If other factors in addition to AGE affect %SCRAPPED, the regression process would have two steps. First, %SCRAPPED would be regressed against these factors without regard to the 100% limit. A Gompertz regression then

TABLE B.1 Auto Scrappage Versus Age (Years)

Age	1	2	3	4	5	6	7	8	9	10	11	12	13	14
% Scrapped	0.3	0.7	1	2	4	7	14	25	38	50	62	72	79	84

would be made of %SCRAPPED against the *estimate* of %SCRAPPED for each point made from the equation derived in the first step. The same pair of equations then could be employed for forecasting purposes.

B.3 The Stock Market Case

Stock markets present many interesting dilemmas for regression analysis. Of particular concern here is the fact that stocks split (e.g., two new shares are given for each existing one) and are combined (e.g., the respective companies merge, or one is bought by the other). An analysis of stock prices somehow ought to take these bifurcations (or "polyfurcations") and unions into account (see Figure B.2). Traditional regression cannot handle these easily.

Stock markets also are places that give birth and preside over the death of many companies. Traditional regression does not include "step" functions—either jumping up from 0 to a given level, or dropping down precipitously to 0 and staying there.

There are two ways in which the initial two might be handled in regression. The first is to reformulate the Y variable. For instance, the prevailing focus might be on the *price* of a stock, which, say, currently is $10 per share. With a 2 for 1 split, the price may drop to $6 per share. Obviously stockholders are better off since they have $12 worth of stock now as opposed to $10 previously. This seems like an improvement since a straight plot of price versus time would show a drop. The alternate approach thus would be to use the *total value* of stock rather than the price. Unions could be approached similarly.

A second alternative is simply to record the fact that the stock split 2 for 1 on a certain date. The future user of the subsequent regression equation then can interpret the results accordingly.

Stock prices (or total values) of new publicly-traded companies "born" during the calibration period can be handled simply by using the data available (if sufficient) since the "birth." If the company is expected to come into existence in the *forecast* period (a forecast itself, which may be highly uncertain), then there obviously is no relationship to go by (see Section B.1). Scenarios can be set up, however, to highlight different possibilities.

Models of stock markets can be either cross-sectional or dynamic. In the former, attention is given to a set of stocks across a group of companies, in the latter to changes in a stock over time. It is difficult for traditional regression to handle the interaction between both of these simultaneously.

Finally, some kinds of experiments can be done on stock markets, at least in terms of which stocks are purchased or sold. This approach allows for a little more definitive analysis than is possible, say, in a using regression to understand the national economy (where nothing can be controlled by the investigator).

A combination of cross-sectional and dynamic models for a stock market can be developed. To illustrate, the price of a stock A can be regressed against the price of stock B at the same point in time as well as that of stock C, say eight days previously or in the future (for another example see the BART case in Secion B.4).

B.4   The San Francisco BART Case

In 1962 people in the San Francisco region voted for an initial bond issue to build BART—the Bay Area Rapid Transit system. A very intensive study was done to determine the impacts of BART [INT-4 Appleguard & Carp] (Dickey, 1985) about five years after its opening. One part of the study was concerned with the traffic impacts. It was hoped that BART would divert travelers from their cars, thereby reducing traffic congestion. A schematic for this "interrupted time series" caused by the permanent "shock" of BART is presented in Figure B.3.

Interestingly, as portrayed in the diagram, traffic did indeed decrease, but it eventually grew back to the same point it was extrapolated to be had BART not been built. The explanation was that, over time, drivers created a kind of economic supply-demand equilibrium. When traffic congestion was reduced (the "price" of travel was lowered) through increased supply (i.e., BART), drivers increased their travel (demanded or "bought" more)

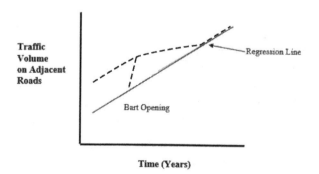

Figure B.3   Regeneration of traffic after opening of BART system.

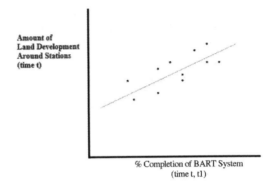

Figure B.4 Adjacent land development vs. completion of the BART system.

until a new equilibrium was reached. The point here, though, is that traditional regression fails to account for such "interruptions."

A second part of the BART study had to do with land use around the BART stations (see Figure B.4). It was hypothesized that various high rise office buildings and shopping areas would develop in a period of years *after* the stations were constructed. In other words, there would be a *delay* of, say, one to three years.

The surprise was that a substantial amount of the land was developed shortly *before* BART was finished. Apparently investors and builders were working in *anticipation* of BART, perhaps expecting land to be cheaper before rather than after the opening.

It might be said for both these kinds of impacts that BART was a *catalyst* for change. A catalyst speeds up a reaction (or, in this case, "preaction") without being consumed in the process. Certainly BART led to a more rapid rate of increase in road traffic (after the initial drop), and it also led to quicker land development near the stations than would have occurred otherwise. The question of whether BART was "consumed" in the process is an open conceptual issue, however. Nonetheless, the point is that traditional regression analysis does not take into account the catalytic impact of certain variables on both time delays and anticipations.

BART's rather quick impact on land surrounding some of the stations (LD) leads to another issue with regression. The coefficient (a) in the (symbolic) relationship:

$$LD = a*BART \qquad\qquad (B.4)$$

presumably would have a very high positive value. Yet if BART started to deteriorate (both physically and financially, as have many such systems in other cities), the reverse impact on land use would take place. Yet this most likely would be at a *much slower rate.* The coefficient thus could be different for a rising versus declining situation.

In fact, the rise and decline processes might take substantially different paths—a kind of *hysteresis* guided by different variables. The rise might be led by land developers, while a fall might be brought about by insufficient funding for operating BART, crime, and a variety of other factors unconnected to developers.

The Bay Area Rapid Transit system thus has presented three main issues for regression analysis:

1. Time-related effects (delay, anticipation, and catalysis) of one variable relative to another;
2. "Interrupted time series" caused by a permanent "shock" (or shocks) (see Figure B.4);
3. The creation of an equilibrium.

The "delay" or "lag" aspect in the first issue is addressed in many books on time series analysis (Hamilton, 1994; Verbeek, 2008). A common approach is to regress the value of the Y variable (e.g., amount of land development around BART stations) at some time (t) against the value of the X variable (e.g., percentage completion of the BART system) at a previous time period (say two years ago, or t-2).

As brought out in the BART case, however, much development came *before* BART. A similar regression approach can be employed for such "anticipation." In this situation:

$$Y[t] = f(X[t+T])$$ (B.5)

where the "+" sign designates the future value and "T" the number of time periods into that future. In the case of BART (see Figure B.4), T might be equal, say, to one year.

Catalysis can affect either a delay or an anticipation, usually (although not necessarily) reducing the former and increasing the latter. A catalyst is a variable that causes these to happen. For instance, some BART station area land development might have occurred even earlier (T) as overall BART funding (F) increased (so that it became more of a "sure thing"). Thus:

$$T = f(F)$$ (B.6)

This equation also can be established via regression.

When a major "shock" (like BART itself or some unplanned event) occurs, regression might be best handled by focusing on the latest trend. This is demonstrated conceptually in Figure B.3, where the regression for Y (traffic volume on adjacent roads) employs only the data for X (time, in years) *after* the BART opening. The data for the preceding years obviously would have less relevance.

Major shocks also can occur during the forecast time horizon period. If the time and magnitude are known, these can be put directly into the appropriate scenario. If they are not (as for, say, earthquakes), simulated values can be put in randomly with timings and amplitudes corresponding to the averages and ranges found historically.

Of course, there is a question of what is meant by a "major" shock. Our lives, and hence the data about them, usually involve both a large number of small ripples and a small number of large ones. Regression centers on the more minor ones but rarely captures all the variation within them. Forecast scenarios thus should include random small variations corresponding to the MAE of the regression line.

The third issue, of equilibrium, generally is handled by inclusion of multiple equations in the overall model. As an example, if traffic on adjacent roads (Y_1) is influenced by BART ridership (Y_2) and income (X), while ridership depends solely on adjacent road traffic, then (assuming linearity for simplicity):

$$Y_1 = a + b*Y_2 + c*X \qquad (B.7)$$

and:

$$Y_2 = g + h*Y_1 \qquad (B.8)$$

Each of these can be established by individual regressions and solved simultaneously to get estimates of Y_1 and Y_2.

Note that while QCQ currently cannot handle such simultaneity, this may not be necessary anyway. There probably are time delays in operation that preclude simultaneous action. A current BART rider, for instance, may have to buy a car before making the switch to driving. This could delay that transition so that it no longer is simultaneous.

B.5   The Trip Generation Case

An issue that comes up periodically with regression is how to address situations that demonstrate "unusual" scatter patterns. An example of one of these is the relationship between the number of daily trips made by members of a household and that household's income.

As shown schematically in Figure B.5, there is a kind of scatter that covers a triangle emanating from the lower left hand corner of the axes. This seems to occur because poor households are restricted in their travel by their incomes, whereas richer ones can travel as much or as little as they like. Members of a rich household, for instance, may like to work at home and stay secluded socially, in which case they might not travel any more than those people in a poor household.

Obviously, no standard regression approach is going to be able to produce a high GoF for this unusual type of scatter.

The issue brought forth by this case is that of what to do with "unusual" scatter. This is a subset, actually, of the more general situation where an unacceptable amount of scatter (error) remains after the "best" relationship has been developed. Both thus can be addressed at one time.

There are at least three ways in which an attempt may be made to reduce undesirable scatter:

1. Try a different form for the equation—for example, an exponential in place of a linear;
2. Add additional variables (and associated new forms of relationship)—for example, for the trip generation case, consider household size as well as income as independent variables;
3. Record a note to the potential user about the situation.

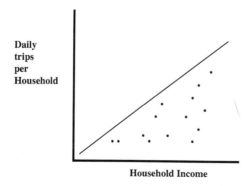

Figure B.5   Variations in daily trips with household income.

The third approach obviously is the last to be taken. The second, which is the "pre-equalization" feature of QCQ (see Section A.12 on the gravity model), has much more potential than the first but makes for more complexity as well as difficulty in forecasting the values of the input (X) variables.

Characteristics of Supernumerary Intelligence (by Step in QCQ Process)

C.1 Overall Process

Encompassing Process: There is a complete, explicit overall set of steps to guide the user in application to a real world situation.

C.2 QCQ Steps

C.2.1 Step 1: Situation Description

1.1 *Aim/Client Identification:* An explicit request is made for the main purpose (goal) of the study; the client for whom intended; etc.

1.2 *Budget Identification:* An explicit request is made for the resources expended on the study.

1.3 *Time Horizon:* An explicit request is made for a time horizon—the point in time in the future for which forecasts are to be made.

1.4 *Developer and User:* An explicit request is made for the name of the model developer and the user of the results.

Supernumerary Intelligence, pages 317–327

C.2.2 Step 2: Theory Search

2.1 *Theories/Analogues:* A request is made for generic concepts (theories) or closely similar situations (analogues) that underlie the model. These "theologues" then can be incorporated into the model.

2.2 *"Real World" Processes:* The equations simulate steps in the associated "real world" process (rather than just correlating variables in it).

2.3 *Variable Identification:* The technique helps in identifying and selecting appropriate variables and variable constructs.

2.4 *Content Analyses:* A search can be made through text material to locate prominent words and phrases in order to discover relevant variables and relationships.

2.5 *Variable Generation:* Variables can be identified through a brainstorming-like process.

2.6 *New Future Variables:* Variables that were not present in the calibration or test period but that are expected in the future can be incorporated.

2.7 *Situation Structuring:* The situation (problem, opportunity) being addressed can be divided (structured) into a small number of relatively homogeneous subcomponents.

C.2.3 Step 3: Theory Development

3.1 *General Theory:* A generic theory is available as backup in case an acceptable one is not found.

3.2 *Anomalies/Paradoxes/Extremes:* A request is made for identification of apparently contradictory statements (paradoxes), highly unusual events or characteristics (anomalies), and excessive conditions (extremes) that need to be addressed by the theory.

3.3 *Policy Capabilities:* The overall model can, if needed, incorporate client policy/strategy/decision variables.

3.4 *Redundant Variables:* Variables that are essentially duplicate measures of the same phenomenon can be recognized and eliminated.

3.5 *Domain Identification:* Boundaries can be identified on the set of variables that will be part of the model.

3.6 *Alternate Causal Sets:* Different groups of (perhaps overlapping) causal variables can be developed into different causal models.

3.7 *Open or Closed System:* A model can be created in which either (a) every variable (except time) is related to another variable (or time) or (b) external policy variables (see 2.5 above) can be admitted.

3.8 *Causal Questions:* A series of questions can be asked to help establish a cause and effect link between one variable and another.

3.9 *Causes, Not Symptoms:* A distinction can be made between a variable that accompanies a causal one (symptom) but is not the actual cause (see 2.16 above).

3.10 *Unknown Relationships:* The technique can be used to help identify relationships when there is no previous theory available.

3.11 *No Cause Correlation:* A distinction can be made between correlations that are a result of cause and effect and those that are not (see also 2.16 above).

3.12 *Direct/Indirect Influences:* X variables can be divided into those that act with no intermediaries (direct) on the given Y variable and those whose effect is through other variables (indirect).

3.13 *Balance of Forces:* The given Y variable can be seen in an equation (model) as being influenced by one or more variables that *raise* the level of Y and are offset (balanced) by one or more that *lower* the level.

3.14 *Causal Diagramming:* A listing and diagram can be created showing the network of possible links or causes in the potential model.

3.15 *External/Policy/Goal:* Variables can be divided into categories like External, Invariate, Goal, Policy, Intermediate, and Reaction Time (and associated Catalyst).

3.16 *2-Way Causality:* A variable can both affect and be affected by another one (possibly simultaneously).

3.17 *Reduction to Invariates:* Variables that are constant over time and/ or space (invariates) can be identified and can be (although they need not be) reduced to a function of these invariates.

3.18 *Cyclical Variables:* A variable that changes regularly about a fixed value (i.e., a stationary process) can be incorporated into the model.

3.19 *Time Delay:* A Y variable can be related to an X variable lagging by one or more time periods.

3.20 *Time Anticipation:* A Y variable can be related to (the prediction of) an X variable leading by one or more time periods.

3.21 *Catalysis:* The reaction (preaction) time in a relationship time delay (anticipation) can vary according to the influence of one or more variables (catalysts).

3.22 *Peaking:* The highest (lowest) values of a variable within a given time period can be forecast.

3.23 *Assumptions:* A request is made to identify and describe the major suppositions behind the theories and/or analogues associated with the given relationship.

C.2.4   Step 4: Data Specification and Collection

4.1 *Many Variables/Relations:* The technique can accept data for a large number of variables and observations.

4.2 *Surrogate Variables:* A variable, with available data, can be substituted for a similar one for which no data are available.

4.3 *Ratio/Nominal Scales:* The measure of a variable can be on either a ratio or nominal scale (or interval or ordinal).

4.4 *Multi-Dimensional Measure:* More than one measure can be employed to describe the same concept.

4.5 *Validity/Precision/Etc.:* A request is made to input data on a variable's validity, precision, definition and measure agreement, reliability, etc.

4.6 *Data Constraints:* A request is made for information on the unobvious limitations on the data and helps them to be identified and described.

4.7 *Eliminating Unusual Observations:* Data that contain highly unique and inappropriate values can be extracted out of the calibration and/or test sets.

4.8 *Statistical Properties:* A request is made for information on the statistical characteristics of the data set (e.g., population, unit of observation, unit of analysis, sample type, and sample size).

4.9 *New Variable Forms:* New variables can be created from old ones. For example, speed = distance/time.

4.10 *Specific Definitions/Measures:* A request for each variable to be defined in depth as well as to be given both a brief and detailed measure.

4.11 *Super Achievement:* A variable that has a limit can be changed, in process, to allow for a higher (or lower) limit.

4.12 *Subjective Measures:* The measure attached to a variable can be either objective or subjective.

4.13 *New Measures:* Historical changes in the measure associated with a variable can be noted, and new measures can be incorporated in the forecast period.

4.14 *Variable Ranges/Limits/Violations:* The range limits of a variable must be identified, and any equation for that variable must not violate those limits.

C.2.5 Step 5: Individual Relationship Development

5.1 *Cross-Sectional & Dynamic:* The technique can be used for data representing one "slice" in time (cross-sectional) and/or for a number of time periods (dynamic).

5.2 *Experimental/Non Cases:* The technique can be employed when data are collected in the context of a formal experimental design and/or when they are not.

5.3 *Interchangeable Variables:* Variables that can be exchanged for each other can be identified and treated as the same.

5.4 *No Y: X Correlation:* X variables that are not highly correlated on an individual basis with the given Y variable but do contribute in conjunction with other X variables can be identified (and not eliminated).

5.5 *Component Decomposition:* The technique can be utilized to divide a variable (or variables) into equivalent component parts.

5.6 *Precedents/"Gates":* The technique allows incorporation of unique antecedents (precedents or gates) that become the new rules of operation from that point in time on.

5.7 *"Accounting" Relations:* The technique allows incorporation of equations that are, by definition, simple sums or multipliers of variables (no regression needed).

5.8 *Deduction Process:* The technique allows incorporation of equations for already developed theory and new equations based on combinations of them (deduction).

5.9 *Value of 1 Case:* The technique recognizes the contribution of a case involving only one observation.

5.10 *Time Discounting:* Weights can be assigned to time series observations for an X variable to give greater or lower importance to their contribution to the current Y value.

5.11 *Curve fitting to Data:* The technique provides a process for calibrating (fitting) a variety of equations to data.

5.12 *Calibration & Test Data:* Data can be divided into those used for curve fitting (calibration) and those employed to test the resultant equations.

5.13 *Direct GoF Optimization:* Equations can be calibrated by optimizing the selected goodness of fit measure (e.g., R^2, MAE, MAPE) directly.

5.14 *Acceptable Structures:* The technique will permit usage only of those forms of relationship that have the "correct" sign, stay within the range limits of a variable (see 4.4 above), and have the correct type of intercept (see 4.15 below).

5.15 *Correct Intercept:* The selected form of X:Y relationship gives only the allowable type of intercept (e.g., at 0, 0) if there is one (i.e., if Y does not approach infinity as X approaches 0). It also gives a 0 value for Y if the situation is such that Y has to be 0 when any X is 0.

5.16 *Covered Y Range:* Every value of Y in its operational range (or at least every value found in the calibration and test data sets) can be obtained in the Y vs. X relationship.

5.17 *Covered X Range:* Every value of X in its operational range (or at least every value found in the calibration and test data sets) can be used in the Y vs. X relationship to get a value of Y within its range.

5.18 *Nonlinear Relationships:* Functions other than linear can be calibrated.

5.19 *Multivariate Relationships:* Functions with more than one independent variable can be calibrated.

5.20 *Multicolinearity:* Alternate measures for a variable that are highly correlated can be reduced in numbers. Different causal (X) variables (for a given Y) that are highly correlated can be accommodated.

5.21 *Implicit Relationships:* Associations in which there is no explicit Y variable can be accommodated.

5.22 *Competitive Relationships:* Associations in which competing forces (including "Nature") control or partially control different X variables can be accommodated. [See any model in which there are "external" variables]

5.23 *Stochastic Relationships:* Associations in which unpredictable variations are included (e.g., Markov chains) can be accommodated.

5.24 *Discrete Event Relationships:* Associations in which there is a flow of discrete entities through a process (e.g., discrete event simulation) can be accommodated.

5.25 *Optimization Relationships:* Associations that have Y reaching a minimum or maximum value somewhere within the range of X can be accommodated.

5.26 *Hysteresis:* An association in which the Y changes at a different rate as X increases vs. when X decreases can be accommodated.

5.27 *"Shocks" (Temporary/Permanent):* Situations in which there are substantial, rapid interruptions ("shocks"), both short and long term, to a time series can be accommodated.

5.28 *Duotonic Relationships:* Associations in which Y can take on two values for a given value of X can be accommodated.

5.29 *"Envelope" Relationships:* Associations in which all of the observations are contained within an overriding "envelope" can be accommodated.

5.30 *"Pre-Equalization":* The technique allows a variety of proposed equations ("pre-equalities," which are not intended to be equal to each other) can be tested before a "final" equation is selected.

5.31 *Missing Values:* Situations in which values for some variables for some observations are missing can be accommodated.

5.32 *Not Applicables:* Situations in which values for some variables for some observations are not relevant can be accommodated.

5.33 *Inappropriate Signs:* Situations in which regression generates an obviously incorrect sign for the coefficient for the X variable can be recognized and appropriate adjustments made.

5.34 *Sign Switching:* Situations in which regression with an additional X variable leads to a switch in sign for the coefficient of a preceding variable can be recognized and appropriate adjustments made.

5.35 *Mis/Disinformation:* Situations in which misinformation or intentional disinformation arise (in the form of additional X variables) can be identified and appropriate adjustments made in the equation and the GoF (so that the GoF does *not improve* with additional variables).

5.36 *Information Confusion:* Situations in which additional information (in the form of additional X variables) lead to information overload and confusion can be identified and appropriate adjustments made in the equation and the GoF (so that the GoF does *not improve* with additional variables).

5.37 *Y in Range if X's in Range:* Estimates of Y will be in its operational range if those for the X's are in their respective calibration and test data ranges. (See 4.4 above)

5.38 *Acceptable Range Union:* The common two-dimensional space that is the intersection of the operational ranges of Y and Xj can be defined and used in selecting eligible relationship forms.

5.39 *Component Constraints:* Constraints tying together different, essentially similar parts of a situation (see 4.5 above) can be identified and used in the solution process.

5.40 *Necessary/Sufficient Variables:* Each of the X variables in an equation (model) is basic (necessary) to forecasting Y, and the *set* of X's leaves no important X out (is sufficient) in making the forecast.

5.41 *Birth/Death Processes:* A variable can go to zero and stay there (death) and, conversely, rise from zero (birth) at any point in the calibration or forecast periods.

5.42 *Irreversible Change:* A variable can be "set on a track" such that it cannot decrease (increase) if it is increasing (decreasing).

5.43 *Variable Division/Joining:* A variable can be divided into parts, or two or more variables can be joined together, in process.

5.44 *Regular Irregularity:* A relationship can be portrayed in which the pattern of connection appears to be almost repeatable, but not exactly (chaos theory).

5.45 *Increase/Decrease Speeds:* The coefficient relating a Y variable to an X can differ in value depending on whether X is increasing or decreasing.

C.2.6 Step 6: Relationship Evaluation

6.1 *Alternate GoF Criteria:* A wide variety of goodness of fit criteria (e.g., R^2, MAPE, MAE, sE) are available for selection.

6.2 *Situational Constraints:* Any restrictions in the situation under study that affect the nature and extent of an association can be identified and accommodated.

6.3 *Relationship Experience:* The previous history of trials and experiments with the association can be documented and assessed.

6.4 *Extrapolation Errors:* A request is made concerning the utility of the relationship for extrapolation (as opposed to fitting data).

6.5 *Degrees of Freedom:* There is recognition of the difference in the number of observations and the number of parameters used in the equation employing these observations.

6.6 *GoF Guidance:* The technique gives the user advice in selecting the goodness of Fit criterion.

6.7 *Lower GoF Possible:* A less-than-the-best value of the selected goodness of fit criterion can be accepted, particularly if the better fitting equation has less appropriate variables or structure, incorrect signs, etc.

6.8 *Heteroscedasticity:* There is recognition of and adjustment for situations where the error about the regression line increases (decreases) as a given X increases.

6.9 *Non-Statistical Evaluation:* Factors other than statistical in nature can be employed in the assessment of the relationship (see, for example, 5.15–5.22).

6.10 *Criteria Tradeoffs:* The relative value of different evaluation criteria can be assessed and used in making decisions about the merit of a particular relationship.

6.11 *Parsimony:* A request is made to check that no more variables and parameters are used than absolutely necessary.

6.12 *Logical Consistency:* A request is made to show that the relationship correctly and coherently follows the rules of induction and deduction.

6.13 *Conceivable Refutation:* A request is made to affirm that there is a possible procedure for disproving the theory represented by the relationship.

6.14 *Skeptic Reproduction:* A request is made to show that a knowledgeable person who doubts the relationship can arrive at the same result using the same procedure.

6.15 *Paradox Resolution:* A request is made to show whether the relationship has settled any previously identified paradoxes and anomalies. (see 2.4 above)

6.16 *Problem Solving Model:* A request is made to show how the technique (and relationship) offers an approach to help get answers to issues.

6.17 *Poses New Problems:* A request is made to describe how the technique (and relationship) brings to the surface issues that have not been addressed before.

6.18 *Changes Thinking:* A request is made to indicate how the technique (and relationship) alter the way in which users envision and approach the situation under study.

6.19 *Demonstrates Novelty:* A request is made to describe how the relationship is new and different from its predecessors.

6.20 *Surpasses Predecessors:* A request is made to show how the relationship is an improvement on previous ones.

6.21 *Testing History:* A request is made to describe how the evaluation of the relationship fits with past assessment practices.

6.22 *Beauty/Harmony:* A request is made to describe the aesthetics of the relationship.

6.23 *Technical Skill:* A request is made to show how development of the relationship required mastery of technique and procedure.

6.24 *Requires Interpretation:* A request is made to describe the kinds of clarifications needed to understand the relationship.

6.25 *Optimum GoF Achievement:* Parameters in the relationship equation can be established to optimize the selected goodness of fit criterion.

6.26 *Close Test Values:* The best calibrated equation can produce estimated values for Y close to those found in the respective test observations.

6.27 *Excessive Scatter:* The technique offers the user guidance on what to do if a large amount of scatter still remains after calibration has taken place.

6.28 *"Unusual" Scatter:* The technique offers the user guidance on what to do if the X-Y scatter is "unique" (e.g., in a triangle in the lower part of the X-Y coordinate plane).

C.2.7 Step 7: Forecasting

7.1 *Scenario Generation:* A new set of future events and/or activities can be proposed and tested.

7.2 *Retrodiction:* "Backcasts" can be made for times before that associated with the earliest observations.

7.3 *Forecasting:* Predictions can be made under different scenarios.

7.4 *Error Analysis:* A forecast range can be created for a given Y variable given the sampling, measurement, and forecast errors in the associated X variables (see 6.4 and 6.5 above).

7.5 *New Shocks:* Future jumps/drops in X variables can be simulated.

7.6 *New Random Variations:* Future series of "small" jumps/drops in X variables can be simulated.

7.7 *Controlling:* The impact of changes in one variable, all others being held constant, can be simulated.

7.8 *Forecast X Variables:* Relationships are created to forecast each of X variables in each relationship unless they are data or invariates (see 2.27 above).

7.9 *Predictability of "Volatiles":* Highly mercurial variables (low predictive validity) can be forecast with accuracy.

7.10 *"True" Variable Effect:* The parameter(s) associated with an X variable can be taken as an accurate measure of the influence of that variable—it will not change substantially as other variables are added to the relationship.

7.11 *Sampling/Measurement Errors:* The likely amount of error resulting from sampling and measurement of influencing X variables can be estimated.

7.12 *Error Propagation:* The spread of errors from one equation to another (where the Y of the first is an X in the second) can be estimated and adjustments made therefore.

7.13 *System "Warm Up":* A sufficient number of time periods (observations) can be used to allow the system of equations to approximate the dynamic equilibrium of the actual system under study (which usually has been in a process of evolution way before the date of the earliest set of observations).

7.14 *Time Series "Leveling":* The forecasted future values will not approach a limiting median value.

7.15 *Mathematical Simultaneity:* The technique can be employed to solve simultaneous equations.

Checklist for Cause and Effect Considerations

"Cause and effect" is a concept derived from observation of the changes that happen continually in both the real world and our inner view of what is happening. The concept of causality is about the relationship that exists between one action, or set of actions, ("the cause") and a second action, or event (the effect) where the second action is a result of the first. The study of causality extends into antiquity and still remains today a staple in current philosophical scholarship.

Influences on the resulting action (effect) is a factor of that effect. There are two types of factors—direct and indirect. A direct factor is a one that affects an effect without any intervening factors. An indirect factor is one that affects the effect by going through an intervening factor, also called an intermediate factors. This concept is the same as used in QCQ to identify variables.

In this Appendix we will propose and give examples of 10 basic elements we feel help to differentiate between a finding of cause and effect, and otherwise. We guess that you will not be surprised to find there still is left an assortment of qualitative judgments to be made.

Supernumerary Intelligence, pages 329–345
Copyright © 2015 by Information Age Publishing
329

D.1 Reasons for Needing to Know About Cause and Effect

Our survival, and then progress, depends on it.

Example:
Starting a fire in an all wood building will *cause* it to burn down (with you possibly in it).

Example:
Growths in population and income (gross domestic product or GDP) *cause* increases in solid waste (trash and garbage) and subsequent disposal problems.

Example:
We save many lives from fires in buildings (action), but not all (realization). We thus are upset (discontent) and try harder (more action).

Example:
Most solid waste is put in landfills (action), but many of these are filled up (realization), so we are aggravated by the problem (discontent) and seek new approaches to disposal (more action).

D.2 Basic Elements of Cause and Effect

- A "client" for whom the explanation is being given.
- An "agent" to carry out the "cause."
- A clear definition of the proposed "cause" (X) factor.
- A subject or "receptacle" to receive the "effect" of X.
- A clear definition of the proposed "effect" (Y) factor.
- A scenario showing the main sets of variables.
- A clear definition of the proposed mode of relationship between X and Y.
- A measure of the "strength" of relationship between X and Y.
- A measure of the "truth" of the X factor.
- A measure of the "truth" of the relationship between X and Y.

D.3 Client for the Explanation

The type of explanation can vary by the "client" for whom it is intended.

Example:
The fire was caused by a careless smoker (client: fire department).

Example:
The fire was caused by the all wood building (client: building code official).

Example:
The fire was caused by the heating of molecules, bringing them to a more active state (client: physicist).

D.4 Causal Agents

An "agent" is a person, group, animal, natural force, or any entity set in motion or place by any of these.

Example:
Lightning (natural force) caused the fire.

Example:
A match (struck by a person) caused the fire.

An agent "causes," "produces," "influences," or "leads to" an effect.

Example:
Lightning produced or lead to the fire.

The agent usually releases or transfers "energy" to the subject.

Example:
The careless smoker (agent) lit the match and tossed it (energy transfer) on the pile of rags (subject).

There can be a large number of agents.

Example:
The fire was caused by the increased activity of billions of overheated molecules.

An "agent" can cause something by doing nothing.

Example:
The fire was caused by lack of fire inspections (by the fire department).

The public can, but science generally cannot, accept a purposeful agent as an explanation (teleology).

Example:
Jim set (caused) the fire because he wanted to (purpose).

Example:
The fire was caused by God to warn people (purpose) about their sinfulness.

The agent may be anticipated rather than existing.

Example:
The fire was caused by anticipation of a good insurance settlement.

The agent may be as "far back" in the "causal chain" as desired.

Example:
The fire was caused by the careless smoker; the careless smoker was "caused" by excessive worry; the worry was caused by family problems; and so on.

The "ultimate" agent ("first cause") may be God, nature, the sun, etc.

The agent may be a trait.

Example:
The fire was caused by the smoker's carelessness (trait).

D.5   Definition of the Causal (X) Variable

Stated in terms understandable to the client.

Example:

The fire was caused by a factor whose LaPlace Transform of its Bessel function had a high variance (not understandable to most clients).

Stated in terms agreed upon by most people.

Example:

The fire was caused by an "emotionally imbalanced" employee (defined differently by different people).

Given with units of measurement.

Example:

The fire was caused by a temperature that exceeded 250 degrees Fahrenheit.

Stated in terms of a given level of aggregation or generality (including for time).

Example:

The fire was caused by striking a match, moving it four feet, and holding it to the flammable rags—all in a period of three minutes (minute hand movements aggregated to three motions; time aggregated to whole minutes).

D.6   Subject or "Receptacle" to Receive the Effect of X

A "subject" is a person, group, animal, natural force, or any entity set in motion or place by a causal agent.

Example:

Lightning caused the fire in the building (subject or receptacle).

Example:

A match (struck by a person) caused the fire in the building (subject).

A subject is "caused," "produced," "influenced," "lead to," or "given energy" by a causal agent.

Example:

Lightning produced or lead to the fire in the building.

The subject usually receives "energy" from the agent.

Example:

The careless smoker (agent) lit the match and tossed it (energy) on the pile of rags (subject/receptacle).

There can be a large number of subjects.

Example:

The increased activity of billions of molecules was caused by the fire.

A "subject" can be affected even if it does not change.

Example:

The building roof (subject) was kept in place during the fire by the concrete columns.

The subject usually is not thought of as a purposeful agent.

Example:

The fire injured Jim (he was a "victim" who could not purposely avoid it).

The subject may be anticipated rather than existing.

Example:

The wooden building caused the fire department to have anticipations of a fire.

The subject may be as "far forward" in the "causal chain" as desired.

Example:

The fire was caused by the careless smoker; the careless smoker was "caused" by excessive worry; the worry was caused by family problems; etc.

The subject may be a trait.

Example:

The fire caused the building to look like a derelict (trait).

D.7 Definition of the Effect (Y) Variable

(See Section D.5 for similar considerations)

D.8 Scenario Showing the Main Variables

There are literally millions of potential causes (and categories thereof) for most effects.

Examples for a building fire:

- Careless smoker
- Gas stove
- Cigarettes
- War
- Match
- Riot
- Pile of rags
- Bad fire alarm
- Wooden building
- Forest fire
- Masonry building
- Earthquake
- Lightning
- Water shortage
- High building temperature
- No fire department
- Heater explosion
- Fire insurance
- No sprinkler system
- Rain outside

- ▪ Arsonist
- ▪ Electric short
- ▪ Disgruntled employee
- ▪ Sun's heat

These are just a few of the immediate ones and do not count ones further down the causal chain.

Example:
Employee gets drunk, has fight with family, is angry, fights with boss, retaliates by setting fire to building.

The list of potential causes depends on the knowledge and memory of those people involved in the investigation.

Example:
The potential cause of "spontaneous combustion" may not be known to an eight year old, so would not be included on his/her list.

Example:
The fire department did not remember to investigate the possibility of spontaneous combustion as a potential cause.

New potential causes may be created.

Example:
The price of eggs in New Zealand went up, thereby causing the U.S. egg processing business to be unprofitable, thereby causing the owner to set fire to his building to collect insurance money.

Shows agent(s), all significant necessary and sufficient X variables, and the effect (Y) variable(s).

Example:
Scenario 1:

Agent: Careless smoker

Causal Variables: Lit match, cigarette, pile of flammable rags, all wood building, careless smoker

Action: Agent tosses lit cigarette on rag pile

Effect: Building catches on fire

Note: The fire could not start without *each one* of the necessary causes existing. *And,* taken as a group, they are sufficient to start a fire.

Can show variables *not* in effect.

Example:
The building did *not* have a smoke alarm or sprinkler system.

Many scenarios can include the same effect(s).

Example:
The fire might have been caused by lightning, a bomb, a fire next door, an electrical short, and so on.

A potential causal variable is selected for a scenario in part because it is true or unusual.

Example:
It is true that there was a pile of rags in the building when it caught fire (so this variable was selected as a potential cause).

Example:
It was extremely hot the day of the fire (so this factor was selected because it was unusual).

A potential causal variable is selected in part because of personal values.

Example:
One physical science definition of a fire includes a need for a fuel, oxygen, and spark but not any human action to start it.

Example:
The President (a Republican) stated that the riots that led to the fires were caused by failed Great Society programs (developed by the Democrats).

A given causal variable can show up in more than one scenario.

Example:
The above-mentioned pile of flammable rags might also have caught on fire in a scenario involving spontaneous combustion.

D.9 Definition of the Type of Relationship Between X and Y.

Something that seems strange is just another instance of something familiar.

Example:
The fire in the wood building was caused by spontaneous combustion of the rag pile (usually we think of spontaneous combustion of leaves or papers).

The type of relationship can be almost anything.

Example:
An increase in the number of fire detectors caused a decrease in the number of fires (change in amount).

Example:
The fire caused the solid pile of rags to turn into a gas (change in state or category).

Example:
Lack of oxygen caused the fire to die out (change from existence to nonexistence).

Example:
The fire caused an explosion (change in speed of reaction).

Example:
The fire was caused by the temperature of the rags exceeding their point of volatility (change above a limit or threshold).

Example:

Quick response by the building sprinkler system prevented a fire (no change).

Example:

The concrete columns in the building caused (allowed) the roof to remain in place during the fire (relationship as static support).

The cause (or the anticipation thereof) occurs before the effect.

Example:

The careless smoker lit the match, then threw it on the rags, which then caused the fire.

Example:

The careless smoker's habit started 20 years ago, which caused the current fire.

Example:

The careless smoker anticipated no retribution if he caused a fire.

The proposed cause, if manipulated (or imagined to be manipulated), would lead to a change in the proposed effect.

Example:

If the building were changed from wood to masonry (stone/brick), there no longer would be a fire.

The proposed cause and effect are correlated, but both are an effect from another cause.

Example:

The fire was caused by smoke (smoke always came before—and during and after—the fire, but both were caused by, say, the cigarette thrown into the rag pile).

The proposed cause and effect appear *not* to be related (correlated?) but are so when divided into categories.

Example:
The number of building fires does not appear to be related to the number of careless smokers until a division is made between fires in wooden and masonry (nonflammable stone/brick) structures.

The proposed cause is a "symptom" (a change in normal function indicating a disorder) not a "real" cause.

Example:
The fire was "caused" by the smoke alarm going off (change in normal function).

Note: A symptom here also is an effect due to another cause.

The proposed cause can be at various distances back in the "causal chain."

Example:
The fire in the building was caused by the careless smoker, whose carelessness was caused by family life stress, which was caused by inability to pay bills, which was caused by...

Depending on the explanative need, the relationship can be presented simply or as a chain (or network).

Example:
In the example immediately preceding this one, the fire could be simply said to be caused by the inability to pay bills.

Cause and effect can be jointly related.

Example:
Fires can be caused by increases in heat, but increases in heat can be caused by fires.

The proposed cause may be a catalyst (a factor that augments the rate of reaction but is not used up itself).

Example:

The fire was caused by the careless smoker but was aided by the high outside summer temperature, which increased the speed at which the fire started.

The relationship may be probabilistic (e.g., Y does not occur every time X occurs).

Example:

A fire is caused many times (but not always) when a careless smoker tosses a lit cigarette into a pile of flammable rags.

The level of aggregation (including time) in the relationship must be established.

Example:

The relationship was determined between the number of fires in a year versus type of building for different cities in the United States.

The relationship might have a time dimension.

Example:

There was a ten minute delay between the time the cigarette was tossed and the time the building was on fire.

Example:

The fire grew in intensity over time.

A relationship usually involves a release or transfer of "energy" from the "cause" to the "effect."

Example:

The careless smoker caused the fire by lighting the cigarette and throwing (transferring/releasing) it on the pile of rags.

There is an "independent" and "dependent" variable in the relationship.

Example:
(Boyle's Law) The volume of a gas at a certain pressure divided by the temperature is a constant $(PV/T = c)$. (Here, in this implicit relationship, any two of the variables can be assigned values and the third computed. There thus is no independent "cause.")

The relationship might depend on the *cumulative* amount of X.

Example:
The smoker was careless because of the buildup of anxieties over home life problems.

The relationship should not be just a definition in disguise.

Example:
The fire was caused by "a rapid but persistent reaction accompanied by the emission of light and heat" (a definition of "fire" from the Mc-Graw Hill Concise Encyclopedia of Science and Technology, 1984).

The type of relationship selected depends on the knowledge, memory, and values of the investigators.

Example:
See examples under Section D.8.

D.10 Measure of the "Truth" of the Relationship between X and Y

May just be a rationalization of the investigator's expectations.

Example:
The fire was caused by the owner just trying to get back some insurance money (expectation) versus the fire was caused by lightning (reality).

May be a logical deduction from two true statements.

Example:

All fires are hot. This is a fire. Therefore this fire is hot.

Depends on the "population" or "range" to which the relationship supposedly applies.

Example:

The relationship between building fires and careless smokers may only apply in places that have wooden buildings (in Israel, for example, most buildings are masonry and do not burn easily).

Depends on the size of the sample from the identified population.

Example:

If the "population" is all the buildings in, say, Los Angeles, and only one building were selected for investigation, the truth of the relationship between building fires and careless smokers would be much more suspect than if 100 buildings were selected.

Depends on the type of sample taken from the identified population.

Example:

In the Los Angeles example mentioned previously, a selection of 100 buildings at random from around the city would be much more representative than only from one block (say in an area with all brick buildings).

Depends on the level of aggregation/generality.

Example:

The average number of fires versus the average number of careless smokers will show an apparent higher correlation than when individual items in those averages are compared.

D.11   Measure of the "Truth" of the X Factor

May just be a rationalization of the investigator's expectations.

Example:

The employee who started the fire was "careless" versus the employee was "overworked and tired."

May be a logical deduction from two true statements.

Example:

All fires are hot. This is a fire. Therefore this fire is hot.

Depends on the "population" or "range" from which the X factor values are drawn or measured.

Example:

Most buildings in Los Angeles are wooden (but most in Jerusalem are not).

Depends on the size of the sample from the identified population.

Example:

If the "population" is all the buildings in, say, Los Angeles, and only one building were selected for investigation, the truth of the statement about wooden buildings would be much more suspect than if 100 buildings were selected.

Depends on the type of sample taken from the identified "population."

Example:

In the Los Angeles example mentioned previously, a selection of 100 buildings at random from around the city would be much more representative than only from one block (say in an area with all brick buildings).

Depends on the level of aggregation/generality.

Example:

An average of the average number of wooden buildings in different parts of the city will show an apparent lower variation than when individual items in those averages are compared.

D.12 Measure of the "Strength" of Relationship Between X and Y

"Strength" is the amount of "energy" passed from X to Y in a given amount of time (also known as "power").

Example:
The lit cigarette on the pile of rags took ten minutes to develop into a small fire.

Presumably most causes are stronger when they are younger.

Example:
The fire grew quickly, then died out over a longer time.

For ratio-scaled variables, the sensitivity or elasticity (% change in Y for a 1% change in X).

Example:
The maximum flame height of the fire grew 0.4% for each 1% increase in the area of rags being burnt.

For nominal scale variables, the difference between the level of Y with and without X.

Example:
Without the careless smoker, there would be no fire.

"Strength" is deemed high when the cause stands out as being "singlehanded" and leading to a complete new item or reversal.

Example:
The fire was caused by an unusual event (riot by farmers).

"Strength" is deemed high when the failure of one part brings the whole system down.

Example:
The fire was caused because the main water valve in the sprinkler system was rusted closed.

APPENDIX **E**

Necessary and Sufficient Conditions

In a relationship between a dependent (Y) variable and one or more independent (X) variables the situation can arise where the presence or absence of one of the latter can strictly determine the presence or absence of the former. In this situation X is known as a "necessary and/or sufficient condition" for Y. Most importantly here, there is an implication for the form of the equation to be employed to reflect this condition.

E.1   Rules to Identify a Necessary and/or Sufficient Condition

When an attempt is made to relate Y to X, there are ten possible outcomes: five for the case where $X = 0$ (or at the finite lower limit, if any), and the other five when $X \diamond 0$ (which, for monotonic functions, might be taken near the upper or lower [if not finite] limits) (See Table E.1).

Supernumerary Intelligence, pages 347–355
Copyright © 2015 by Information Age Publishing
All rights of reproduction in any form reserved.

TABLE E.1 Possible Outcomes in Attempting to Relate Y to X

When X = 0	Symbol	Interpretation
Y unknown	??	Get more information
Y not causally related	nR	Drop X from equation
Y can take on any value	nN	Not NECESSARY
Y must (always will) = 0	N0	NECESSARY Condition
Y must (always will) <> 0	N#	NECESSARY Condition

When X <> 0	Symbol	Interpretation
Y unknown	??	Get more information
Y not causally related	nR	Drop X from equation
Y can take on any value	nS	Not SUFFICIENT
Y must (always will) = 0	S0	SUFFICIENT Condition
Y must (always will) <> 0	S#	SUFFICIENT Condition

The definition of a *necessary condition* thus is:

If, no matter what the values of other influencing variables, when X is set to 0, Y must or always will be 0, then X is a necessary condition.

or

If, no matter what the values of other influencing variables, when X is set to 0, Y must or always will be <> 0, then X is a necessary condition.

On the other side, a *sufficient condition* is:

If, no matter what the values of other influencing variables, when X is set to be <> 0, Y must or always will be 0, then X is a sufficient condition.

or

If, no matter what the values of other influencing variables, when X is set to <> 0, Y must or always will be <> 0, then X is a sufficient condition.

To test for these two conditions in practice, it probably is easiest to start by imagining that all the other possible independent variables are held at their current values. The X variable being tested then is changed to be either 0 (for a check for a necessary condition) and subsequently to be not 0 (for a check for a sufficient condition).

The process can be illustrated, and many other lessons learned, with the help of the list of variables in Section 5.2. These are ones presumed to affect COC (carbon monoxide concentrations from mobile sources) in the proposed AIRPOL model. This is illustrated in Table E.2. Keep in mind that almost all the variables have a lower limit of 0, with essentially no upper limit (i.e., infinity).

TABLE E.2   Possible Factors Influencing COC and Their N&S Status

Economic:

N0 nS	Household income to buy and operate new vehicles.
nN nS	Interest rates (for loans).
nN nS	Federal spending for pollution control.

Legal:

nN nS	Compatible court decisions.
nN nS	Enforcement of emission control regulations.
nN nS	Number of localities/states having emission control laws.

Political:

nN nS	Amount of local political defense of local industry (e.g., auto manufacturing in Detroit).
N# nS	State legislators supporting environmental laws.

Managerial:

N# nS	Number of governmental personnel dealing with the problem.
nN nS	Time needed to produce a required budget.
nN nS	Time required to implement an environmental program.
N# nS	Personnel with environmental training.

Technological:

N# nS	Use of catalytic converters.
N# nS	Use of lighter, more fuel efficient cars.
N# S0	Use of no emission fuels.
N0 S#	Vehicle CO emissions.
nN nS	Miles of expressways and arterial streets.

Ecological:

nN nS	Heating degree days.
nN nS	Area covered by vegetation.
N# S0	CO dissipation rates.
?? ??	Number of atmospheric inversions per year.
?? S0	Wind speed.
?? ??	Terrain (maximum height differential).

Sensual:

nR nR	Degree of "smell" of CO.
?? ??	Number of days that big buildings can be seen from a given distance.

Social:

nN nS	Geographic distribution of jobs vs. housing location.
nN nS	School segregation (impact on geographic distribution).

(continued)

TABLE E.2   Possible Factors Influencing COC and Their N&S Status (continued)

N0 S#   Travel behavior (vehicle miles of travel).

N0 nS   Total population.

Religious/Ethical:

nN S0   Degree of remorse of drivers about polluting the environment.

nN nS   Number of clergy preaching environmental morality.

Intellectual:

nN nS   Number of studies indicating travel as a polluting factor.

nN nS   Number of newspaper articles on the topic.

Cultural:

nN nS   Frequency of automobile advertisements.

N0 S#   People seeing the auto or truck as a symbol of "individual freedom."

Health:

nN S#   Leaks in catalytic converters.

nN nS   Mental health of drivers (people drive faster if under a lot of time stress).

The first test uses travel behavior (VMT) as the designated X variable. Is it a necessary and/or sufficient condition for COC? To start we must use great imagination to envision a situation where all other variables on the list are at their current values, but there is no travel (VMT = 0) in a year. Must or will COC always be 0? The answer is "Yes." If nobody is traveling, then there are no emissions and thus no concentrations of CO. VMT consequently is a *necessary* condition for COC. It is of type "N0" (see table above) as opposed to type "N#".

Next imagine that all the other variables on the list are at their current values and VMT is some value other than 0. Must or will COC always be 0? The answer is an obvious "No," so VMT has failed the first question for sufficiency. Yet it is true that if there is VMT, there must or always will be some CO. VMT therefore is a *sufficient* condition (of type "S#") for CO.

In sum, VMT is both a necessary and sufficient condition for CO.

The preceding example helps bring out some other points to be addressed. First, exact definitions and measures are required in making the determination of necessity and sufficiency. Note, for instance, that COC was defined as the concentration arising *from mobile sources*. If the definition had included other sources (like home wood heating fires), then COC would not *always* be 0 when VMT was 0, thereby eliminating VMT as a necessary condition. (This also illustrates the fact that an independent variable [VMT] in the relationship for one component or category [COC from *mobile* sources] of a broader entity [CO from *all* sources] can never be a necessary or sufficient condition in the relationship for that broader entity).

Second, the definition of both necessity and sufficiency (N&S) state that they occur "no matter what the value of other variables." Suppose, though, that fuels were developed that had no carbon monoxide emissions (see under "Technological" on the variable list). A similar situation has occurred for lead emissions from gasoline, which now are almost nil (Environmental Protection Agency, n.d.). VMT no longer would be a sufficient condition. No matter how much travel, there would be no emissions and thus no concentrations. The N&S definitions thus should be amended formally to exclude such cases, but this would make the definitions much too complicated from a practical standpoint in QCQ.

Third, the test for N&S must take into account the unit of analysis for the variables being considered. In this case each data point is a "year." Now consider the impact of GDPPC (Gross Domestic Product per Capita) on COC. If there were no GDPPC for one year (only), there still might be some travel and thus some CO. People might, for instance, use their savings (not considered income) to help pay for fuel, and so on. On the other hand, these savings eventually would run out. Over a *period* of years, then, travel (and hence COC) also would vanish. GDPPC consequently might not be considered a necessary condition for COC for a one year interval, but may be considered as one for a longer period.

Sometimes it is difficult to answer the questions to determine N&S. As an example, "terrain" (taken here to mean simply the height differential between the lowest and highest spots in the urban area) is identified as a factor influencing COC. This certainly appears to be true in the Los Angeles area, where the mountains help to keep pollutants caught in the basin next to the ocean. It is doubtful, however, that all 200+ cities included in the COC measurement have had analyses done of the impact of local terrain, so nobody really knows if terrain could be a necessary and/or sufficient condition. More information and/or a good theory is needed before the N&S questions can be answered.

Several other questions arise as an attempt is made to determine N&S for the variables in the table.

Q: Can there be more than one necessary variable?
A: Yes. 12 have been identified in Table E.2.

Q: Can there be more than one sufficient variable?
A: Yes. 8 have been identified in Table E.2.

Q: Can there be more than one variable that is both necessary and sufficient?

A: Yes. 5 have been identified in Table E.2.

Q: If an X variable is both N&S for Y, should there be a perfect fit with the Y variable?

A: Not generally. The "necessary" condition represents only one point (X = 0) and the "sufficient" condition represents any (unspecified) point where X <> 0.

The implication of the last answer is that, while it is desirable to include variables in a relationship that are N&S, they may need to be, and can be, supplemented with those that do not fulfill those conditions in order to get a good fit.

E.2 Connection to Equation Development

The questions to establish X as a necessary and/or sufficient variable for Y also have implications for the *form* of the equation used to estimate Y. This can be illustrated initially for the situation where:

(a) there is only one X in the relationship;
(b) both X and $Y \geq 0$; and
(c) Y is increasing monotonically with X.

For instance, if Y must be (or always is) 0 when X is 0 (necessary condition "N0"), then the equation for Y versus X obviously must go through (0,0). Hence, a power curve (or, less generally, a straight line) would be an acceptable form:

(a) If X = 0, then Y must = 0 example: $Y = a*(X^b)$

On the other hand, for the necessary condition "N#":

(b) If X = 0, then Y must > 0 example: $Y = a*(e^{(b*X)})$

For the sufficient condition "S0," which is not very interesting, and actually is precluded when the slope is known to be positive:

(c) If X > 0, then Y must = 0

and lastly for sufficient condition "S#":

(d) If X > 0, then Y must > 0 example: either $Y = a*(X^b)$ or
$Y = a*(e^(b*X))$

Attention now turns to those situations where X is both necessary and sufficient. There are four of these, representing the four possible combinations of the two necessary and two sufficient conditions:

(e) Where X = 0, then Y must = 0
AND where X > 0, then Y must = 0: example: Y = 0
(degenerate case)

(f) Where X = 0, then Y must = 0
AND where X > 0, then Y must > 0: example: $Y = a*(X^b)$

(g) Where X = 0, then Y must > 0
AND where X > 0, then Y must = 0
(not very interesting)

(h) Where X = 0, then Y must > 0
AND where X > 0, then Y must > 0: example: $Y = a*(e^(b*X))$

The interesting fallout from these eight representations is that in almost all practical cases only two questions need to be asked, and these concern the intercept. The first is "When X = 0, must/will Y = 0?" If the answer to this is positive, a linear (through 0,0) or power-type form is required.

If the response is negative, the second question is posed: "When X = 0, must Y > 0?" A positive response presupposes a regular linear or exponential form. A negative response means that X is neither necessary nor sufficient, so any form can be employed (starting in QCQ with a standard linear form).

When the slope of a relationship is expected to be negative (again with both X and Y ≥ 0), then Y cannot be 0 when X is 0 (except for the degenerate line Y = 0). This means that the "N0" and "S#" conditions are not possible. In fact, there may not even be an intercept at X = 0, as in the equations:

$$Y = 1/X \text{ or, more generally, } Y = a*(X^{-b}) \qquad \text{(E.1)}$$

E.3 Relationships Containing Necessary and Sufficient Variables

An important question is "What happens when there are two X variables in a relationship, one of which (X_1) is, say, a necessary condition of type 'N0'?" To insure that Y will be 0 whenever $X_1 = 0$, no matter the value of X_2, the forms for the two variables should be *multiplied together*.

As an example, as shown above, VMT is a necessary and sufficient condition for COC: there obviously will be no carbon monoxide concentrations from travel if there is no travel (and there will be some if there is travel). The amount of federal air pollution control expenditures (PE), however, is neither necessary nor sufficient (although it should help reduce COC).

The simple linear form for the COC versus VMT would be:

$$COC <=> a*VMT+b \qquad (E.2)$$

but that is not acceptable since COC = b when VMT = 0, which violates the necessary condition. The alternate is:

$$COC <=> a*VMT \qquad (E.3)$$

or more generally:

$$COC <=> a*(VMT^b) \qquad (E.4)$$

The simplest form for COC versus PE is:

$$COC <=> -c*PE+d \qquad (E.5)$$

where c has been assigned a minus sign since COC presumably decreases as PE increases. This form actually is not acceptable because COC could go negative if PE were large enough. But, for purposes of illustration, it will be maintained.

The simplest combination of these two variables would be to use forms {E.3} and {E.5} to get the traditional multiple linear:

$$CO <=> a*VMT - c*PE + d \qquad (E.6)$$

This, however, is unacceptable since CO may not be 0 when PE is 0. This would violate the necessary condition for VMT. Multiple linear regression thus is not appropriate in this circumstance.

A solution, as suggested, is to multiply the two forms together:

$$CO <=> a*VMT*(-c*PE + d) \tag{E.7}$$

Here, if VMT is 0, the whole right side becomes 0.

More generally:

$$CO <=> a*(VMT^b)*(e^{(-c*PE)}) \tag{E.8}$$

is an example of a pre-equation that also contains an acceptable form for PE.

The next question is "What happens when two or more variables have N&S conditions that conflict with each other?" The answer assumed in QCQ is that a necessary or sufficient condition that makes a zero value (N0 and S0, respectively) for Y will prevail.

This can be illustrated with the COC versus VMT relationship again and with the COC versus "Leaks in Catalytic Converter" variable (LCC: see under the "Health" category in Table E.2). VMT, as brought out previously, is N&S for COC. LCC is not necessary (if there are no leaks, there still will be emissions and thus concentrations), but is sufficient (if there are leaks, there definitely will be emissions and thus concentrations).

What happens, then, if there are leaky converters but no VMT? Obviously, if the vehicle is not running, nothing will be going through the converter, leaky or otherwise, so the COC will be 0. The "zero out" condition prevails. Of course, if people ran their vehicles (with leaky converters) without moving (so there would be no VMT), there would be emissions and then concentrations. So the assumption employed in QCQ is not perfect but still is felt to be the most appropriate (future versions might leave this decision to the user).

APPENDIX **F**

Data

Supernumerary Intelligence, pages 357–359
Copyright © 2015 by Information Age Publishing
All rights of reproduction in any form reserved.

Obs	Name	B: APE	C: COC	D: COE	E: FBPS	F: FPE	G: GDPPC
1	1975	0	11.68	83	2.4	2.5	20034
2	1976	0	11.09	84	2.3	4.2	19802
3	1977	1	10.37	85	2.1	4.4	20870
4	1978	0.5	9.84	86	2.2	4.7	21417
5	1979	0	9.38	81	2	4.8	22382
6	1980	0	8.68	78	1.8	5.6	22840
7	1981	1.4	8.64	76	1.7	5.2	22567
8	1982	0	8.01	77	1.9	5.1	22911
9	1983	0	7.82	78	2	4.3	22246
10	1984	1.2	7.74	78	1.7	4.1	23038
11	1985	1.3	6.99	77	1.6	4.5	24485
12	1986	0	7.11	73	1.6	4.9	25264
13	1987	-2	6.67	72	1.4	4.9	25898
14	1988	1	6.42	71	1.4	4.9	26518
15	1989	0	6.32	65	1.4	4.9	27362
16	1990	-1	5.9	58	1.3	5.1	28062
17	1991	0	5.6	62	1.3	5.8	26262
18	1992	0.5	5.2	61	1.3	6	27633
19	1993	0	4.9	61	1.4	5.9	28365
20	1994	0	5.1	62	1.3	5.9	28747
21	1995	0	4.5	54	1.2	6.4	29550
22	1996	0	4.2	53.1	1.3	6	29941
23	1997	0	3.9	53.3	1.2	6.2	30703
24	1998	0	3.8	52.4	1.1	6.3	31716
25	1999	1	3.6	51.6	1.1	6.7	33671
26	2000	0.9	3.4	50	1	7.2	33748
27	2001	0.7	3.2	49	1.2	7.4	35080
28	2002	0	2.9	48	1.3	7.5	35102
29	2003	0	2.7	47	0.9	8	35405
30	2004	0	2.5	46	1	8.3	35976
31	2005	0.2	2.3	45	0.8	7.9	36920
32	2006	0	2.2	44	0.7	8.3	37701
33	2007	0	2	42	0.9	8.3	38341
34	2008	0.6	1.9	43	0.7	7.9	38699
35	2009	0.4	1.8	43	0.6	8.1	38336
36	2010	0.5	1.8	42	0.5	11	36676
37	2011	0.5		41	0.7	10.8	37330
38	2012	0.5			0.6		37691
39							
40							
41							
42							
43							
44							
45							
46							
47							
48							
49							

	H: PE	I: POP	J: VMT	K: YEAR
1	2.5	215.9	1.33	0
2	4.2	218	1.412	1
3	5.4	220.2	1.477	2
4	5.2	222.6	1.548	3
5	4.9	225.1	1.529	4
6	5.6	227.2	1.521	5
7	6.6	229.5	1.556	6
8	5.1	231.7	1.592	7
9	4.3	233.8	1.653	8
10	5.3	235.8	1.72	9
11	5.8	237.9	1.774	10
12	4.9	240.1	1.835	11
13	4.7	242.3	1.921	12
14	5.9	244.5	2.026	13
15	4.9	246.8	2.096	14
16	5	249.6	2.148	15
17	5.8	253	2.172	16
18	6.5	256.5	2.247	17
19	5.9	259.9	2.296	18
20	5.9	263.1	2.358	19
21	6.4	266.3	2.423	20
22	6	269.4	2.486	21
23	6.2	272.7	2.56	22
24	6.3	275.9	2.619	23
25	7.7	279.1	2.667	24
26	8.1	282.2	2.748	25
27	8.1	285	2.776	26
28	2.5	287.6	2.851	27
29	8	290.1	2.882	28
30	8.3	292.8	3.01	29
31	8.1	295.5	3.031	30
32	8.3	298.4	2.964	31
33	8.3	301.2	2.959	32
34	8.5	304.1	2.964	33
35	8.5	306.8	2.93	34
36	11.5	309.3	2.945	35
37	11.3	311.6	2.946	36
38		313.9		37
39				
40				
41				
42				
43				
44				
45				
46				
47				
48				
49				

APPENDIX **G**

Warrant-Based Equation Development

Warrant	Number of the Warrant
Function Name	Type of basic function
Sign	Underlying positive or negative slope
Linearizing	Basic form from linearizing
Y Limits	Any Limits (upper, Lower, Both) on Y Axis?
X Limits	Any Limits (upper, Lower, Both) on X Axis?
Add or Multiply	Add or multiply terms when combining $f(X_i)$ with $f(X_j)$
b Range	b parameter should be either <0 or >0
Upper Reach	Y value can reach upper limit
Lower Reach	Y value can reach lower limit
0Intercept	Y value when X = 0

Schematic of Any Limits (Upper, Lower, Both) on Y axis?
Warrant Determination Parameters

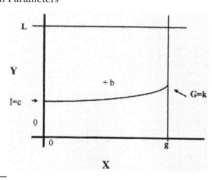

Supernumerary Intelligence, pages 361–365

	A	B	C	D	E	F
1						
2	**Warrant**	1	2	3	4	5
3	**Funct Name**	Linear	Linear	NonLin	Linear	NonLin
4	**Sign**	Plus	Minus	Plus	Plus	Minus
5	**Linear Form**	b*x	b*x	d*ln(b*x)	b*x	d*ln(b*x)
6	**YLimits**	None	None	None	None	None
7	**XLimits**	None	None	Lower	Lower	Lower
8	**Add/Multiply**	Add	Add	Add	Add	Add
9	**b Range**	>0	<0	>0	>0	>0
10	**UpperReach**	Y	Y	Y	Y	Y
11	**LowerReach**	Y	Y	Y	N	Y
12	**0Intercept1**	0	0	MINUSINF	0	PLUSINF
13						
14	**Warrant**	12	13	14	15	16
15	**Funct Name**	Linear	NonLin	NonLin	NonLin	Linear
16	**Sign**	Plus	Plus	Plus	Minus	Minus
17	**Linear Form**	b*x	d*ln(((g-x)/g)^b)	d*ln((x/g)^b)	d*ln(ln(x/g)^b)	b*x
18	**YLimits**	None	None	None	None	None
19	**XLimits**	Both	Both	Both	Both	Both
20	**Add/Multiply**	Add	Mult	Mult	Add	Mult
21	**b Range**	>0	<0	>0	>0	<0
22	**UpperReach**	N	Y	N	y	N
23	**LowerReach**	N	N	Y	Y	N
24	**0Intercept1**	0	0	MINUSINF	PLUSINF	0
25						
26	**Warrant**	23	24	25	26	27
27	**Funct Name**	LogLin	LogLin	NonLin	LogLin	NonLin
28	**Sign**	Minus	Minus	Plus	Plus	Minus
29	**Linear Form**	x^b	e^(b*x)	[x]^b	e^(b*x)	[x]^b
30	**YLimits**	Lower	Lower	Lower	Lower	Lower
31	**XLimits**	Lower	Lower	Upper	Upper	Upper
32	**Add/Multiply**	Mult	Mult	Mult	Mult	Mult
33	**b Range**	<0	<0	<0	>0	>0
34	**UpperReach**	Y	N	Y	N	Y
35	**LowerReach**	Y	Y	Y	Y	0
36	**0Intercept1**	c	c	PLUS	c	0
37						
38	**Warrant**	34	35	36	37	38
39	**Funct Name**	NonLin	LogLin	LogLin	LogLin	LogLin
40	**Sign**	Minus	Minus	Minus	Plus	Minus
41	**Linear Form**	ln((x/(g+h))^b)	(g-x)^b	e^(b*(g-x))	e^(b*x)	e^(b*x)
42	**YLimits**	Lower	Lower	Lower	Upper	Upper
43	**XLimits**	Both	Both	Both	None	None
44	**Add/Multiply**	Mult	Mult	Mult	Mult	Mult

	G	H	I	J	K	L
1						
2	6	7	8	9	10	11
3	Linear	NonLin	Linear	NonLin	Linear	NonLin
4	Minus	Plus	Plus	Minus	Minus	Plus
5	b*x	d*ln(b*x)	b*x	d*ln(b*x)	b*x	d*ln(ln(x/g))
6	None	None	None	None	None	None
7	Lower	Upper	Upper	Upper	Upper	Both
8	Add	Add	Add	Add	Add	Add
9	<0	<0	>0	<0	<0	>0
10	N	Y	N	Y	Y	Y
11	Y	Y	Y	Y	N	Y
12	0	PLUSINF	0	MINUSINF	0	MINUSINF
13						
14	17	18	19	20	21	22
15	NonLin	NonLin	LogLin	LogLin	LogLin	LogLin
16	Minus	Minus	Plus	Minus	Plus	Plus
17	d*ln((x/g)^b)	d*ln(((g-x)/g)^b)	e^(b*x)	e^(b*x)	x^b	e^(b*x)
18	None	None	Lower	Lower	Lower	Lower
19	Both	Both	None	None	Lower	Lower
20	Mult	Mult	Mult	Mult	Mult	Mult
21	<0	>0	>0	<0	>0	>0
22	Y	N	Y	Y	Y	Y
23	N	Y	Y	Y	Y	N
24	PLUSINF	0	c	c	0	c
25						
26	28	29	30	31	32	33
27	LogLin	NonLin	NonLin	LogLin	LogLin	NonLin
28	Minus	Plus	Plus	Plus	Plus	Minus
29	e^(b*x)	ln(((g-x)/g)^b)	ln(((g-x)/(g+h))^b)	x^b	e^(b*x)	ln((x/g)^b)
30	Lower	Lower	Lower	Lower	Lower	Lower
31	Upper	Both	Both	Both	Both	Both
32	Mult	Mult	Mult	Mult	Mult	Mult
33	<0	<0	<0	>0	>0	<0
34	Y	Y	Y	N	N	Y
35	N	Y	N	Y	N	Y
36	c	0	c	0	c	PlusInf
37						
38	39	40	41	42	43	44
39	LogLin	LogLin	LogLin	LogLin	NonLin	LogLin
40	Plus	Plus	Minus	Minus	Plus	Plus
41	x^b	e^(b*x)	x^b	e^(b*x)	[x]^b	e^(b*x)
42	Upper	Upper	Upper	Upper	Upper	Upper
43	Lower	Lower	Lower	Lower	Upper	Upper
44	Mult	Mult	Mult	Mult	Mult	Mult

	A	B	C	D	E	F
45	b Range	<0	>0	>0	<0	>0
46	UpperReach	Y	N	N	Y	Y
47	LowerReach	N	Y	N	Y	Y
48	0Intercept1	PLUSInf	c	c	c	c
49						
50	Warrant	45	46	47	48	49
51	Funct Name	NonLin	LogLin	NonLin	Nonlin	LogLin
52	Sign	Minus	Minus	Plus	Plus	Plus
53	Linear Form	$[x]^b$	$e^{(b*x)}$	$\ln((x/g)^b)$	$\ln((x/(g+h))^b)$	$(g-x)^b$
54	YLimits	Upper	Upper	Upper	Upper	Upper
55	XLimits	Upper	Upper	Both	Both	Both
56	Add/Multiply	Mult	Mult	Mult	Mult	Mult
57	b Range	<0	>0	<0	<0	>0
58	UpperReach	Y	Y	Y	Y	N
59	LowerReach	Y	N	Y	N	N
60	0Intercept1	MINUSinf	c	MINUSinf	c	MINUSinf
61						
62						
63	Warrant	56	57	58	59	60
64	Funct Name	NonLin	NonLin	NonLin	LogLin	NonLin
65	Sign	Minus	Plus	Plus	Minus	Minus
66	Linear Form	$d^{b\wedge x}$	$(1-e^{(b*x)})$	$a*(L-d*e^{(b*x)})$	$e^{(b*x)}$	$d*e^{(b*x)}$
67	YLimits	Both	Both	Both	Both	Both
68	XLimits	None	Lower	Lower	Lower	Lower
69	Add/Multiply	Mult	Mult	Add	Mult	Mult
70	b Range	>0	<0	<0	<0	<0
71	UpperReach	Y	Y	Y	Y	N
72	LowerReach	Y	Y	N	Y	Y
73	0Intercept1	c	L	c	L	c
74						
75	Warrant	67	68	69	70	71
76	Funct Name	NonLin	NonLin	LogLin	NonLin	NonLin
77	Sign	Plus	Plus	Minus	Minus	Minus
78	Linear Form	$a*(x/g)^b$	$a*(x/(g+h))^b$	$((g-x)/g)^b$	$((g-x)/(g+h))^b$	$a*((g-x)/g)^b$
79	YLimits	Both	Both	Both	Both	Both
80	XLimits	Both	Both	Both	Both	Both
81	Add/Multiply	Add	Add	Mult	Mult	Add
82	b Range	>0	>0	>0	>0	>0
83	UpperReach	Y	N	Y	N	Y
84	LowerReach	N	N	Y	Y	N
85	0Intercept1	c	c	L	c	L

	G	H	I	J	K	L
45	<0	<0	>0	>0	>0	<0
46	Y	Y	Y	N	Y	N
47	Y	N	Y	Y	Y	Y
48	MINUSinf	c	o	c	0	c
49						
50	50	51	52	53	54	55
51	LogLin	NonLin	NonLin	LogLin	LogLin	NonLin
52	Plus	Minus	Minus	Minus	Minus	Plus
53	e^(b*(g-x))	ln(((g-x)/g)^b)	ln(((g-x)/(g+h))^b)	x^b	e^(b*x)	d^b^x
54	Upper	Upper	Upper	Upper	Upper	Both
55	Both	Both	Both	Both	Both	None
56	Mult	Mult	Mult	Mult	Mult	Mult
57	>0	<0	<0	>0	>0	<1
58	N	Y	Y	N	N	Y
59	N	Y	N	Y	N	Y
60	c	0	c	c	c	0
61						
62						
63	61	62	63	64	65	66
64	LogLin	NonLin	NonLin	NonLin	LogLin	LogLin
65	Plus	Plus	Minus	Minus	Plus	Plus
66	e^(b*x)	a*e^(b*x)	(1-e^(b*x))	a*(1-e^(b*x))	(x/g)^b	(x/(g+h))^b
67	Both	Both	Both	Both	Both	Both
68	Upper	Upper	Upper	Upper	Both	Both
69	Mult	Add	Mult	Add	Mult	Mult
70	>0	>0	>0	>0	>0	>0
71	Y	N	Y	Y	Y	N
72	Y	Y	Y	N	Y	Y
73	c	0	c	0	0	0
74						
75	72					
76	NonLin					
77	Minus					
78	a*((g-x)/(g+h))^b					
79	Both					
80	Both					
81	Add					
82	>0					
83	N					
84	N					
85	c					

References

Literature

Argyres, N., & McGahan, N. (2002). An interview with Michael Porter. *Academy of Management Executives, 16,* 43–59.

Babbie, E. (1998) *The practice of social research.* Belmont, CA: Wadsworth.

Babbie, E. (2013). *The practice of social research* (13th ed.). Belmont, CA: Wadsworth Centage Learning.

Barnes T. J. (1998). A history of regression: actors, networks, machines, and numbers. *Environment and Planning, 30,* 203–223.

Belsley, D., Kuh, E., & Welsch, R. (1980). *Regression diagnostics: Identifying influential data and sources of collinearity.* New York, NY: Wiley.

Berkovec, J. (1985). New car sales and used car stocks—A model of the automobile market. *RAND Journal of Economics, 16,* 195–214.

Birdsall, I. (2004). *It seemed like a good idea at the time: The forces affecting implementation of strategies for an information technology project in the Department of Defense.* Unpublished doctoral dissertation, Virginia Tech.

Chanlett, E. (1982). Environmental protection. In S. Parker (Ed.), *McGraw-Hill concise encyclopedia of science and technology* (pp. 691–692). New York, NY: McGraw-Hill.

Checkland, P. (1981). *Systems thinking, systems practice.* New York, NY: John Wiley

Ching P. C., & Chih P. C. (2008). Improvement of causal analysis using multivariate statistical process control. *Journal of Software Quality Control, 16,* 377–409.

Clausewitz (1832). *On war.* (M. Howard & P. Paret, Trans. and Ed., 1984). Princeton, NJ: Princeton University Press.

Supernumerary Intelligence, pages 367–372
Copyright © 2015 by Information Age Publishing
All rights of reproduction in any form reserved.

Cohn, L., & McVoy, G. (1982). *Environmental analysis of transportation systems.* New York, NY: Wiley Interscience.

Dawkins, R. (1989). *The selfish gene.* Oxford: Oxford University Press.

Deming, W. E. (1986). *Out of the crisis.* Cambridge, MA: Massachusetts Institute of Technology Center for Advanced Educational Services.

Dickey, J., & Watts, T. (1978). *Analytic techniques in urban and regional planning.* New York, NY: McGraw-Hill.

Dickey, J. (Senior Author), (1983). *Metropolitan transportation planning* (2nd ed.). New York, NY: McGraw-Hill.

Dickey, J. (1995a). Quantitative CyberQuest: A new tool for analytic discovery. In R. Wyatt, R. & H. Hossain (Eds.) *Proceedings of the fourth international conference on computers in urban planning and urban management.* Parkville, Victoria: The University of Melbourne.

Dickey, J. (with Hovey, J.) (1995b). *CyberQuest: Innovation support system: Conceptual background and experiences.* Westport, CT: Greenwood.

Dickey, J. (1996). Tools/procedures for continuous innovation in next generation manufacturing systems. In L. F. McGinnis, M. M. Ahmad, & W. G. Sullivan (Eds.), *Proceedings of the sixth international flexible automation and intelligent manufacturing conference.* New York, NY: Begell House.

Dickey, J. (2009). *The public administration (PA) genome project: Capturing, mapping, and deploying the "genes" of PA.* Charlotte, NC: Information Age.

Dickey, J., & Larkin, G. (2003). *Conceptualizing barriers: Technology infusion and learning in pre-service teacher education.* Presentation to the National Education Computing Conference. Seattle, WA.

Dickey, J., & Malhotra, P. (2003). QCQ conceptual model visualization in the CAVE. In K. Miyamoto (Ed.), *Proceedings of the 8th international conference on computers in urban planning and urban management.* Sendei, Japan: Tohoku University.

Dickey, J., & Birdsall, I. (2006). Information, technology and decision-making. In G. Morcol, (Ed.). *Handbook of decision-making* (pp. 371–394), Boca Raton, FL: CRC Press.

Eden, C., Jones, S., & Sims, D. (1983). *Messing about in problems: An informal structured approach to their identification and management.* Oxford: Pergamon Press.

Forrester, J. (1968). *Principles of systems.* Cambridge, MA: Wright Allen Press..

Friend, J., & Jessop, W. (1969). *Local government and strategic choice.* London: Tavistock Publications.

Gilbert, H. (1992). *Basic concepts in biochemistry.* New York, NY: McGraw Hill.

Gleich, J. (1987). *Chaos: Making a new science.* New York, NY: Penguin Books.

Guba, E. G., & Lincoln, Y. S. (1981). *Effective evaluation.* San Francisco, CA: Jossey-Bass.

Hall, P., & Pfeiffer, U. (2000). *Urban future 21: A global agenda for 21st century cities.* London: Spon.

Hamilton, J. D. (1994). *Time series analysis.* Princeton, NJ: Princeton University Press.

Harding, G. H. U. (1960). *Planning and design for traffic and traffic generation.* ITTE, Berkley: University of California.

Ishikawa, K (1982). *Guide to quality control.* Tokyo: Asian Productivity Organization.

Kim, K. S., & Dickey, J. (2006). Role of urban governance in the process of bus system reform in Seoul. *Habitat-International, 30,* 1035–1046.

Kim, K. S., & Kim, G. C. (November, 2006). Bus system reform in Seoul: Achievements and lessons. In K. S. Kim (Ed.), *Proceedings of the international conference on "Toward Establishing Sustainable Planning and Governance."* Seoul: Sungkyunkwan University.

Kim, K. S., Kim, G. C., & Dickey, J. (2007), *The Seoul bus system reform case and the public administration genome.* The 10th International Conference on Computers in Urban Planning and Urban Management. July 11–13, 2007, Iguassu Falls, Brazil. 298–299.

Landers, A. (1994, August 24). Accident insurance claims. It happened this way. *The Roanoke Times and World News.*

Langley, P., Simon, H., Bradshaw, G., & Zytkow, J. (1987). *Scientific discovery: computational explorations of the creative process.* Cambridge, MA: MIT Press.

Lewin, K. (1943). Defining the field at a given time. *Psychological Review, 50,* 292–310. Republished in *Resolving social conflicts & field theory in social science.* (1997). Washington, DC: American Psychological Association.

Lincoln, Y. S., & Guba, E. G. (1985). *Naturalistic inquiry.* Beverly Hills, CA: Sage Publications.

List, J. (1995). *Black–white differences in postsecondary educational attainment.* Unpublished dissertation, Virginia Tech

Mackie, J. L. (1988). *The cement of the universe: A study in causation.* Oxford, England: Clarendon Press.

Mannheim, J. B., & Rich, R. (1991). *Empirical political analysis* (4th ed.). New York, NY: Longman.

McLuhan, M., & Fiore, Q. (1967). *The media is the message: An inventory of effects.* London: Penguin Books.

Meadows, D., Meadows, D., Randers, J., & Behrens, W. (1972). *The limits to growth.* New York, NY: Universe Books.

Meadows, D., Randers, J., & Meadows, D. (2004). *Limits to growth: The 30-year update.* White River Junction, VT: Chelsea Green.

Moore, E. F. (1957). The shortest path through a maze. In *Proceedings: International Symposium on the Theory of Switching.* April 2–5, 1957. Cambridge: Harvard University Press.

Morehead, P. D. (2002). *Roget's college thesaurus.* Colchester, UK: Signet Books.

Parker, S. (Ed.). (1982). *McGraw-Hill concise encyclopedia of science and technology.* New York, NY: McGraw-Hill.

Pedhazur, E. (1982). *Multiple regression in behavioral research*. New York, NY: Holt, Rinehart and Winston.

Pedhazur, E., & Pedhazur-Schmalkin, L. (1991). *Measurement, design, and analysis*. Hillsdale, NJ: Lawrence Erlbaum Assoc.

Perrow, C. (1984). *Normal accidents: Living with high-rise technologies*. New York, NY: Basic Books.

Pompa, L. (1990). Causal explanation, common sense, and realism. *Inquiry*, 355–372.

Rapoport, A. (1965). *Operational philosophy*. New York, NY: Wiley.

Roblyer, M., & Edwards, J. (2000). *Integrating educational technology into teaching*. Upper Saddle River, NJ: Merrill.

Roe, A. M., & Dickey, J. (1992). *Socio-technical change and organizational learning*. Bethlehem, PA: Report to the Center for Innovation Management Studies, Lehigh University.

Root Bernstein, R. (1989) *Discovering: Inventing and solving problems at the frontiers of scientific knowledge*. Cambridge, MA: Harvard University Press.

Rosen, R. (1985). *Anticipatory systems: Philosophical, mathematical & methodological foundations*. Oxford: Pergamon Press.

Seoul Development Institute. (December, 2005). *Toward better public transport: Experiences and achievements of Seoul*. Seoul: SDI.

Shareef, R. (2010). What business schools can learn from public management—and vice versa. *Journal of Public Administration Education, 16*, 645–652.

Shaw, M. (1980). *On becoming a personal scientist*. London: Academic Press.

Skiadis, C., & Skiadis, C. (2008). *Chaotic modeling and simulation*. London: Chapman & Hall.

Spradley, J. P. (1979). *The ethnographic interview*. Chicago, IL: Holt, Rinehart and Winston.

Steers, R. (1981). *Introduction to organization behavior*. Glenview, IL: Scott Foresman.

U.S. Bureau of the Census (various years), *Statistical abstract of the United States*. Washington, DC: USGPO.

Verbeek, M. (2008). *A guide to modern econometrics*. New York, NY: John Wiley and Sons.

Vinzant, D., & Vinzant, J. (1996) Strategy and organizational capacity: Finding a fit. *Public Productivity and Management Review, 20*, 139–157.

Wells, G., & Gavanski, I. (1989). Mental simulation of causality. *Journal of Personality and Social Psychology, 56*, 161–169.

White, P. (1990). Ideas about causation in philosophy and psychology. *Psychological Bulletin, 108*.

Woodward, J. (2003). *Making things happen: A theory of causal explanation*. Oxford, England: Oxford University Press.

Yasuda, Y. (1991). *40 years, 20 million ideas: The Toyota suggestion system*. Cambridge, MA: Productivity Press, Inc.

Internet (INT) Sources

[INT-1] Air trends (2013). Retrieved November 14, 2013 from http://www.epa.gov/airtrends/agtrends.html

[INT-2] American Geophysical Union (1995). U.S. National Report to IUGG, 1991–1994. Rev. Geophys. V33 Suppl. Unsuccessfully retrieved December 2, 2014 from http://www.agu.org/revgeophys/penner00/node3.html

[INT-3] Analytics (n.d.) in Wikipedia. Retrieved February 13, 2013 from http://en.wikipedia.org/wiki/Analvtics

[INT-4] Appleyard D., & Carp, F. (n.d.) The BART Residential Impact Study: A longitudinal empirical study of environmental impact. Retrieved August 11, 2013 from http://www.edra.org/sites/default/files/publications/EDRA04-Appleyard-296-307.pdf

[INT-5] Jean le Rood d'Alembert. (n.d.) Retrieved October 31, 2014 from http://newworldencyclopedia.org/entry/Jean_le_Rond D'Alembert

[INT-6) Asset Visibility (2000). What does asset visibility mean? Retrieved December 10, 2014 from http://www.definitions.net/definitions/asset%20visibility

[INT-7] Big Data (n.d.) in Wikipedia. Retrieved February 13, 2013 from http://en.wikipedia.org/wiki/Big Data

[INT-8] Francis Galton (n.d.). Retrieved October 31, 2014 from http://newworldencyclopedia.org/entry/Francis Galton

[INT-9] Johann Carl Friedrich Gauss (n.d.). Retrieved October 31, 2014 from http://newworldencyclopedia.org/entry/Johan Carl Friedrich Gauss

[INT-10] Kever, J., (2011, February 13). Inspector General questions accuracy of U.S. Census. *Houston Chronicle*. Retrieved December 19, 2012 from http://www.beaumontenterprise.com/default/article/Inspector-General-questions-accuracy-of-U-S-Census1011942.php

[INT-11] Lanxon, N. (2011, January 31). *How the Oxford English Dictionary started out like Wikipedia*. Retrieved December 11, 2014 from http://www.wired.co.uklnews/archive/2011-01/13/the-oxford-english-Wiktionary

[INT-12] Prive, T. (2012). What is crowdfunding and how does it benefit the economy? Retrieved on December 11, 2014 from http://www.forbes.com/sites/tanyaprlve/2012/11/27/what-iscrowdfunding-and-how-does-it-benefit-the-economy/

[INT-13] Public Administration Genome Project (n.d.). Case list. Retrieved November 11, 2014 from http://pagenome-compass.pbworks.com/PA+Genome+Case+List

[INT-14] Public Administration Genome Project (n.d.). Frontpage. Retrieved November 11, 2014 from http://pagenome-compass.pbworks.com

[INT- 15] Public Administration Genome Project (n.d.). Hurricane Katrina case. Retrieved November 11, 2014 from http://compass1.pbworks.com

[INT-16] Public Administration Genome Project (n.d.). PA Ontology. Retrieved November 30, 2014 from http ://pagenome- compass/PA- Ontology/pbworks.com

[INT-17] Regression. (2008). Retrieved December 19 , 2012 from http: //www. encyclopedia.com/topic/Regression.aspx

[INT-18] Rosenberg, T. (n.d.) (fixes). Crowdsourcing a better world. Retrieved December 10, 2014 from Opinionator.blogs.nytimes.com/2011/03/28/ crowdsourcing-a- better-world/?_r=O

[INT-19] *Smithsonian magazine* (2012, April). Looking back on the limits-of-growth. Retrieved December 10, 2014, from http://www.smithsonianmag. com/science-nature/Looking-back-on-the-limlts-of-growth/125269840/ ?no-ist

[INT-20] U.S. Census Bureau, population forecasting estimates. Retrieved November 15, 2013 from http://www.census.gov/population/www/documentation/twps0050/twps0050.html

[INT-21] U.S. Department of Defense, U.S. TRANSCOM. Joint Total Assets Visibility. Retrieved December 12, 2014 from http://www.almc.army.mil/ ALOG/issues/MayJun00/MSS37.htm

[INT-22] U.S. Department of Education, PT-3 Program. Retrieved October 23, 2014 from http://www2.ed.gov/programs/teachtech/index.html

[INT-23] V'Yugin, V., (n .d.). On calibration error of randomized forecasting, algorithms. Russian Academy of Sciences, Retrieved August 10, 2013 from http://www.iitp.ru/upload/publications/885/Finalversionvyugin.pdf

[INT-24] Whither qualitative/quantitative? (Journal) Qualitative & Qualitative. Retrieved December 21, 2012 from http://link.springer.com/ article/10.1007%2Fs1135-006-9041-7?LI-true

[INT-25] Woods, D. {2009, September). The myth of crowdsourcing. Retrieved December 11, 2014 from http://www.forbes.com/2009/09/28/crowd-sourcing-enterprise-innovation-technology-cio-network-jargonspy.html

[INT-26] Your PAPG Strategy Guide. Retrieved on December 15, 2014 from http://papgstrategycases.pbworks.com/w/page/48605574/Strategizing %20Process

About the Authors

John Dickey

Dr. John W. Dickey is Professor Emeritus at Virginia Tech, where he continues his research and outreach activities through academic appointments in the Center for Public Administration and Policy and in the Department of Urban Affairs and Planning. He received his BS degree in civil engineering from Lehigh University and his MS and PhD degrees in civil engineering (transportation) from Northwestern University before joining Virginia Tech in 1966.

Dr. Dickey is president of IdeaPlex, Inc. and formerly was CEO of Logos Software, Inc. He has been involved in over 40 years of research and consulting in scientific, teaching, engineering, computer, and management endeavors. He has worked on projects in over 30 countries around the world and with a wide variety of firms and public agencies. He has written extensively for scientific journals and proceedings, as well as given international presentations before groups in over 20 countries. Dr. Dickey has been urban/regional advisor to the U.S. Dept. of State (Agency for International Development); twice an NSF exchange scientist to India; twice a visiting scientist, Commonwealth Scientific and Industrial Research Organization, Australia; visiting professor at the University of Sao Paulo (Sao Carlos, Brazil); and distinguished visiting professor, Universiti Teknologi Malaysia (Skudai, Malaysia). Dr. Dickey has directed about 200 management/planning workshops and given congressional testimony. He has authored 13 books and a similar number of software packages, and he was the founder of the Public Administration Genome Project.

Supernumerary Intelligence, pages 373–375

Ian Birdsall

A 22-year veteran of the United States Air Force, Dr. Birdsall provided leadership at practically every level in the Department of Defense, ranging from the Pentagon to combat-ready units. Among other postings, he was a project manager on the Secretary of Defense staff, deployed to Haiti with the Army's 82nd Airborne Division, commanded over 300 people as a squadron commander and was an exchange officer with the Royal Air Force.

As a senior consultant to LMI, a non-profit, public service agency, Dr. Birdsall authored over 20 professional studies including how to apply robotics to logistics processes in the U.S. Army, a mathematical tool to perform trade-off analyses for vaccine management and the concept of operations to incorporate sensors with radio frequency identification technology (RFID) tags to remotely sense environmental conditions of naval ordnance.

Dr. Birdsall has 10 years experience in higher education teaching history, defense policy, leadership, strategy, and public administration. He co-authored a book chapter on decision-making and has been published in journals such as *Administration and Society* and the *Journal of Emergency Management*.

Dr. Birdsall holds a PhD in public administration and policy from Virginia Tech, an MS in management science from the State University of New York, and a BS in industrial management from Georgia Tech. He is an outstanding graduate of the National Defense University, and a graduate of the Defense Systems Management College, the RAF Staff College, the U.S. Marine Corps Command and Staff College, the U.S. Air Force Command and Staff College.

G. Richard Larkin

G. Richard Larkin is the director of the PhD program in Public Policy and Administration at Walden University. Prior to his employment at Walden, Dr. Larkin held faculty and administrative positions at the University of West Georgia, Auburn University, the University of Southern Mississippi, the West Virginia College of Graduate Studies, and Concord College.

Dr. Larkin received his BA in political science from Concord College and his MURP in urban and regional planning and PhD in public administration and public affairs from Virginia Tech. He also has studied as a program scholar at the University of Michigan's Inter-University Consortium for Political and Social Research summer program in quantitative methods in social research.

Dr. Larkin is a managing member of PRISM Associates, a planning and management consulting firm. He has over 30 years of research and consulting experience in a variety of areas, including comprehensive planning, new town and resort planning, sustainable development, coastal policy, electoral redistricting, public defender case load studies, educational technology utilization, economic development, and agricultural policy. Dr. Larkin has authored or co-authored numerous consulting reports and academic articles. He has delivered over 80 presentations and workshops and given testimony before the U.S. House of Representatives.

Kwang Sik Kim

Kwang Sik Kim is Professor Emeritus of the Department of Public Administration, Sungkyunkwan University, Seoul and a Contract Professor at the Universiti Teknologi Malaysia. He is a graduate of the Seoul National University and obtained his PhD in urban planning from the University of Washington, Seattle. Over the past 30 years, he has been involved in about 200 research projects in the area of urban spatial planning as well as transportation planning. He has authored or co-authored several books and has published approximately one hundred journal articles in the fields of transportation studies and urban planning. He has served as the director, Sustainable Urban Development Institute and professor, Department of Public Administration/ Graduate School of Governance at Sungkyunkwan University (SKKU) Seoul, Korea. He was the dean, College of Social Science; dean, Graduate School of Public Administration; and director, Research Institute of Social Science at University Technology Malaysia (UTM) Skudai, Johor, Malaysia. He served as president, Korean Association of Urban Policies (KAUP) Seoul, Korea and senior research scientist, Department of Transportation Economy, Korea Institute of Science and Technology (KIST) Seoul, Korea. He has also served as president of the Korean Society of Transportation, which has accommodated 2,000 members over the last two years.

A sample of publications dealing with bus system reform:

Kim, K. S., & Dickey, J. (2006). Role of urban governance in the process of bus system reform in Seoul. *Habitat-International, 30,* 1035–1046.

Kim, K. S., & Kim, G. C. (2006, November). *Bus system reform in Seoul: Achievements and lessons.* In Proceedings of the International Conference on "Toward Establishing Sustainable Planning and Governance." Sungkyunkwan University, Seoul.

Seoul Development Institute. (2005). *Toward better public transport: Experiences and achievements of Seoul.* Seoul, Korea: Author.

Index

A

Annie's Mailbox, 62
Accounting Equations, 140
Accuracy, 16, 38, 139, 140, 142
Agreement, 142
Artificial Intelligence, 5, 13, 18, 98, 251
Assumptions, 30, 108, 113, 320

B

Babbie, Charles, 16, 106, 107, 110, 140,
    142, 143, 257
Balance
    Ecological, 58
    Equation, 157
    Force Field, 100
    Trade, 99
Barnes, T. J., 293
Birdsall, Ian, 19, 269, 272, 277, 278,
    367, 368, 374

C

Case Information, 54
Catalysis, 96, 110, 111, 117, 313, 319

Catalysts, 8, 26, 41, 95, 96, 102, 110,
    111, 112, 192, 213, 319
Categories of Knowledge, 4, 212
Categorize Variables, 122
Causal Chain, 250, 332, 334, 336, 340
Causal Variables, 25, 68, 71, 318, 336
Cause/Effect, 45, 100, 109
    Analysis, 96, 104, 106, 117
Ching and Chih, 105
Clausewitz, Johann von, 98
Coefficient Magnitudes, 160
Coefficient of Determination (R^2), 38,
    51, 163, 167, 178, 301, 302
Completeness, 25, 142
ComPASS, 6, 27, 231, 236, 238, 286
Constrained Values, 143
Constraints, 5, 44, 136, 146, 189, 191,
    303
    component, 323
    data, 320
    legal, 93
    resource, 70
    situational, 96, 97, 108, 115, 117, 324
Content Analysis, 54, 56, 68, 70, 73, 92
Correlation coefficient (R), 14, 37, 78,
    145, 155, 178, 293, 302

Supernumerary Intelligence, pages 377–381
Copyright © 2015 by Information Age Publishing

Correlation, 14, 19, 66, 80, 161
   No-cause, 154, 319
   No Y: X Correlation, 321
   Symmetric, 154
Coverage of Extremes, 25, 142
Crosscutting Concepts, 18
Crowdsourcing, 68, 75, 76
Curve fitting, 14, 18, 138, 182, 183, 293, 321
Cyberquest, xvii, 5, 68, 70, 81, 83, 88, 89, 93
Cyclical Stationary, 103, 104

D

D'Alembert, Jean Le Rond, 14, 293
Data, 2, 14, 15, 16, 17, 18, 19, 44, 49, 140, 216, 269, 286, 357
   Analysis, 20, 272
   Availability, 77, 108, 141, 145
   Big/Wide, 18, 19, 20, 24, 40, 288
   Calibration, 46, 134, 146, 195
   Codes, 272
   Errant, 77
   Forecasted, 102
   Protocols, 272
   Qualitative, 3, 4, 286, 288
   Quantitative, 3, 140, 151, 286, 288
   Reduction, 272
   Requirements, 163
   Specification and Collection, 3, 17, 25, 26, 33, 46, 76, 139, 195, 230, 287, 320
   Synthesis, 272, 273
   Visualization, 290
Database, 19, 32, 54, 58, 59, 70, 81, 83, 84, 92, 145, 231
Dataflow, 3, 25, 287
Dated Material, 68, 86
Degrees of Freedom, 142, 182, 195, 324
Deming, 33
Dickey, John, 5, 27, 81, 146, 245, 256, 311, 370, 373
Dickey, J. and Birdsall, I., 272, 277
Dickey, J. and Larkin, G., 253
Dickey, J. and Malhotra, P., 290
Dickey, J. and Watts, T., 142

Domain, 70
Duotonic, 103, 218, 323

E

Element, 2, 7, 46, 88, 90, 143, 330
Equations, 159, 162, 164, 178, 201, 304
   Accounting, 139, 140, 144
   Outside, 139, 140, 144, 184
Error Avoidance, 116
Evaluation, Qualitative, 208, 210
Evaluation, Quantitative, 206

F

Forecasting, 3, 25 27, 39, 49, 50, 65, 78, 134, 157, 211, 221, 287, 326
Forecasts, 15, 164, 224
   Make Forecasts, 223
   Negative, 154
   Scenarios, 221, 224
Forrester, J., 15

G

G-score, 90, 91
Galton, Francis, 293
Gauss, Johann Carl Friedrich, 14, 293
Goal List, 60
Goodness of fit, 14, 15, 36, 37, 47, 134, 152, 163, 167, 169, 171, 172, 178, 180, 185, 201, 293, 298, 299, 300, 301, 302, 321, 324, 325

H

Hall, Peter, 10

I

Image Maps, 60
Institutional Analysis and Development (IAD), 27, 85, 232
Incorrect signs, 156, 189
Intercept types, 175
Invariates, 68, 70, 73, 74, 98, 100, 102, 319, 326

J̄

Joint Total Asset Visibility (JTAV) Project, 269
  Data Analysis, 272
  Data Synthesis, 273
  Methodology, 272
  Relationships, 278

K̄

Kelly, George, 87
Kim, K.S., 19, 369, 375
Kim, K.S., and Dickey, J., 257
Kim, K. S. and Kim, K. G., 369
Kim, K.S., Kim, K. G., and Dickey, J. 255, 256

L̄

Larkin, George, 19, 245, 253, 368, 374
Legendre, Adrien-Marie, 293
Langley, P., Simon, H., Bradshaw, G. and Zytkow, J. xviii, 18
Limits, upper, 166, 167, 169, 172, 175, 186
Limits, lower, 34, 145, 146, 166, 167, 169, 175, 179, 186, 188
Lincoln, Y. S. and Guba, E.G., 17
List, J., 185

M̄

Mannheim, J.B. & Rich, R., 142, 143
Mathematical Structure, 96, 103, 105, 108, 117, 152
Maximum Absolute Deviation (MAXAD), 296
Maximum Absolute Percentage Deviation (MAXPD) 296, 297
Measure, 14, 15, 38, 39, 45, 78, 106, 117, 139, 140, 141,142,163,178, 215, 320, 330
Mean Absolute Deviation (MAD), 294, 295
Mean Absolute Error (MAE), 298, 305

Mean Absolute Percentage Deviation (MAPD), 295
Mean Absolute Percentage Error (MAPE), 299, 305
MINIMAX, 299, 300
MINIMAX%, 300
Model of a Model (Meta-Model), 6, 7, 24
Monotonic, 47, 103, 173, 174, 347
Moore's Algorithm, 126

N̄

Necessary and Sufficient Condition, 63, 65, 107, 162, 176, 347

Ō

Ostrom, Elinor, 27, 86

P̄

Pedhazur, E., 14, 294
Pfeiffer, Ulrich, 10
Potential Sphere of Influence, 142, 143
Preaction, 96, 102, 109, 110, 111, 112, 145, 192, 193, 312, 319
Precision, 38, 46, 142, 320
Pre-equalization, 152, 166, 198, 316, 323
Project InSight, 243, 244, 245
  Barriers to Infusion, 245
  Lessons Learned, 249
Public Administration Genome Project, xviii, 6, 26, 229, 286
  Building and Contributing a Case, 232
  Ontology, 260
  Overview, 230
  PAGP (Temporary Interruption to Use the PAGP) 30
  Using the PAGP, 85, 93, 237
  Views of a Case, 234

Q̄

Qualitative Analysis, xvi, 13, 209

Qualitative Evaluation, 208, 210
Qualitative Research, 5, 13, 17, 40, 287
Quantitative Analysis, 13
Quantitative CyberQuest (QCQ), xv,
xvi, xvii, 3, 5, 13, 24, 27, 40, 253,
272, 286, 287, 317
   QCQ Step 1, 25, 28, 44, 53, 54
   QCQ Step 2, 25, 29, 44, 67, 81
   QCQ Step 3, 25, 29, 45, 95, 109, 119
   QCQ Step 4, 25, 33, 46, 139
   QCQ Step 5, 25, 34, 47, 151, 165
   QCQ Step 6, 26, 38, 48, 201
   QCQ Step 7, 26, 39, 50, 221
Quantitative Evaluation, 253

R

Ratio, 143
Reachability, 146, 152, 176, 187, 206
Redundancy, 99, 100, 260
   Elimination, 99
Regression, xvi, xix, 13, 14, 34, 38, 40,
51, 63, 64, 77, 78, 79, 133, 178,
192, 216, 303, 307, 309, 310, 311,
315
   Disadvantages/Drawbacks of 14, 93,
133, 152, 154, 157, 159, 160,
225
   History of, 293
Relationships, 1, 3, 6, 24, 38, 41, 67, 70,
73, 95, 115, 156
   Accounting, 144, 160
   Bivariate, 126
   Competitive, 322
   Deduced, 160
   Discrete Event, 322
   Duotonic, 323
   Envelope, 323
   Equality, 26
   Implicit, 322
   Individual, 25, 152
   JTAV, 278
   Linear, 14
   Multivariate, 322
   Necessary and Sufficient, 354
   Nonlinear, 15, 322
   One way, 159

Optimization, 322
Outside, 144
Public Administration Genome
Project, 27, 286
Quantitative Cyberquest, xviii
Qualitative, 41
Quantitative, 6, 41, 151, 173
Semantic, 17
Stochastic, 322
Supernumerary, 5, 287
Temporal, 109, 112
Unknown, 319
Variable, 6, 9, 32, 95
Reliability, 2, 25, 142
Representativeness, 142
Research Methodology, xvi, 5, 13, 16,
17, 287
Roe, A. M. and Dickey, J., 17
Root-Bernstein, R., 39, 83, 201, 209

S

Sample Size/Type, 142
Scenarios, 26, 39, 221
Seoul Bus System, 255
Sequentiality, 143
Shaw, Mildred, 87
Shulman, R, 105
Sign Switching, 160, 323
Simultaneity, 192, 327
Situation Description, 3, 25, 27, 28, 44,
53
Situation Structuring, 71, 87, 88, 122,
318
Source/Reference, 142
Spradley, J. P., 17
Standard Deviation, 297
   Tutorial, 294
Standard Error, 301
Supernumerary Intelligence (SI), 2, 20,
40, 285, 290
   Art and Science, 3
   Characteristics of, 317
   Contribution to Analytics, 288
   Contribution to Education, 289
   Contribution to Management, 289
Systems Analysis and Dynamics, 15

T

Theologues, 67, 70, 73, 83, 96, 113, 318
Theory, 113
    Development, 3, 25, 29, 44, 95, 109,
        119, 318
    Grounded, 17
    Search Process, 3, 25, 29, 44, 67, 71,
        81, 318
    Systems, 15
Time Affinities, 26, 100, 109
Time availability, 187
Type of Measurement Scale, 143

U

U.S. Dept. of Education: Preparing To-
    morrow's Teachers for Technol-
    ogy (PT3) Program, 243
    Project InSight, 244
        Barriers to Infusion, 245
        Lessons Learned, 248

V

Validity, 142
Variables, 6, 24, 67, 73, 161, 186, 249,
    318, 319, 320, 321, 322, 323, 324,
    326, 335, 347, 354
    Accounting, 144
    Categories, 122

    Catalyst, 102 (*See* catalyst)
    Causal, 71, 106
    Combinations, 63, 126
    Definitions, 140
    Description, 267
    External, 7, 102, 221, 245, 247
    Goal, 8, 54, 56, 102, 246, 248
    Identifying, 56, 71, 73, 81, 95, 97
    Intermediate, 8, 102
    Invariate, 102 (*See* invariate)
    Links, 100
    List, 85, 91, 93, 234, 236
    Minimum Time Paths, 126, 126
    Operational Range, 145
    Policy, 155
    Pre/reaction time, 7, 102
    Quantitative, 13, 223
    Qualitative, 13
    Relationship, 6, 73
    Roles, 102
    Strategy, 7, 102, 221, 246
    Surrogate, 93, 222
    Systems Theory, 15
    Time clock, 8, 102
Virginia Tech, 10, 11, 290

W

Warrants, 34, 35, 172, 179, 185, 198,
    361

Made in the USA
Columbia, SC
23 April 2019